ORIELTON

Some other books by the same author

THE ISLAND

SHEARWATERS

PUFFINS

GREY SEAL, COMMON SEAL

MAN AGAINST NATURE

OCEAN WANDERERS

SEAL WOMAN

THE PRIVATE LIFE OF THE RABBIT

ORIELTON

The human and natural history of a Welsh manor

*

RONALD LOCKLEY

Illustrated by
C. F. TUNNICLIFFE R.A.

ANDRE DEUTSCH

First published 1977 by
André Deutsch Limited
105 Great Russell Street London WC1

Printed in Great Britain by
Cox & Wyman Ltd.
London, Fakenham and Reading

British Library Cataloguing in Publication Data

Lockley, Ronald Mathias
    Orielton.
    1. Zoology – Wales – Orielon
    I. Title
    591.9'429'63   QL258

    ISBN 0–233–96928–4

Apologia

The story of Orielton as related in this book has been produced from the diaries and records kept by the author, who accepts responsibility for any sins of commission and omission. It has not been possible to mention every one of the good people who came to Orielton and gave practical help and advice, including my sisters and other relatives. To these I offer both my sincere apologies and my warmest thanks.

I am also grateful to the *Reader's Digest* which published a condensed version of That Rabbit's story. And I acknowledge with pleasure the consent, where necessary, of the authors named, for permission to use the quotations under the chapter headings.

I

*Remote from universal nature, and living by complicated artifice, man
in civilization surveys the creature through the glass of his knowledge
and sees thereby a feather magnified and the whole image in distortion.
We patronize them for their incompleteness, for their tragic fate in
having taken form so far below ourselves. And therein we err, and
greatly err. For the animal shall not be measured by man. In a world
older and more complete than ours they move finished and complete,
gifted with extension of the senses we have lost or never attained, living
by voices we shall never hear. They are not brethren; they are not under-
lings: they are other nations, caught with ourselves in the net of life and
time, fellow prisoners of the splendour and travail of the earth.*

HENRY BESTON
The Outermost House

On the sheltered side of the gentle hill stood the old manor, with
creeper and clematis in charming disarray framing its hundred
windows as it gazed towards the morning sun over half-wild parkland beautiful with cowslips, primroses, cuckoo flowers and
orchids. Below lay a tree-embowered lake fringed with yellow
iris, white with water-lilies.

For nearly eight hundred years the Orielton estate had been the
home of a succession of adventurers, and knights, who had loved,
hatched, matched and dispatched here. In books, and in records
stored in the archives at the National Library of Wales, I had
read of stirring events at the old manor. And some tales had come
to me from local witness or hearsay.

The first Norman owner had built a fortified house in independent style, above a spring of pure water – essential in case of
siege – which still made the foundations rather damp, although
hidden in a deep stone-roofed cistern under the present barrel
cellar. And he and his Wiriet heirs had maintained armed men
and numerous serfs to provide protection and labour for the
forests, farm, fish-pools, mill, columbarium and coneygarth:
those attributes now much decayed of which I had come into
possession, but without the armed men or the serfs.

7

Here, about a hundred and fifty years ago, at the coming-of-age of Sir Hugh Owen, descendant of the original Wiriet, had been the last of the giant house parties of the last century with five thousand guests and a correspondingly gargantuan dinner. Even at the beginning of the present century the young squire, returning from the Boer War, had been met at the gates by cheering tenants and retainers who had unharnessed the horses and dragged the carriage triumphantly on foot the half mile to the flag-decorated mansion.

'Those were the good times, sir,' said white-haired Levi, my informant, who had shared in that welcome; but shaking his head doubtfully as he looked at me. As well he might, for it was almost by accident I had just become owner of the gracious old manor, and its demesne of 260 acres enclosed by a solid stone wall. No one had lived here for the last twelve months.

Old Levi could see that I was a forlorn creature, wearing battered country clothes. He had cycled from the nearest hamlet ostensibly to offer his occasional services as handyman, but I suspected that his main motive had been natural curiosity to examine the new 'squire' and make sure it was true that I intended to live here.

'Of course, not reg'lar full-time work, sir. Drat the gover'ment – 'twould take away me pension if I earn'd more'n a few shillings a week. I've still got childer to feed.'

'You have?' I said, hiding my astonishment as I gazed at his ragged white locks. Evidently Levi had been twice married. I must have betrayed my surprise, for he reassured me:

'Two lots o' childer we 'ad, like, but 'twas the same 'ooman each time. We just 'ad a bit of a rest, like, in between.'

'I understand, Levi. Well, just come when you feel able to. Bring a hoe and you can begin right away, on the thistles and weeds here, around the house.'

Levi was one of a series of idle locals who came and stared and told good stories about Orielton's past and, their curiosity satisfied, went away, rarely to return. Levi came irregularly that summer, helping to cart the rough hay, mostly scented ladies' smocks and meadowsweet – useless as stock feed – which I was obliged to clear off the weedy undergrazed park. One warm day Levi consumed a lot of cider and, falling asleep, rolled too near a wasp's nest and got badly stung. I gave him an antidote and an extra day's wages, and saw him no more – save casually at *The Speculation*, the local inn.

It was not possible to get reliable retainers locally. None wished to live at the old manor, which was three miles from the nearest shop, the sleepy small town where the station had been classed as redundant since the Government had nationalised the railways. The nearest Labour Exchange offered me the unemployable dregs of the unemployed. A few of these ventured as far as Orielton's echoing empty house; only to shudder and hurry away. It was known to have had a ghost as far back as the twelfth century; might it still be there?

Someone must be found to dust and clean and care for the great public rooms and the dozen or so huge bedrooms, if I was to become a genuine squire inhabiting this wonderful old mansion. It would fall to pieces if I did not take action soon. Already the lead-and-slate roof leaked. The bats, owls and bees had long been the real owners in possession – and I was pleased at this thought. But soon I would have the hundred-acre farm on my hands . . .

Impressed by the courtesy and cleanliness of a Spanish couple employed by a friend living in London, I wrote to the agency from which she had obtained them. After weeks of delay, passport red tape, and several cheques had passed, a likely young couple arrived: a lean, dark, scowling Jack Spratt, and his smiling curvaceous wife. They had two words of English. I bolstered my schoolday Spanish with a traveller's phrase book.

'But surely you are not Jesus?' I muttered, half to myself. 'It would be blasphemous to shout for Jesus in these marble halls!' (And could anyone named Jesus be married to a woman called Victoria?)

Jesus's big ears caught only their names as I uttered them. A smile lit up his olive countenance as he nodded eagerly:

'Si, Don Ronald; she, Victoria, yes?' pointing first to her stomach and then to his own. 'I Jesus, yes?'

He pronounced his name the Spanish way, phonetically *Chroesus*; not unappropriate, I was to find. His main, and perfectly legitimate and perhaps admirable, preoccupation was to make as much money as quickly as possible, so that they could return to their village in Spain and buy enough land to keep a few cows. In the advertisement I had received from the agency Jesus had

9

been described as a trained houseman. He began by breaking several windows, and in his apology I was not surprised to learn that his real occupation had been with a demolition firm.

As for Victoria, described as a trained housemaid, I fell in love with her radiant smile and good looks. She had never been employed before, except in helping her mother at home, and she proved to be a poor housemaid, but soon became a very good cook and found her way to our affections via our taste-buds. She had been married five years, and had only one serious disability – in her view – she had never had a child, or even conceived one. This caused her at intervals of one month a profound melancholy and in due course she was to confide this terrible affliction as she rapidly learned to speak her sort of English.

'We try and try,' she wailed one day, months later. 'But we can't get baby. It's terrible! Who look after Jesus and Victoria when we too old to work? It's ver' sad, and damn bad, for Spanish woman have no baby – it's ver' damn bad!'

She dried her tears bravely when my wife said that perhaps our local doctor could put this right with hormone treatment. He examined her and tested Jesus (this had to be a secret arrangement: Jesus submitted reluctantly, convinced that his virility was perfect, as so it proved to be) and gave her suitable pills. He warned Victoria she was too fat; after one year at Orielton she had, I fear, almost doubled her weight. She would have to go on a diet.

Victoria was to continue childless – to her great vexation. Their little noisy disputes took place not in the peaceful love-nest of the bedroom at the top of the house which Victoria had furnished in garish Spanish style, with a Madonna and red light at which she prayed for help from the Virgin Mary; their disagreements flared up in the kitchen, where Jesus snatched away second helpings from under his wife's knife and fork. Victoria loved her food too well.

She loved everything worthy of her affections. Especially did she croon over Mr X, the neuter cat, black with a white shirt front. Under that love he became fatter and lazier than ever; he was the substitute for the child she could not get. This pleased me, for I like cats best when they stay indoors and confine their hunting to mice and rats – and leave the wild birds alone.

*   *   *

Before committing myself irrevocably to its purchase I wandered for many days in that spring time around the little estate, cogitating in the luxury of imagined ownership, distilling its exhilarating essence, perfumed with wild flowers, its splendid natural disorder, without the liability of having to spend a penny on its upkeep. I roamed the spacious public rooms, marvelling at the Adam ceilings, the Italian marble fireplaces, the white stone staircase, planning the future vaguely, optimistically, and now and then troubled by the thought of buying a white elephant. (Curiously enough there was a white teakwood ornamental elephant from Burma lying with the junk in the basement, part of certain unwanted household fittings and furniture I was invited to purchase at valuation, if I bought Orielton. I placed it in the study window to remind me each day I visited the house that I was a fool even to think of signing the agreement to purchase.)

I was bemused by the air of utter peacefulness, the lucent Atlantic light slanting through the tall windows and the bowers of ancient beech, elm and silver fir surrounding that glorious patchwork of spring flowers which covered the parkland between the eastern front of the great house and the three-acre lake. The spirit of the place awaited someone to cherish it, who would sense and respect its history and preserve its mellow beauty. Its voice seemed to be loud in the song of a woodlark which soared above, pouring out its sustained bell-like phrases, between magic, expectant pauses. Like the nightingale, which does not migrate so far west, the woodlark often sang at night and was always first to greet the dawn, and with none of those vulgar squeaks which the nightingale interposes now and then.

My favourite walk was from the Grecian porch to the Lily Pond, admiring the ancient Japanese maples and the rich assortment of red, pink, white and yellow rhododendrons which screened from view the utilitarian buildings of the north side – the huge disused stables and laundry blocks. Then across the causeway damming the lake where I would linger to watch coot, moorhen, wild duck and heron feeding, scarcely heeding me, so long had this pool been their sanctuary. For many years no gun had disturbed them.

Of course the dam, long neglected, half overgrown with alder, wild rhododendron, camellia and willowherb, leaked a good deal, spilling into a shallow pond below, and this in turn fed a third pond. All three waters were storage for a disused timber mill, originally the corn-mill of the Norman lord of the manor.

The small middle pond was called the Japanese Garden, for here, more than a hundred years ago, had been constructed a willow-pattern-plate affair of latticed footbridges, meandering streams and pools. On the far bank lay huge blocks of water-worn stone, chosen for their picturesque, often grotesque, shapes, and brought – it was said – by steam engine from the limestone shore eight miles distant. Giant ferns smothered the narrow paths between these tall rocks, where montbretia ran wild. One single ancient palm tree seemed to be the last exotic extravagance left to tell the tale of the departed elegance of the landscape gardener's efforts to amuse his aristocratic patron – or more likely, patroness, for the place somehow still had a dainty air: a Japanese garden is surely not a country squire's amusement?

Strolling eastwards past this warm, sheltered confusion of rocks and ferns, where I seemed to hear the silver-black water-shrews whisper their scandal in safe burrows beneath, I passed along the high wall of the four-acre vegetable garden and orchard. This wall is a solid structure, beautifully built of red sandstone, lined with brick. Erected more than two centuries ago by cheap labour (how proud, nevertheless, the masons must have been of the result!) its cost today would be astronomical. A line of cypress trees stands sentinel here, above a path choked with bluebells, violets and wild arum. Framed in an archway covered with climbing roses long unpruned is a wrought iron door opening into the enclosed garden.

I had found the woodlark's nest with richly freckled eggs in the thin grass of this bosky enclosure. It was a fresh second laying, not yet near hatching, for the male ceases to sing when it has nestlings to feed.

This southern half of the garden, partly shaded by the high wall and the cypress trees, had been allowed to go wild by Alf Hitchcox.

Now over seventy years old, he was tenant of a cottage in the far corner. He was always welcoming, with offers of tea, sherry, a posy of flowers, some fruit. He paid a nominal rent, grew tomatoes principally in some decrepit glasshouses against the south-facing wall, and chrysanthemums and everlasting (*statice*) outside. He retained his customers by his modest charges. He made wreaths

12

cheaply, using the abundant ferns and wild flowers from the woods, to set off his cultivated blooms. With a twinkle in his eye and pithy comment on their character he told lugubrious tales about local undertakers and bereaved persons who patronised his packing shed.

'. . . There was Sam Lewis, a reg'lar mean bloke, who buried his father in the old man's second best suit, to save buying a new one for himself. But although he saved a few quid that way he didn't know he had also buried the old man's savings; it didn't come out until the will was found and read that the old man, who didn't trust the bank, had sewed his life savings in £10 notes into the lining of that second-best suit!'

Alf had worked hard variously as an apprentice, and head gardener to sundry great houses in Cheshire; he had migrated to Orielton before the last owners, the Gaddums, arrived from that same county. And now . . .

'Hope you'll let me stay here – to end my days in peace. I'm too old to move any more. Help yourself to anything you can see in the gardens – veg, flowers or fruit – all free to you. Give me a call if you want anything I've got, and I'll send it up to the house. I don't make money here, but I can just get by, and I love the peace of the old place – and so will you. I can't afford any longer to keep more than half these four acres in proper order; for that I apologise, but times have changed and wages are too high to afford a regular man today. And although I'm old, I'm too old to have joined any pension scheme. I want to drop dead in harness . . .' He hitched his braces and patted a splendid stomach.

'Wait – I haven't bought Orielton – yet! But don't fret, Mr Hitchcox. I'm delighted you've allowed the shady north-facing side of your garden to go wild. For it's there the woodlark is nesting. Listen, isn't he in grand voice?'

Could I win a living from Orielton? I was nearly fifty, with two young sons barely old enough for school. Yet here I was, dreaming the hours away, hearing the woodlark sing, watching a long-tailed tit family flitting through the cypress trees, with nuthatch, wren, goldcrest and other small birds for company. These first summer parties of young birds kept together for mutual protection, stimulating but not unduly competitive as they foraged through the wooded grounds, each species feeding in its special way on the abundant insects and wild fruits.

13

Those cypress trees were all curiously forked, just above wall height. Alf Hitchcox explained: 'The Mackworth-Praed family, who leased Orielton just before the Gaddum family bought it, had a son – you probably know him – he's a keen naturalist and crack shot. 'Twas him who started up the old duck decoy before you came along. One day Cyril was out after woodcock when he dropped by the gardens here, for a chat, as was his custom. At that time I was young enough to keep the whole four acres in tip-top production. I told him everything was going fine, except that those young cypresses were beginning to top the wall, and soon they would throw too much shade over my apples and pears for my liking. "H'm, that's easy," Cyril said, "I'll soon put that right!" And before I could stop him he shot the leading tips off all twelve cypresses, at wall height, never missed one first time. But of course, it's ruined their appearance. Not that it matters to me now; as I say I don't use that shady side of the gardens any more.'

'They're ugly as they are, with ragged twin heads – doesn't suit a conifer's beauty. I would cut them all down if I had my way. I want to recreate that Japanese Garden,' I said, mentally reserving the right to reprimand Cyril Mackworth-Praed next time I encountered him at those ornithological meetings in London we attended.

Yes, I would get rid of those deformed trees which were now shading the limestone blocks of the Japanese Garden outside the wall. Already I was planning to restore to the sunlight their water-worn beauty hidden under fern and moss and shadowed by the trees. I dreamed I would revive the tranquil beauty and order of that miniature landscape of oriental design. I would repair the leaking lily pond dam, and the two lower ponds which supplied power to turn the huge iron water-wheel of the ivy-clad sawmill. Alf had said that, although the mill had not been used for the last ten years, the machinery was there, still sound, apart from some new belts needed, and you only had to mend the storage ponds and the sluices to 'give the wheel enough head of water, and it'll turn as sweet as ever. Next real rainy day I'll show you.'

Yes, I would restore all this and more, of the delectable place, with its columbarium, folly tower, and other relics of feudal magnificence yet to be explored. For instance there was the American Garden which I had lately rediscovered; Alf had casually mentioned its existence 'buried in the woods by that old gazebo tower'.

Exploring along the wooded heights of the estate, I followed the great wall to where this tall Folly or watch-tower stood astride the disused southern gateway. Approached from the outside by a lane now blocked with thorn trees, this hollow stone shell gazed towards the sea, far across sweetly fertile fields, here and there a hamlet half-hidden in a fold of land, but marked by the tall, battlemented towers of Norman churches.

The gatehouse was square with two storeys, both with corner fire-places; but the floors and the roof had long mouldered away. Perhaps, after all, I ought not to restore this Folly? It belonged to the birds which had made their homes there: the owls and the starlings, and above all the ravens, which, wheeling and croaking in the sky, expressed their disapproval of my visit. I recognised

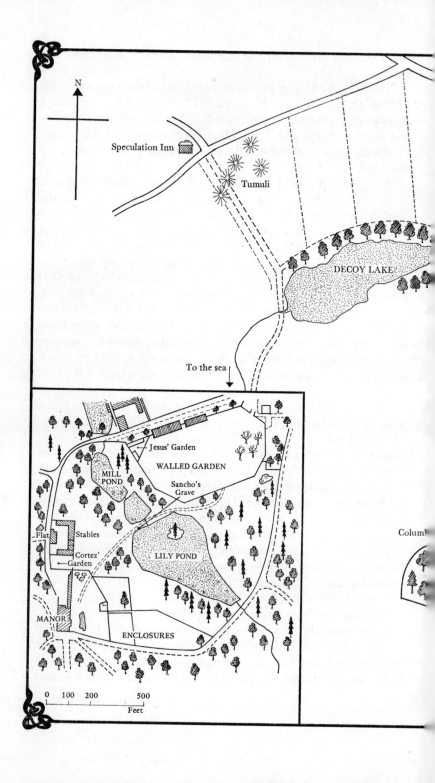

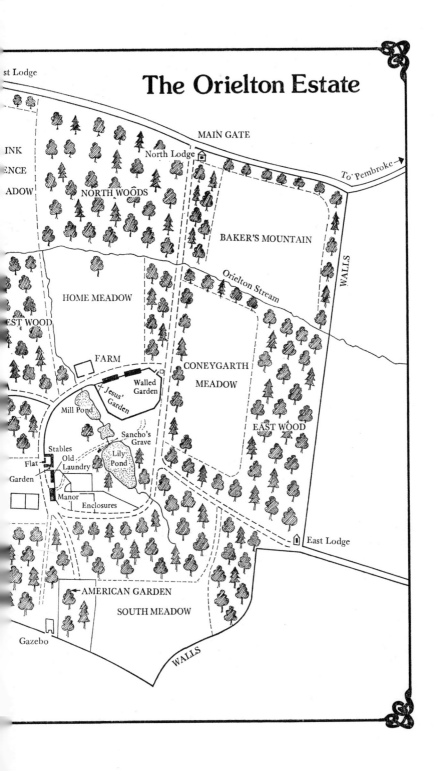

The Orielton Estate

st Lodge

MAIN GATE

North Lodge

To Pembroke

INK

ENCE

ADOW

NORTH WOODS

BAKER'S MOUNTAIN

WALLS

Orielton Stream

HOME MEADOW

EST WOOD

FARM

CONEYGARTH
MEADOW

Walled
Garden

Jesus'
Garden

Mill Pond

EAST WOOD

Sancho's
Grave

Stables

Lily
Pond

Flat

Old
Laundry

Garden

Manor

Enclosures

East Lodge

AMERICAN GARDEN

SOUTH MEADOW

Gazebo

WALLS

their bulky stick nest, filling the broken top of the chimney, with delight. 'Welcome, Bird of Odin!' I shouted in answer to the deep croaks of their greeting. These rare and intelligent birds were to live there under my protection henceforth, although neighbouring farmers were to ask, and be refused, my permission to shoot them for their alleged lamb-killing. (I explained to them that ravens certainly ate lambs, but only when they were dead, or rarely they would attack a sickly lamb too weak to live more than a few hours. Not convinced, my nearest neighbour set up a timing device to fire automatically at set intervals a blank cartridge in his field close under the outer wall of the Folly. The ravens were at first startled, but soon ignored the noise. So birds in their territory will sing in the heart of the cannonade.)

At ground level heavy oak double-doors still closed this southern entrance to the estate against human access; nor, to judge from the thick stems of green ivy clasping the giant hinges and crossbar, had they been opened for many a decade. Only the badgers had dug a passage in one corner for themselves, and for the foxes, hares, rabbits and hedgehogs, whose various footprints marked a narrow track there.

A short walk to the east of the Folly was yet another landscaped enclosure – the American Garden. Walled on all sides, its northern limit was a stone ha-ha, pigeon-holed near the top to take cultivated plants (holes now occupied by ivy-leaved toadflax, herb robert, stonecrop, and hartstongue fern) with a half-filled ditch below. In the centre the now gateless entrance was approached from the manor by a wooded walk painted in season with snowdrops, orchids, violets, bluebells and other wild flowers. Quite overgrown, the four acres of this enclosure were enchanting in natural disorder where still a decayed North American maple and swamp cypress lingered in competition with the dominant native sycamore, ash, elm and elder.

Said to have been constructed about the time of the colonising adventures of scions of Orielton stock in Canada and the eastern American dependency some 200 to 250 years ago, it was designed to disguise the raw wound of the quarry from which had been hewn the red sandstone for rebuilding the manor in 1656. On crossing the ha-ha you passed a little summer house – one ivy-clad wall and a paved fountain surviving – and presently descended into the quarry to reach a flight of stone stairs which narrowed to reach an elevated promenade two feet below the top of the outer wall of the estate. Here the view, as from the Folly, embraced the southern horizon of the sky and the Severn Sea, with hamlet and rolling plain, its pattern of fields bounded by low hedges clipped by the salt wind.

Upon these once well-groomed ramparts, so charmingly supported by an inner wall of embrasured chiselled stone, had strolled the eighteenth- and nineteenth-century squires, with their wives, children, sweethearts, nursemaids and friends of the Owen dynasty. Among them were some amateur poets who have captured in rhyme, blank verse and doggerel, glimpses of the romance of those distant leisured hours.

In my pocket book were some poems which I had copied from the Orielton papers, deposited in the archives of the National Library of Wales. One page of five verses, signed by E. Owen, is headed *Addressed from a Sincere Friend*, promising eternal love 'if to your Betsy you'l prove true . . . and when the Nuptial Knot is Ty'd . . .

> Oh! happy then will be Our Lot
> Whether in the Pallace or in Cot
> I'll Envy not the Great
> If destin'd for an Humble State
> Well pleas'd I'll Chear my Chosen Mate
> Nor murmur at my Fate.'

Another maiden whose poems are preserved for posterity in these papers is more cautious in her view of matrimony. Miss Fowler declares that

> A vergin state is crowned with much content
> Its allways happy as its innocent
> No blustering husbands to create yr tears
> No childrens crys for to offend your ears.

I quote another in full; she lays down conditions for marriage . . .

> No blooming youth shall ever make me err
> I will the beauty of the mind prefer
> If himans rites shall call me hence
> It shall be with some mane of sence
> Not with the great but with a good estate

Not too well read nor yet illiterate
In all his actions moderate grave and wise
Redyer to bear than offer Injuries
And in good works a constant doer
Faithful in promise and liberall to the poor
He thus being qualified is allways seen
Ready to serve his friend his country and his king
Such men as these you'l say there are but few
Their hard to find and I must grant it too
Butt if I ever hap to change my life
Its only such a man shall call me wife.

'Humbly Dedicated too Mrs Anne Barlow. C. Fowler.'

(Anne Owen, who married John Barlow, was born about 300 years ago. Evidently she enjoyed matrimony, for she was twice married.)

Also in C. Fowler's handwriting is *A Receipt to Cure a Love Sick Person who can't obtain the Party Desired*:

'Take two oz: of the spirits of reason three oz: of the Powder of experience five drams of the Juce of discretion three oz: of the Powder of good advise and a spoonfull of the Cooling watter of Consideration make all these up into Pills and be sure to drink a little content affter ym and then the head will be clear of the maggotts and whimsies and you restored to yr right sences but the persons that wont be ruld must become a sacifise to Cupid and dye for love for all Docters in the world cant cure ym.'

Yes, I would be able to spend nostalgic hours amusing myself in this American Garden, trying to reconstruct it from what I could find both in the archives of the layout of the terraces, walls, ha-ha and summerhouse, and as I gradually removed the humus and debris of a century of neglect . . .

Or should I? Was not all this inspiration an evanescent dream? If I restored it, who would maintain it afterwards – who could *afford* to maintain it these days? Why not leave it to the happy affairs of the wild ones who now inhabited it – the birds, rabbits, badgers and foxes which had their long-established homes and dens in the ever-encroaching rhododendron thickets which flourished in this mild climate.

Where – if I really did buy Orielton – should I begin? Within the walls there were one hundred acres of grass fields dispersed between some hundred and fifty acres of old mixed woodland; and in addition those dozen acres or so of parkland, ponds and walled gardens. Possession of the farm, with its limited stock shedding (converted from the lumber mill buildings) had been promised when the tenant, a local grazier, gave it up on a year's notice. I knew that the soil and climate might provide conditions suitable for profitable combinations of Jersey cattle for milk, and early potatoes followed by a fodder crop in the same year – from my practical experience of such mixed farming elsewhere.

Most of the woodland was tall ancient beech, elm and ash, grand to walk and wander under, the ground white with snowdrops in January, but many of the older trees were stagheaded with age and Atlantic gale damage. There was no profit there, nor did I feel any desire to fell this natural and planted forest which sheltered the fields and gave the estate its wonderful feeling of sanctuary.

What about the huge stables, with their stall space for twenty-four horses, four carriages, looseboxes, hayloft, coachman's flat, harness rooms and clock tower? What would I do with them? They were still empty, their doors still painted with the labels of their occupation more than a decade ago by the Royal Air Force during the last war . . . the clock was irretrievably silent at 3.30 hours, its inner mechanism missing possibly removed by some airman as a souvenir on the departure of his squadron when peace came. Above it the weathervane cock was rusted permanently, optimistically, with its open beak facing the sunset of the midsummer solstice.

Old Levi told me that Squire Saurin was the last to ring the stable bell to summon his coach or horse; he showed me the lever fixed to the ornamental iron balustrade on the left side of the front porch, which connected by pulley and wire along hidden conduits to the bell in the stable yard a hundred yards distant. The wire had long perished, but the solid bronze bell had not been stolen; it was still firmly hung under the eaves of the coachhouse, half concealed by the cup nests glued against it of the house-martins.

Swallows were nesting in the harness room and darting through the broken window panes. When I climbed the stairs to the hayloft I heard a continuous chittering of bats concealed behind the plaster of the slate roof. It was a hot day, and they were too warm there, anxious for the coming of dusk, when they would issue in a stream lasting for half an hour, as they fluttered forth to feed. Pipistrelle, long-eared, horseshoe or whiskered? I longed to find out which species inhabited Orielton.

At that moment of the evening you could stand on the cobbled floor of the large loosebox in one corner of the stable block, and hear strange muffled noises erupting beneath your feet. Years ago a pair of badgers had tunnelled a dry warm hibernaculum and nursery there, entering by way of the outfall of the main drain to the yard, outside the walls. Grunting and scratching, the boar, sow and young cubs were preparing for the nightly sortie.

The loosebox floor had sagged somewhat as a result, but this did not dismay me. Perhaps this was the opportunity to put an observation window in the floor directly above the sett?

The way the wild ones had almost completely taken over the estate excited me. I should not disturb them. I should study them.

That is, unless . . . and if . . . ?

2

Wou'd she walk from dew secure?
Sancho can her clogs procure;
Wou'd she for attendance ring?
Sancho pulls the well-known string.

Sancho! thee this song I give:
Long in plenty mayst thou live!
And when Ruthless Death appears
Honor'd still by Emma's tears.

Thus wrote the young woman in three tattered pages marked
(possibly by her devoted papa?) 'Verses by Miss Emma Owen',
preserved in the Orielton papers. There are twelve such verses in
this *Ode to my dog Sancho*, who brought such happiness to his young
mistress by his 'bushy tail and pendant ear, auburn feet and sable
hair', by his instant attention to her needs, who

Soon the missive Stick explores,
Brings it to the applauding shores
Shakes his mazy ringlets dry
Then awaits his Lady's eye.

Whom, when ruthless death came to this beloved spaniel, Emma
buried, doubtless with many tears, in the little pets' graveyard
which I discovered by accident when cutting away wild rhododendron to give better access to the edge of the lake. I uncovered
three small burial plots, each two-feet long, and enclosed by low
iron rails a foot high. One had a cast-iron plate embossed SODA;
another, older, cast-iron plate, askew upon railings rusted thin,
was embossed SANCHO.

We may suppose that young Emma lived a secure and happy
childhood at Orielton; but those days had their exciting moments.
She was the eleventh of twelve children born to Sir Arthur Owen
by his wife Emma, only daughter of Sir William Williams of

Denbighshire, one time Speaker of the House of Commons. Doubtless Arthur had met Emma senior during his early service as Member of Parliament for Pembrokeshire, beginning in 1695. He is said to have galloped all the way (250 miles) to Westminster to give his vote for the Whigs against an amendment by the Tories to the Abjuration Oath (February 1703) which required all MPs and holders of public offices to renounce the Scottish Stuart succession; the amendment was defeated by 118 votes to 117, thanks to Sir Arthur's timely arrival.

He was a barrister of Gray's Inn and a figure of distinction and some notoriety. In the 1708 election he was accused by his rival Lewis Wogan of bribery and fomenting violence in unfairly winning the seat for Pembroke Borough. But the petition to decide the issue was not resolved by the Committee of Privileges in Wogan's favour for another three years, during which Sir Arthur enjoyed the advantages of sitting member. In 1714 he successfully contested Pembroke County against John Barlow (High Sheriff of the county in 1705) whose second wife was Sir Arthur's sister Anne (to whom Miss Fowler dedicated her poem – see Chapter One). Barlow also petitioned against sundry malpractices of Sir Arthur, who had intimidated electors likely to vote against him by sending men armed with halberds to harry and prevent them from reaching the ballot-box. The petition came to nothing, and Emma's father continued to sit for the county until 1727, when he was unseated by a young neighbour of the house of Cawdor, John Campbell of Stackpole Court.

Sir Arthur was now sixty-three years old, and he devoted the remainder of a long life to the enjoyment and embellishment of the Orielton estate. After bearing him so many children his wife had died three years earlier, at the age of fifty-two, and he buried her at Monkton, the nearest church, where so many earlier and later Owen tombs and memorials may be seen. At that date Emma was hardly in her teens, but with her sister Margaret, a little older, and the younger Elizabeth, formed a trio of young daughters to console the widower. But already Sir Arthur had had the satisfaction of seeing his son and heir William elected MP for Pembroke Borough in 1722, while yet only twenty-five years old.

William continued to represent borough or county for over fifty years to 1774; again not without those electioneering disputes and petitions by opponents which were to trouble the Owen family to the end. Thus in the election of 1741 the supporters of his rival, Rawleigh Mansel, alleged that 'they were obstructed and prevented from going into the Town Hall by a great number of persons who were placed on the stairs leading to the said Hall, armed with pitchforks and other offensive weapons; that during the whole time of the election several persons friends to the said William Owen, stood at the head of the stairs, with their Backswords or Scymitars in their hands, and when any of the Burgesses (attending with intent to vote for the Petitioner) attempted to go into the Town Hall to vote for the petitioner, they called out to other persons so placed on the stairs as aforesaid, to knock them down, saying they were none of our friends . . . whereby the said William Owen unfairly . . . was by the said Mayor declared duly elected – not one of the petitioners' electors being permitted to come into the Hall'.

The Owen heirs continued to be elected to Parliament, whether by undoubted merit and favour or by certain malpractices, or both, often followed by expensive litigation. This was to ruin the last Owen to occupy the manor, Sir John, whose enormous expenses in contesting elections caused the property to be mortgaged. In 1842 all the furniture and plate were sold; and in 1857 the balance of the estate, 5,800 acres, was sold at auction in London. Thus ended over 700 years of occupation by the descendants of the Norman founders, the Wiriet family.

To return to Sir Arthur, he was happily living at home, embellishing the manor, making new plantations, helping his son to win elections, scheming to marry off his daughters advantageously and, like his father before him, was interested in local sailing ships carrying cargoes of corn and anthracite between Milford Haven, Ireland and Brittany. He liked to entertain distinguished guests. Although neighbour John Campbell had defeated him in the election of 1727, it was a matter of courtesy and etiquette that Campbell should bring William Pitt to Orielton when the Prime Minister was visiting Stackpole Court, a vast medieval mansion (since pulled down) barely four miles away. A letter dated 5 September 1736 describes the occasion. Campbell showed Pitt the curious medieval chapel of St Govan wedged in a fissure in the cliffs near Stackpole, and on the next day they gazed upon the harbour of Milford Haven:

> ... an exceeding fine haven for ships but there would be no
> guard from an enemy, the entrance being too broad for guns
> to reach the ships that should attempt to come in. We then
> went to Orielton where we dined, and Sir Arthur showed
> all the rarities of his house. One thing I thought odd, and
> that was Sir Arthur called for his horse. I thought it was to
> send us part of the way home, but that was to ride about his
> gardens to show his plantations. He was extremely pleased
> with Mr Pitt for approving his designs.

Not really odd, for a man who had ridden at a gallop 250 miles to
Westminster at forty-seven. He was in his seventy-second year
when he showed Pitt and Campbell through the woodlands – and
probably the American Garden, then newly created.

In that year he gave in marriage his lately-widowed youngest
daughter Elizabeth (probably the Betsy of the love-poem in Chapter One) to his sister Anne's son Hugh, by John Barlow, Arthur's
unsuccessful rival in the 1714 election. Elizabeth's first husband,
her cousin William Owen of Anglesey, had died without issue,
and Elizabeth continued childless in her second consanguinous
marriage. When her brother William won the election of 1747 for
both Pembroke Borough and County against her husband Hugh,
he allowed his brother-in-law by favour to sit for the borough;
the rivalry of the previous generation was less important than the
retention of power in the present family.

William the eldest and Elizabeth the youngest of Sir Arthur's
quiverful of twelve remained close, living longer than their
spouses. Hugh Barlow died in 1763, and William's wife died in
1764: she was his first cousin Anne, daughter of John Williams –
brother of Emma, Sir Arthur's wife. The relationship was intricate – Anne was the only child of the marriage of Sir Arthur's
eldest sister Catherine to the said John Williams, second son of
Sir William Williams, Sir Arthur's father-in-law. Sir William Owen
died in 1781 aged eighty-four. His childless sister Betsy died in
1788, her large estates passing to Hugh Owen, son of Hugh
Barlow's sister Anne (daughter of Sir Arthur's sister Anne) who
had married her cousin Wyrriot Owen of Nash, on condition that
young Hugh took the name of Owen – he became Hugh Owen
Barlow. His father Wyrriot had been returning officer in the
notorious fraudulent election of 1741, when he had deliberately

26

omitted to give notice of the time of the poll to the burgesses of Wiston known to favour William's rival Rawleigh Mansel.

It was an age of arranged marriages between the wealthy and privileged, often between cousins in order to keep properties intact and, preferably, enlarged. Families were large, and mothers died young. Sir Arthur's father, the second baronet Sir Hugh Owen, had married in 1664 his second cousin Anne Owen of Anglesey, by whom he had twelve children (five dying as infants) before she died and he married again; but he died aged fifty-three without further issue. Of Sir Arthur's twelve children six died young, and the mother as we have seen aged fifty-two. The tangle of relationships of the Owens, bearing the same first names in successive generations, took me several months to unravel. Later I had the assistance of an amateur genealogist who claimed kindred with the house of Wiriet and Owen, and with princes and kings and other noblemen: one Ifor ap Rhys, who appears in later chapters.

Of Sir Arthur's three daughters to survive infancy, none had issue. Margaret died unmarried, but at last a husband was found for Emma; in 1751 she married William Bowen of Williamston on the north shore of Milford Haven. Emma was then close to forty, no longer perhaps writing poems. Her husband was elected High Sheriff in 1761, but was otherwise unremarkable; he died in the next year. The redoubtable Sir Arthur died in 1754, approaching his ninetieth year. Emma died in 1777.

* * *

Many tantalising glimpses of the human history of Orielton arose in this way: Emma's ode to Sancho, Sancho's grave, a search of the genealogical record – in that order were my little discoveries, or uncoveries, made in one instance. In others I experienced a nostalgic delight in finding a ruined arbour in the woods; a lead pipe uncovered between the Folly and the manor where a gushing spring filled a man-made grotto, now ruined; an archway bricked up in the basement – of late Norman provenance; and one day, inserting new wires under a floor, I found a layer of golden sand which told me convincingly which room had been the Owen children's playroom. The fine sand, with some fragments of toys and George II coins, had filtered through the joints between the wide floorboards, shed from shoes and clothes of generations of children returning home from happy hours on the yellow sands of the bays on the nearby coast.

Long before deciding to buy the estate, however, I already knew something of its natural history. A hundred years ago, when the estate extended to around 8,500 acres, it had embraced a flourishing duck decoy sited on a small lake made by damming the Orielton brook as this issued westwards from beneath the demesne walls. Originally this lake had five decoy pipes screened by trees and rush fences in the traditional manner. At that time it was used to snare a few thousand migratory duck each winter, which were sold for profit to poulterers, or eaten by the people of the manor. During the First World War when the surrounding land passed into the hands of the neighbouring farmer, the decoy became derelict.

Afterwards, when ornithologist and sportsman Cyril Mackworth-Praed was temporarily resident as a young man with his parents at Orielton, he initiated a scheme in partnership with a man of similar tastes (known as Barmy Gilbert from his extravagant footloose pursuit of birds with binoculars and gun; his devastating punt-gunning made him notorious among more law-abiding duck-shooters) to revive some of the catching pipes of this decoy for a new purpose; to study migration by leg-banding with numbered rings and releasing the waterfowl unharmed. Catching and marking wild birds in this way is a sporting science, or scientific sport, which satisfies the hunting instinct and intelligence of man without harming the quarry and ultimately, through the knowledge thus gained of their individual migrations, longevity, moult and other behaviour, provides a better understanding of how to protect them.

The study of birds by marking the individual had long been my passion. I had banded many thousands of sea birds in twelve years of living on the remote island of Skokholm, fourteen miles as the raven flies from Orielton, before the commencement of the Second World War. During this period, I had visited the decoy in winter occasionally to help the decoyman Greenslade, and learn how to lure the ducks. By that time Cyril Mackworth-Praed had left Orielton, and the decoy was financed from his office in the British Museum of Natural History where (when he was not too busy making money as a stockbroker) he was compiling a handbook of six volumes on the birds of Africa. This mammoth task had been interrupted by the Second World War, when Cyril served in the Scots Guards; this war also put a stop to the work of marking ducks in the decoy.

Thus it was that I first met those enthusiastic nature-lovers Arthur and Alice Gaddum when they bought the Orielton estate, now reduced to the walled area enclosing 260 acres, intending to retire and enjoy its peace and beauty. Arthur was a stockbroker, Alice the daughter of a sometime Lord Mayor of Manchester. They had invited me to tea – my first visit to the old house.

'We married very late in life,' Alice told me ingenuously, 'much too late to expect to have children. So you can judge my surprise and joy when, soon after our return from our long honeymoon cruise around the world, I found myself the mother of a darling baby daughter! I can still hardly believe it!'

The darling daughter was now a substantial size, and just then as doting on dogs as evidently Emma had been, over two hundred years ago. Whenever I called at Orielton Mary pestered me to buy one of the pups from her kennel of pedigree Corgis. Now I like Corgis as they were first intended – originating in North Pembrokeshire – as a useful cattle dog. Their merit in my view had been their original skill in snapping at the heels of Welsh cattle to muster the herd and, because of their size, they avoided being kicked. But the show Corgi today is an example of the breeder's perverse pleasure in producing the extreme by line-breeding for defects. It has been selected for dwarf twisted legs and dachshund length; and the unfortunate male is obliged to waddle around unhappily on four stumps, with sagging back, and his sheath rubbed raw when he attempts to run across rough country.

Young Mary was offended when I pointed out her stud dog running aground amidships as we walked over thick clumps of grass on the way to the stableyard where she exercised her dogs on the smooth cobbles. Nor would she listen to my suggestion that she started a kennel of the original hardy, lithe, Pembrokeshire Corgis still bred by cattlemen in the hills of the (Welsh-speaking) northern half of our county. She was determined to make me buy one of her line-bred pups. But I had, I fear, lost interest at that moment, and drew her attention to the handsome cock black redstart, a rare bird here, flitting about the eaves fly-catching in the shelter of the vast, empty stables.

Unfortunately the Second World War interrupted the idyllic

retirement of the Gaddum couple. The duck decoy was closed, and I no longer visited Orielton. When the War Department requisitioned the manor, stables and laundry block for RAF Coastal Command, the Gaddums stoutly refused to leave. They were reluctantly allowed to inhabit the attic and the basement.

Five years later the RAF withdrew. Once more the Gaddums settled down to enjoy the peace of wild nature and the woodland scene. Sadly, not for long. Slipping one day on the polished white freestone staircase which is such a magnificent feature as it rises through the well of the house, Arthur fell headlong – to his death.

Alice, courageous but inwardly inconsolable, stayed on with her daughter. Now almost blind, she could feel her way about the spacious house, if necessary independently of the assistance of Mary, and one maid, and the occasional help of a manservant Ronnie Williams who lived in one of the lodges, and acted as gardener and chauffeur. She continued to visit the tenants of the estate cottages, making them little presents and refusing to raise their minimal rents.

After the Second World War, I was living only ten miles from Orielton and when it was decided to re-open the duck decoy, Mackworth-Praed and Peter Scott asked me to supervise the work of a part-time decoyman, Harold Greenslade. There was little money available: local naturalists would be expected to volunteer to help the decoyman with the duck-banding and make the repairs to the pipes. Alice Gaddum, now a lonely woman, asked me to call whenever I could and talk with her.

It was a pleasure to enter the grand old house, and afterwards to stroll through the once bustling outbuildings and huge stables to see how Nature was assuming command of the deserted 'appurtenances'. Occasionally in a dreaming mood I imagined myself as Norman overlord, one of the Wiriet (sometimes spelt Wyrriot) knights; perhaps Sir David Wyrriot, who attended the court of Dame Joan de Valence, Countess of Pembroke in 1300. David was a descendant of Stephen Wyrriot who had to deal with an 'unclean spirit' which haunted Orielton, as described by Giraldus Cambrensis in 1188. Or I may have been the swashbuckling Sir Arthur Owen of 1700, for by then these old buildings would have been newly-erected on the site of the earlier Wiriet manor . . . Pleasant dreams enlivened by the birds and other animals, and wild flowers, which had taken possession. Along the sunlit tops of lime-rich walls, many-coloured toadflax, wild thyme and erigeron daisies delighted the eye and nose.

Alice loved to hear me speak of the small events of nature which she could no longer witness with her eyes. She too had certain confidences to make. Her mind was increasingly clouded about the future: not hers, but her daughter's – Mary would never be able to manage Orielton on her own, she was still very young and unlikely to marry for a long time . . .

The decoyman was managing the work of banding ducks fairly well, so I came less often – the twenty-mile journey was a deterrent in winter, and another volunteer had turned up to assist Greenslade. But soon a tragedy occurred to bring me daily to attend the decoy, and release and band the day's catch of waterfowl. When Greenslade had fallen ill and been bedridden for many weeks, I had arranged with volunteer Ted Elsdon to take turns in the work. Ted was a reformed egg-collector, deeply interested in birds and able to spare time since his retirement from business in Pembroke, only three miles from the decoy. But with a weak heart he had to take things quietly.

It was exciting to creep behind the reed screens hiding you from the ducks feeding on the water. But absolute silence was necessary; and you carried a smoking peat on a shovel – this was supposed to disguise your scent. The pipes had been well-baited with wheat and barley the day before – these grains sank to the bottom of the shallow water; the ducks would be happily dabbling and feeding there, and afterwards resting on a low bank provided, close to the high netting entrance.

Peeping through slits in the rush screens to ascertain that ducks were present and tranquilly occupied, you now 'showed the dog'. Any small dog sufficed, but the fox-like Corgi we used was specially trained by Greenslade. It was taught to pop in and out of each screen all the way up to the bend in the pipe. The ducks, ever curious, would swim after it, convinced that as long as they stayed in the water, they were safe. As soon as they passed the bend in the gradually narrowing pipe, you showed yourself in the gap facing the closed end of the funnel, and (unseen by any waterbirds still on the lake) you panicked all those birds by your sudden appearance into flapping down the narrowing pipe-end into hoopnets, where they could be collected and released. The marked ducks might yet return to be caught at a later date, in another winter. About ten per cent of those marked at Orielton were subsequently recovered abroad, perhaps shot by a hunter in Europe, or even in Russia – anywhere from the Arctic to the Volga.

One wild December day Ted, ignoring his doctor's warning not to work the decoy in bad weather, suddenly collapsed in the water beside one piper. It was dusk, rain had set in and his companion, an older man who had never been there before, was an hour finding his way to the nearest house, wandering for a while in the wooded perimeter of the decoy lake.

Ted had died at once of heart failure – I felt sure his sudden swift death was what he would have wished. But the loss of this good friend brought sadness to Orielton for a while. Now all the work at the decoy became my responsibility – until, later, Greenslade got up from his sick bed.

It was a gloomy hour. Alice told me she too was hoping for such a swift end – soon. She longed to die. As a helpless blind old woman she was, she declared, useless and boring, tying her daughter to dull routine when the young woman ought to be free to enjoy the company of those of her own age.

'We are too isolated here. It's too lonely for Mary in this remote corner of Wales. No one near of her own age. All my friends are so old – far away in my old home, Manchester, or dead. Even when they come here, which is hardly ever, they are boring to a young girl, although Mary's too kind to complain. I have offered to go into a home for the blind – although, as you can imagine Ronald, I can't really bear the thought of that! I love this old house. Anyway, Mary wouldn't agree – she's a country girl. So I wish I were dead. Then she'd be free; and I would too – to join dear Arthur.'

A splendid long-legged house spider had spun its silken lines in and out of the crystal chandelier above our heads. But Alice could not see the cobwebs, the dust, and general shabbiness. Neither could she see the solitary bat which had silently entered the drawing-room in the falling dusk; it was snatching up the flies and moths under the lofty Adam ceiling. Nor could Alice witness the rich glow of sunset lighting the tall pyramidal beeches with their leaves still russet, or the leafless elms lining the parkland slope below the French windows, or the silver water of the lake winter-free of lilies, with its reflection of a young fir tree on the little island in the centre. Ducks which I had caught and banded in the decoy were happily dabbling there, well aware that they were safe in this sanctuary to which they had flown (but soon they would fly by night to eat the grain I had put down in the pipe entrances).

Alice put one frail hand out to feel for the edge of the silver tray, and asked me to help us both to another cup of tea. She was transparently thin and white like the fine china of her tea set.

'Did you ring many ducks this afternoon? There's another thing I want to talk to you about. When I die – soon I hope – what's going to happen to Orielton? Oh, I know you and your naturalist friends will keep the decoy going if you can. But the decoy is not on my land, although you say it's essential for the wildfowl to have our little lake and streams and marshy fields as part of their refuge – when the decoy is disturbed by fishermen in the summer. When I die Orielton will have to be sold. I would turn in my grave if it were bought by the wrong person – some land speculator, perhaps, who would convert this lovely old house into flats, or pull it down and divide the land into building plots.'

'I don't believe he'd get permission these days for that sort of development, from the planning authorities.'

'I wish you could take it over, Ronald. I know you would

33

respect Arthur's wishes and mine, to keep it as a sanctuary for wild creatures and plants. Wouldn't Peter Scott help – he's world famous, isn't he? Remember you brought him to see me one day? Surely you naturalists could do something about it? Between you, couldn't you buy it cheaply from me and keep it as a sanctuary for wildlife? What do you say? Is it possible?'

'It would be wonderful!' The idea leaped gladly in my too-receptive mind. But I spoke hesitantly: 'Why, Alice, you mustn't talk like this. You'll live many more years yet. In any case I have no money myself. Yet I would try to raise enough somehow, if a scheme of managing Orielton as a nature reserve could be devised, and approved by enough supporters. That is, if you decide to . . . to – well, it's a marvellous thought, but I have no idea what is involved financially – I've a poor head for figures.' I fumbled for words, while my thoughts raced.

I listened fascinated as she poured out her hopes and fears for Orielton and the future, to which she had lately given much thought: 'When we bought Orielton some years before the War, we paid – I think I am right in saying, but my memory is so bad these days – £5,000 for it. It was in a bad state, and we've spent much more than double that on it since. I remember Arthur, who had such a good brain for figures, saying before we bought it that it would cost us twice as much to put it right to live in, and having to bring all our furniture from Cheshire. You see, I've been talking with my lawyer lately; for I don't feel I have much time left now. He says the estate is worth at least £15,000 today, at present inflated market values. I've argued with him, I've told him that I was going to ask you, Ronald, to take it over when I die, if you can, for not more than I – we – paid for it. That is, what it cost us to buy it and live here: say about £10,000. If I could I would give Orielton to you, on trust. But my lawyer says that's ridiculous – he's a good man, a little pigheaded but very kind at heart – and he won't let me do that, or even lease it to a nature-lovers' trust. Says death duties on the estate, even if I gave it away, would be too heavy. And I couldn't afford to give it to the National Trust, even if they would want such a remote place, in lieu of death duties. I have to think of my daughter's future, it would be unfair to poor little Mary; although goodness knows she's well provided for by Arthur's will. And that's another complication – his will rather ties me down, the lawyer says. Anyway,

Ronald, I've finally told my lawyer that you are to have first refusal before Orielton is put up for sale after my death. I hope you won't mind me saying all this? And meanwhile if you can be thinking of some way of buying it at a low price as a nature reserve and be planning to take it over, you yourselves or with your fellow naturalists, I would go to my grave a happier woman. What do you say?'

Never very talkative, always a good listener, it was a considerable effort for Alice to make these confidences and what seemed to me to be a generous offer. Afterwards she seemed happier; she relaxed with her head upon the faded lace antimacassar of the arm-chair, her sightless eyes closed, her thin face less wrinkled with care.

'I don't know what to answer, immediately,' I said at last. 'But first, thank you sincerely for the honour and trust your offer implies. I would love to take Orielton on myself, if only I had the means; but I haven't that amount of money, alas. However, you've given me a chance I shan't neglect. I'll certainly talk with a few influential friends who would be interested. Surely, between us, we ought to be able to raise enough. It will take time, but perhaps I'll be able to come to you and discuss a plan later? It would be wonderful if we could buy Orielton while you are still living here, Alice; for then you would enjoy knowing it was safe as a nature reserve, for all time. Wouldn't that please you? We'd want you to stay on indefinitely, of course.'

'Indefinitely, Ronald? My time is finite, and very soon . . .'

In my heart I was astonished, delighted, yet a little embarrassed, all at once. Embarrassed because I did not like to think that Alice, gentle, guileless lover of nature, was about to die – as surely, from her present fragile appearance, and her own desire, she was soon to do? I was also uneasy, in the silence which followed; I could feel that dangerous optimism rising – that weakness of mine of over-enthusiasm for any large enterprise of saving wild places and pristine country which had led me into so many adventures of building nature reserves which, when completed (and some were not), I would abandon to the care of less pioneering spirits. Selfishly too, I began to think – at that moment of utter silence in the winter dusk – with the bat still moth-hunting above our heads, of the exciting possibilities and the challenge of living in this lovely, attractively forlorn place. Since the war had driven me from my dream island of Skokholm after twelve years of happiness there, I had not gone back to live that idyllic but weather-beaten life. I had returned only long enough to re-establish the bird observatory I had created there and then hand it over to the West Wales Naturalists' Trust, of which I was a co-founder. Just now I was living very comfortably in an old rectory near Tenby, beside the Norman church of Gumfreston, which had a military-style watchtower with white owls and bats, a pre-Reformation bell, warm springs in its graveyard which were said to have miraculous healing powers, and hardly any human congregation. It was good bird country, with a great marshland below, and a noble view of Caldey Island and the Severn Sea . . .

Even if I could find the money, it would take time to adjust to such a change, plunging at my age into the work of managing forest, farm and manor house. As to the last, what should I do with that white elephant? The woods and the farms I could certainly cope with – as a lifelong naturalist and farmer. Yet in my heart I knew I was ready and eager to begin any such exciting adventure. I was ever a restless devil, a push-ahead-regardless pioneer rather than a satisfied squatter.

'It would take time,' I said to Alice again.

'There's very little left,' she sighed.

*   *   *

When Alice died a few weeks later, I was offered the first refusal of the Orielton estate at £12,500, lock, stock and barrel: the 260 acres of woodland, farm and water, with mill buildings, four cottages subject to existing tenancies at low rents, the four-acre walled gardens with tomato, peach and rose glasshouses (all very dilapidated, several with no glass left), 'Lily Pond and Ornamental Gardens and Walks now somewhat neglected'; and 'the Manor House with splendid public rooms and separate quarters for staff'. This option was open for ten days only. Otherwise Orielton would be advertised for sale at £15,000, and if not sold within a certain period, would probably be put up for auction.

It was a bad moment financially for me, and as it happened for the nation generally. There was no possibility of my raising so large a sum alone. I discussed the project with Lord Merthyr (President of our local naturalists' trust), Peter Scott, Julian Huxley, Max Nicholson, Fraser Darling and others, and at the Council (of which I was a member) of the wealthy Royal Society for the Protection of Birds, but no one offered much hope. So many more important, less risky conservation schemes needed immediate support.

One day Fraser Darling came to me at Gumfreston to say that he had been greatly tempted to buy Orielton for himself and his young family, but (I quote from my diary): 'I could just about find the money, but not the time to enjoy the lovely old place. I'm engaged with a three-year contract to study Highland red deer for the Nature Conservancy. They give me two fieldmen I must supervise. Then the Americans want me to advise on conservation projects. I'm torn to bits, for I've just walked in the peace and beauty of that historic estate and I'd love to retire and study there, in this mild Lusitanian climate.'

Peter Scott wanted me to pioneer a refuge like the one he was building at Slimbridge on the Severn Estuary, where I served on his scientific advisory committee. If I bought Orielton he would help me stock the wetland area with wild geese and ducks surplus to his collection at the Severn Wildfowl Trust. A generous offer from a generous and far-seeing friend.

'Thanks. But consider first all those foxes, otters and badgers; and the peregrine falcons and buzzards, which roam wild in Wales! The otters sometimes catch the ducks in the decoy pipe before we do! Greenslade keeps an otter trap going – when I am not there to prevent him!'

'Otters are a damn nuisance to a wildfowl collection,' said Peter. 'They'll bite through wire-netting. I don't blame Greenslade; we have to set humane vermin-traps at Slimbridge.'

Perhaps I am lazy, but I thought that I should hate to have to gamekeep Orielton for the sake of preserving a wildfowl zoo. And did I want thousands of human visitors like Peter? He had been wise in siting his splendid collection of water birds halfway between two large centres of population and patronage, Bristol and Gloucester; also it was on the flight-line and a wintering place of thousands of wild geese which visited the saltings there. But who would travel over a hundred miles to visit remote Orielton?

I have great respect and admiration for this talented naturalist, artist, champion glider pilot and amateur international helmsman, from many occasions when our lives have touched. One such was when Peter rang one day to ask me to take him out to

Ramsey Island, off the Pembrokeshire coast, in the middle of the winter.

'Whatever for?'

'It's fine weather just now. Aren't there lots of seals there?'

'They've finished pupping months ago.'

'Surely some left to look at?'

'A few worn-out bulls, I daresay, and the resident cow seals will be moulting.'

'That's fine. Besides, I hope we'll see some wild geese. Just for a few hours. I'm bringing one friend, only – male.'

The friend proved to be Peter Dawnay, an equerry of the Royal Household. I engaged a fast boat and we had a fine calm day roaming the island. We watched seals, saw no geese, but witnessed the gathering of a million starlings, wintering flocks from northern Europe, to roost in the safety of this rugged island, which has just one farm and no good harbour.

Peter Scott never confessed to me the true reason for this sudden unusual visit, but I was to find out when in the following summer H.M. Yacht *Britannia*, on a west coast cruise, suddenly diverted from its scheduled route and anchored off Ramsey. Queen Elizabeth, her husband and children, went ashore for a picnic on their own, watching sea-birds and seals. The plan and suitability – perfect seclusion, scenic beauty and natural amenities – for the royal adventure had been a well-kept secret for six months.

Julian Huxley – at a meeting of the scientific committee at Slimbridge – suggested that Orielton manor house should be made to pay as a retreat and research institute for scientists, biologists especially: 'Juliette and I would be the first to patronise you, dear boy. You know how we love your Pembrokeshire. And talking of ducks, do you remember that famous occasion during the war, when food was rationed, how we discovered nine mallard drakes, deep in moult, in a cave in the Island Farm cliffs? They had not lived in vain!'

I remember it well; not altogether without shame. A summer's day on holiday, idling in my Irish-built curragh along the north coast of Pembrokeshire. Perfect weather, the sea air gave you a vast appetite. Those drakes were fat, they could not fly, their old wing quills dropped; nor could they escape past us in the narrow cave where they were hiding by day. We dispatched all nine, I fear, consoling ourselves that the mallard is polygamous: a female mallard would never lack a male, but we at that moment of the war desperately lacked protein.

Discussing Orielton over lunch at the Savile Club with those good naturalists G. P. Wells, Eric Linklater, Richard Church and Compton Mackenzie, Compton spoke of his manor house at Denchworth:

'I'm happy there. I once thought I would go back and live on sweet Jethou in the Channel Islands after the war. I sighed for those jewelled days of island beauty – and all the semi-tropical shrubs I planted there. Of course the Germans had made a hell of a mess of the old house. But one must never go back in life. Go forward, and keep your sweet dreams of the past. They are more marvellous in memory than in fact, for in the dream the bitter winds are forgotten, the sun forever shining, the flowers never cease to bloom. Don't go back to your wild windy Welsh island of Skokholm, Ronald. Go forward to your lovely old Norman manor of Orielton. If I were your age, I'd have a crack at it myself! It looks wonderful, in the auctioneer's brochure. But I've got Denchworth Manor for my old age. It's not so old or grand or large as Orielton, but it's wonderful. Come and see it. I'll guarantee you the very best Scotch, unlimited!' (Sir Compton Mackenzie had just been awarded a bottle of whisky a week for life by the Whisky Distillers Association, for the publicity given in his famous farce *Whisky Galore*.)

The financial recession continued. Orielton remained unsold, and I was quoted a figure of £10,000 for a private sale, no time limit mentioned.

Six months, nine months, a year passed.

'A mortgage can be arranged.'

The helpful agent was on the phone again. He admitted he was troubled that the estate was proving difficult to sell. It was too remote and there was a continuing heavy liability for upkeep of its ancient manor and its old cottages. A caretaker had to be paid, the drives and outbuildings kept in reasonable repair. Why not make an offer? He would prefer to see me as owner. Did I know that before she died Alice Gaddum had told him that if Ronald Lockley wanted Orielton as a nature reserve he was to have special consideration over the price?

'Sorry, I've done my best to raise some money, but its useless. It's too tight everywhere.'

'Well, come and see me, and we'll arrange a mortgage.'

I did not go. I was busy trying to complete a book contract, as well as work out the coast path for the new Pembrokeshire National Park which I had helped Julian Huxley, Clough Williams-Ellis, Leonard Elmhurst, Lord Merthyr and others to plan.

A few weeks later the agent was again on the phone. His voice seemed to ooze some new delight.

'Come and see me – quickly! Good news!'

'What does that mean?' I whispered, suddenly hoarse with contagious excitement.

In his old-fashioned office in sleepy Pembroke town, in the shadow of the limestone walls of the castle which the Wiriet followers of William the Conqueror had helped to build, I was told I could have the Orielton estate for £5,000.

'Can you make it? It must be cash down. No other conditions whatsoever, except a reply within ten days. The solicitors are agreed you would be the most desirable owner because of Alice Gaddum's well-known wish, and your record of establishing nature reserves. There is nothing in the Gaddum will to say so; but we would have sold Orielton to Dr Fraser Darling for the same reason, if he'd been able to buy. I must say, however, the price then was considerably higher. I must add also that we have had to put a time limit on the offer because we have had other and higher, offers from less desirable sources. One is from a caravan park developer, the other is from a shooting syndicate.'

I was astounded, confused, delighted and a little wary. Where was the catch? Ready cash was one.

I had not got £5,000, in fact I was probably in debt, as usual, at the bank. I owned Gumfreston Old Rectory and a few acres around it; and now it seemed incredible that I had paid £500 more for that property than I was quoted for Orielton and its 260 acres! But in the present financial slump I would be lucky if I got £4,000 for Gumfreston.

My bank manager listened to the proposition with a frown. He reminded me once more that I was impecunious, and always short of cash, adding, with a sudden conciliatory smile, that all the same I had never let them down – so far. I was no longer impressed by this opening gambit; my brother – a successful business man living abroad – had lately advised me that bank managers (of whom I used to be scared) could easily be frightened by threatening to withdraw your overdraft, on which banks depended for their main profit.

'I need £5,000 immediately,' I told the manager, adding as he frowned without replying, 'and if you let me down, I shall have to go elsewhere.'

This bluff made him roar with laughter.

'Listen,' he chuckled, 'we lend money on the man himself, rather than his other assets. I have ascertained your account today is actually £13 13s 6d in credit. I'm surprised you didn't ask for £10,000, like the crafty borrowers who start by doubling the sum they really want. You might have got it. But your modesty is in your favour. That property as it stands is a dead loss; needs developing and the cottage rents should be trebled. I know the place well, I've walked it lately with one or two speculative buyers – including the caravan bloke and the sporting fraternity. But you're different – you're peculiar, if I may say so. You've no idea about money, and therefore I've a hunch you're the right person for Orielton, just what that glorious unprofitable place needs. I believe you'll win in the end. So I'm going to help you. You'll need to borrow up to at least £6,000. Well, you can have it. Just let me keep the title deeds safe in the bank – as security. No, don't thank me, this is strictly a business deal. Any time I can help, come and talk to me.' He added, as I appeared to be, and indeed was, stupified: 'Good, that's settled then. Oh, by the way, if you want a spare gun when the woodcock and woodpigeons come in November, I'll be grateful. Last time I walked those damp spinneys they were full of 'em. Not at all, not at all!'

My heart began pounding again, as it rose to its proper place from my boots.

*　　*　　*

'What on earth are you going to do with it? I thought you hadn't a sou in the world? I can tell you now – I'm certainly not coming to live in that great barn of a house, with fifty rooms, antiquated plumbing and a leaking roof!'

Thus my wife – and many other critics – at first. Later she, and some of the others, relented.

What indeed was I going to do with it? I did not know, precisely. I only knew I was tremendously excited. There was also that wish and half-promise, or rather burden of responsibility, that if I became owner I would maintain Orielton as a nature reserve, which haunted me when I remembered Alice Gaddum's dying request. If only that request had proved to be a practical bequest, with full financial support!

Yet, strangely, as I walked for the first time as owner in the beautiful woods and fields at midsummer, and beside the laughing stream and the lake white with water lilies, I forgot the financial liability. I was uplifted – as I had been in those first days of possession of Skokholm 27 years ago – by the wonder of the sight of and music of wild birds in their pristine environment. For watching them and nature had ever been my passion, and here, once more, it would find fulfilment – in the possession of this marvellously serene place, just the same size as that island, and ringed with a splendid ancient stone wall in place of the white Atlantic surf!

3

In the house of Stephen [Orielton] the spirit in a more extraordinary manner conversed with men, upbraided them openly with everything they had done from their birth, and which they were not willing should be known or heard by others. I do not presume to assign the cause of this event, except that it is said to be the presage of a sudden change from poverty to riches . . .

GIRALDUS CAMBRENSIS
Itinerary through Wales

Each evening the sight of white owls hunting around the lawns and fields warmed my heart anew. They were beautiful as they emerged at sunset from a gap in the eaves behind the lead box-spout which, handsomely decorated with the coat of arms of the Owen family, received the roof water at the top of a downpipe discreetly hidden by creeper and ivy. They would sit together for a few moments, like dignified miniature footmen: gold coat, white breast, trousers and spats, black eyes with upper lids decorously lowered against the rosy evening light.

They would preen, and talk, with a polite twittering conversation which now and then degenerated to less agreeable bill-snapping noises, as they took stock of weather, of food prospects, but little notice of the naturalist in faded corduroys who studied them through his binoculars forty feet below. Then one would silently depart, swinging away to the west side to look for the voles which were plentiful in the overgrown grass of the tennis courts; and its partner invariably coasted down towards the lily pond.

For many months the white owls had been the largest and most conspicuous inhabitants of the old manor. But they were not alone. There were a few thousand smaller individuals of many species when I became the first human for more than a year to sleep at Orielton. In order of size these were: owls and long-eared bats in the roof; mice and toads in the cellars; horse-shoe bats in the cavernous ice-house; honey bees passing under the eaves to

43

a vast ancient natural hive (which proved inaccessible to man) beneath the rafters; and numerous species of spiders, insects, mites, bacteria and fungi. This does not include the plant kingdom; the virginia creeper, ivy, clematis and old-fashioned musk roses – where many small birds nested and roosted – climbing at will over the exterior walls, reaching to the eaves, even beginning to block some of the windows; or the white and orange and goatsbeard lichens painting the exposed stonework and slates.

On the ground floor (called the 'public rooms' in the advertisement) and in the larger bedrooms there was still some old-fashioned furniture, which I had been requested to buy at valuation: those larger items which, on the death of Alice Gaddum, her daughter had not wanted for the much smaller home she now lived in, far from Orielton. These noble pieces had been there for many decades, some dating perhaps to the Owen dynasty over a hundred years ago. Dilapidated yet mellow, they pleased me because they seemed to have grown into the scene. Their presence had given the house a less forlorn and echoing state during the period it remained empty.

Arthur Gaddum had been fond of billiards: he had installed a full-size table and a parquet floor in one of the main bedrooms on the first floor. Its immense weight was having some effect on the thick centuries-old joists, so that its dead level had had to be adjusted at intervals as the floor groaned and subsided slowly, a few millimetres annually. One of the first things I did was to move this table two storeys down to the huge basement kitchen, which had a solid cobble floor hundreds of years old; an operation requiring four men and an expert from the firm who built the table. At the same time we moved the modern Esse stove which the Gaddums had installed in the kitchen up to the butler's pantry on the ground floor, where the afternoon sun flooded warmly through the western windows. That basement kitchen might have been good enough for servants in the feudal centuries, and it had a servants' hall close by, but it was almost windowless, looking out on a dark alleyway leading to the ice-house and the fuel caverns. I daresay Victoria wouldn't have complained, having seen similar sunless working quarters in the great houses of her native Spain. But what a lot of running up and down stairs to answer the bells it would mean, and what loading and unloading of trays and buckets etcetera that crazy hand-operated service lift entailed!

Besides, the basement kitchen had been the home of thousands of cockroaches during its last occupation. Fortunately they had all died in the period when the house was empty and cold, leaving their brown pupal cases behind the fittings which we had uprooted. I intended they should never re-colonise.

Victoria was to be content in the butler's pantry. As a kitchen it might be a bit small, but its windows were large, its ceiling high, and it was easy to adapt one window for the transit of supplies delivered by van over a little footbridge, crossing the alleyway below, which I put in.

I was alone that first night at Orielton, stretched out upon the enormous brass double bed in the vast principal bedroom. I doubt whether this monster had been moved from the room since the Owens had slept in it. The friendly ghosts of the Wiriets, Owens, Saurins, Mackworth-Praeds and others seemed to people the shadows of this splendid sleeping place. The bed was very soothing and welcoming with a modern mattress a foot thick, above an ancient well-sprung box mattress eighteen inches high.

Vaguely, as I drifted on the borders of a well-earned sleep, I remembered the poltergeist. In the last year, searching assiduously books and local archives, I had collected a growing file on Orielton's history. The earliest reference seems to be that of the nobleman Giraldus Cambrensis (Gerald the Welshman). A descendant of a Norman knight and a Welsh princess, he lived at Manorbier Castle, seven miles east as the raven flies from Orielton, at that time inhabited by Stephen Wiriet. In his *Itinerary of Archbishop Baldwin through Wales*, which took place 'in the year 1188 from the incarnation of Our Lord . . . when Saladin, prince of the Egyptians and Damascenes, by a signal victory gained possession of the Kingdom of Jerusalem, Baldwin, Archbishop of Canterbury, entered Wales' to preach the Third Crusade. In this book Giraldus, who accompanied Baldwin, relates the following ghost story:

> In this part of Penbroch, unclean spirits have conversed, not visibly, but sensibly, with mankind; first in the house of Stephen Wiriet, and afterwards in the house of William Not; manifesting their presence by throwing dirt at them, and more with a view of mockery than of injury. In the house of

45

William, they cut holes in the linen and woollen garments, much to the loss of the owner of the house and his guests; nor could any precaution, or even bolts, secure them from these inconveniences. In the house of Stephen, the spirit in a more extraordinary manner conversed with men, and, in reply to their taunts, upbraided them openly with everything they had done from their birth, and which they were not willing should be known or heard by others. I do not presume to assign the cause of this event, except that it is said to be the presage of a sudden change from poverty to riches, or rather from affluence to poverty and distress; as it was found to be the case in both these instances. And it appears to me to be very extraordinary that these places could not be purified from such illusions, either by the sprinkling of holy water, or the assistance of any other religious ceremony; for the priests themselves, though protected by the crucifix, or the holy water, on devoutly entering the house, were equally subject to the same insults. From whence it appears that things pertaining to the sacraments, as well as the sacraments themselves, defend us from hurtful, but not from harmless things; from annoyances but not illusions.

Those holes in the superstitious William Not's and his guests' clothing had obviously been made by the larvae of sundry clothes moths, several species of which are plentiful in such old houses. I had noticed their attacks upon the horsehair stuffing of the ancient chaise-longue in the first floor gallery, and hoped that the bats which every evening circulated there were taking due toll of the adult clothes-moths.

As for Stephen's poltergeist, goodness knows I had plenty of sins on my conscience, but at least the Wiriet evil spirit could not upbraid me in front of other men tonight, for there were none present. Besides, hadn't I read or heard somewhere that a later tenant of Orielton, a certain nobleman His Excellency Count Ramirez de Avellano, a devout who rented the house for a while, had set up a chapel in the dressing-room next door and had exorcised the ghost with the assistance of a priest? I must find out the truth of this sometime . . . and it was while my mind was wondering about the poltergeist and whether I was on the verge of poverty or affluence that it toppled over into sleep.

'Eeee-ee-yee-hi!'

I sat up violently, heart pounding disagreeably and scalp prickling.

But I could hear only the west wind moaning gently around the house; a sound eerie and inhuman enough in the darkness, to my half-awake senses.

'Eeee-ee-yee-hi!'

The terrifying screech was repeated, clearly to my ears now. It seemed to come from the gallery outside my door.

The silence which followed was soon broken by a muffled whispering and, as I prepared to defend myself against burglars, I waited breathlessly, fancying that I could hear ghostly footsteps approaching the door.

The whispering became a distinct hissing, and then a loud growling and snoring noise arose.

Of course, those white owls! They must have a second brood up there in the roof! I rushed to the gallery, laughing with relief, and listened through the open window to the owlish conversation above my head. Clearly I could hear the family reunion. The screeching had announced the return of the adults to the nest, laden with a mouse, vole or young rat, perhaps a bat; the young owls responding by hissing and squabbling over who should be served first, their enormous eyes gathering the weak midnight light like those of a cat.

On another occasion I heard a white owl strike the window of my lamp-lit room with a thud, and looking up I saw its ghostly form slip away into the night, leaving behind a powdery down from its feathers where wings and body had crashed momentarily against the glass. With very little imagination that transparent imprint could have been turned into an evil face with devil ears, and with the shrieking and hissing noises of the owls added, it could have given rise to the legend of the Wiriet ghost. It is easy for the non-naturalist to be terrified by the white owl's shrieks by night. They resemble the long wail of a human being in agony, as at the tightening of rack or thumbscrew – a torture popular in the days of Stephen and Giraldus.

When Jesus and Victoria first heard that blood-curdling owl shriek, they wanted to leave next morning and had to be restrained and soothed by my laughing explanation that it was a perfectly natural phenomenon, that these owls lived on rats and mice, which Victoria feared. Jesus vowed he would get rid of the owls. He wanted to shoot them.

'I, Jesus, I crack shot, sure gun-man, served in Spanish army. Won medal. Please lend Jesus gun, Señor Don Ronald.'

I forbade him to handle any gun, making the excuse that it was a serious offence for a foreigner in Britain to go about armed. Jesus knew I had a gun locked up in the armoury cupboard which I had inherited as part of the office or study, where former squires had kept their weapons, including Sir Arthur Owen his halberds. But this gun was not mine. Alf Hitchcox had given it to me on permanent loan, saying he was too old to handle it any longer; but it was, he said, a lovely tool, had belonged to his gamekeeper father and its only weakness now was that it was liable to fall apart when fired, which was why I should keep the stock carefully bandaged. I had told Alf I did not want a gun, I never used one. But he had thrust it into my arms, with cleaning rod and a box of very old cartridges.

I was soon to realise that Jesus, a superstitious peasant at heart (but with certain admirable traits of tenaciousness) nursed and enjoyed a vendetta; it pleased him for many months to occupy his idle moments with plotting to overthrow these night birds which disturbed his sleep. He warned me that they were considered evil in Spain and would bring bad luck to those who harboured them. He would tell Victoria not to look when he saw one of an evening.

'Some birds wicked, others ver' good. If stork make nest on house, that's ver', ver' lucky. It means baby soon.'

No such luck; I did not tell Jesus that storks were never seen wild in Wales. Poor owls! From the Bible onwards the owl is reputed to be an abomination to man, unclean, a funereal bird of ill omen. Pliny wrote 'the scritch-owl foretells always some dark news, and is most execrable and accursed in presaging of public events'. Shakespeare says:

> The scritch-owl, scritching loud,
> Puts the wretch that lies in woe
> In remembrance of a shroud.

Perhaps Jesus had been taught to believe in the Latin prescription (which Pliny scorned as a magician's lie) for discovering the truth about a woman's character: 'Lay the heart of a scritch-owl upon the left pap of a woman as she lies asleep, she will disclose and utter all the secrets of her heart.'

He was at last to have some satisfaction in the matter of screech owls one day a year later.

In the uncut grass of the unused tennis courts the numbers of field voles were building up, and in that summer the cycle was at a peak – usually reached every third year. As a result of this abundant food supply the owls again raised a large brood in the manor roof.

When the young owls began to fly they were at first inexpert and needed to perch often. On one overcast afternoon a newly-fledged white owl, obviously too hungry to wait until dusk, wavered across the tennis lawns, made an unsuccessful grab at a vole in the grass, then flipped up to perch upon a fence post. Jesus and I, having a cup of tea beside the kitchen window, saw a large hawk suddenly descend from a nearby tree and, hardly pausing in flight, snatch up the owl and fly towards the cover of the woodland. I was surprised, for buzzard and owl are rival predators of much the same size, although the owl weighs a good deal less.

Jesus was delighted, but I leaped out of the window, and ran after the buzzard. It dropped its victim, which flew feebly into the deep wood. The buzzard followed. Neither was seen again; but a year later the same thing happened.

This time I rescued the owl, which was too wounded to fly away (the rapier-sharp talons of the hawk are invariably driven deep into the body of its victim) and nursed it indoors. It sat upright, gazing wisely at me with its splendid ebony eyes. But it refused to eat and died a few days later. Jesus, expert at eviscerating poultry, asked for the corpse, saying he wanted to stuff it. He dissected it carefully, and informed me that it had died of a 'bleeding heart' . . . whatever that might mean in the hidden recesses of his superstitious mind.

While the beautiful young owl lived it was perfectly tame, and allowed me to stroke and examine it, and study its remarkable visual and auditory acuity. Generally birds have small well-hidden ears, but those of the owl, although masked by the wide facial ruff surrounding the large eyes, are funnel-shaped receptors which can be directed upon and tuned to receive the faintest nocturnal sound of nature – the insect or mouse moving in the grass, the

itch of the sparrow sleeping in the ivy on the wall. The vibrations set up by these weak noises cause sound waves to strike through the flexible opening of the owl's outer ear to the auditory nerve attached to the drum of the inner ear and, translated to electrical impulses of varying intensity, reach the information centre of the brain. In the owl the number of special nerve sells or neurons which receive and analyse this auditory information in the medulla is relatively enormous, nearly 10,000, which is far in excess of that of many larger birds and mammals.

Further, as the ear openings of owls are asymmetrical, being placed higher on one side of the head than on the other, it can the more quickly detect the source of the sound (of hidden prey) in relation to the owl's position and line of vision. In other words it can receive two sound images from the same (or from separate) sources but at different intensity and 'home' (navigate by two co-ordinates) on to its prey the more accurately. In the dusk its ears become as the eyes of birds, such as waders and game species, which have 'side vision', that is a wide field of perception between 180° and 360°. But while the comparatively small eyes of the woodcock (fixed close to the top of its head) have a total field of view of 360°, the owl's huge eyes are rigid in their sockets and directed forward, giving it a highly concentrated binocular vision of only about 70° of the field.

The owl's eyes are relatively very much larger than ours (in the largest owls they can weigh as much as a man's) with much greater acuity to distinguish the fine details of objects at close range. In man, a similar binocular vision is not accompanied by the same considerable sensitivity to make the best use of poor light, which owls and other night birds possess in common with the nocturnal cats. The eyes of these night creatures have a large protruding cornea or window to admit all the available light to the almost round lens (much flatter in diurnal animals) which throws a brighter image on the retina. In the owls the back of the eye is less pigmented and therefore less light-absorbing. Instead, any unabsorbed light is reflected back through the eye, increasing the sensitivity of the receptor cells, which are numerous and may be packed in layers. No wonder then that the eyes of my poor sick owl shone so brilliantly with light reflected from the lamp in my hand when, about dusk, I brought its supper of mouse which it was too ill to eat.

The owl's method of hunting is to beat slowly over its familiar home territory, eyes focused upon the ground, ears tuned to catch the familiar sounds of prey it might not first see. Informed by ear of the position of hidden prey, it hovers above, ready to pounce, perhaps upon the blades of grass disturbed by its victim. The long talons reach down into the grass in a vigorous snatch, often without success. Then it resumes its hunt, noiseless because the flight feathers have downy, trailing edges which cause no resonance. If successful the owl takes its prey in its claws to a perch where it devours it at leisure, or, transferring it to its bill, carries it to the nest.

Small mammals burrowing in the grass and forest litter were

the main food of the three species of owl breeding at Orielton. In the autumn it was common to find lying in the open many adult shrews, which, worn out after one intensive breeding season – their short life-span of eighteen months completed – had died suddenly, often still in good condition. Few scavengers would pick up these corpses. The shrew has an unpleasant musky smell distasteful to cats and dogs, but the owls, seeking moving prey, readily devour live shrews.

Shrews, voles and mice were commonly taken alive in the Longworth traps we used at Orielton. These traps are ingenious, with a funnel entrance to a larger compartment where bait and a bunch of dry grass attract the hungry visitor; a trip-bar closes the door behind the entrant, and usually I would find the prisoner asleep in a nest it had fashioned out of the hay by the time I made my morning inspection. I marked each by clipping its fur with scissors and released it after weighing and measuring.

In the damp woodland the handsome water shrew *Neomys fodiens*, black above and white beneath, went about its affairs in the low vegetation and in tunnels in the ground. In the Lily Pond and the pools in the Japanese Garden it swam in search of young fishes, caddis-worms, beetles, tadpoles, young frogs and dragonfly larvae, a silvery torpedo with translucent air bubbles clinging to its dense velvet fur. Like the mole, its fur is reversible, which enables it to dry out quickly by squeezing its body – forwards or backwards – through the narrow passages of its underground runways. Surplus moisture which might chill the body is swiftly dissipated; in fact, the water shrew's fur is as dense and oily as a seal's.

Altogether *Neomys fodiens* is a fascinating creature, living happily in water or damp ground. It digs its own burrow system which usually has an entrance under water as well as a vent for air and exit in the dry bank above. We found a few nests with young some distance from water. It produces three litters in summer, each of five to seven blind naked young. The weaned water shrew leaves home early, and wanders far in search of winter quarters. We would find one occasionally, warmly holed up behind household junk stored in the dank basement.

Like all shrews it is carnivorous and has a tremendous appetite during its active life in summer, and is said to eat its own weight in food each day then. The bite of the water shrew is somewhat poisonous, enabling it to paralyse its prey for the purpose of storing it temporarily, in a moribund condition, in a special underground chamber or larder. To assist in swimming, its feet and tail are fringed with long stiff hair or bristles which act as auxiliary flippers and rudder respectively.

The common and pigmy shrews *Sorex araneus* and *minutus* lived semi-commensally in the drier habitats at Orielton, eating much the same insect and small invertebrate food. Sometimes we caught both in the same trap, in a hedge or woodland site. It is a rule in nature that two related species cannot co-exist, except parasitically or in ecological isolation, and I soon found that the pigmy qualified under the latter definition. It lived in smaller burrows than its larger cousin, and could forage above ground in bush and low trees, occasionally adopting an abandoned nest in one of our bird boxes. This climbing ability, not possessed by the common shrew, explains its longer, partly prehensile, tail.

When caught in the same trap, the pigmy stayed as far from the common shrew as the space permitted, frequently screaming fear or defiance; or they fought to the death, the survivor usually devouring the vanquished.

Shrews live at a tremendous pace. Except when breeding, they are solitary and aggressive, driving out their own young as soon as they are old enough to leave the nest. They run and dart through the daily or nightly search for food, which they devour alive as they press it to the ground.

Years ago, when we were making a film of the life of the gannet* on Grassholm, a remote islet in the Atlantic, some twenty miles west of Orielton, Julian Huxley gave me a copy of a book of poems Blackwell had published while he was still a young man. I make no further excuse, in rounding off this glimpse of the Orielton shrews, than that he gave me permission to quote this amusing comment on the life of the shrew:

> Timid atom, furry shrew,
> Is it a sin to prison you?
> Through the runways in the grass
> You and yours in hundreds pass
> An unimagined world of shrews,

* *The Private Life of the Gannet*, backed by London Films, which won an Oscar in America.

A world whose hurrying twilight news
Never stirs but now and then
The striding world of booted men.
Fear and greed are masters there,
And flesh and blood go clothed in hair;
Life hurries without Power, and Mind,
Cocooned in brain, is almost blind.
And yet 'tis wild, and strange, and free –
And all that shrews can ever be.
What is it, Shrew? I fain would know. . . .
– Dumbness and fright, I let you go!
'Tis not by holding in the hand
That one can hope to understand;
Truth was never prisoned yet
In cage of Force, in Matter's net.
The body of a shrew is small,
Of man is big; but after all
Not so am I more great than you –
It is the soul that makes the shrew.
Go back to twitter out your life
Of obscure love and timid strife!
To learn the secret of your kind,
I will pursue you with my mind.

*   *   *

Eric Hosking had told me of his harrowing experience (later described in his autobiography *An Eye for a Bird*) when a tawny owl, whose nest he had been photographing, suddenly attacked him, striking his face and tearing out one eye. It made me nervous and careful when I suddenly came face to face with a tawny owl sitting on a nest at eye level in a hole in the ha-ha of the American Garden. I stepped back hurriedly. She rustled her wings slightly, expanding her feathers so as to appear enormous, glaring at me with dark shining eyes.

She was to get used to my periodic visits, and developed the amusing habit of winking at me, usually with her right eye. I say *she* because I believe that only the female incubates. She is larger than her mate. From a safe distance, since I dared not handle her, I sprayed a spot of white paint on her golden crown feathers, so as to identify her.

The tawny owls were rarely active by day. But early in spring, as darkness closed in on a fine calm night, you would hear their conversational calls, the male singing his musical hoot to attract a mate and receiving a clicking answer from the hen bird.

'Hoo-oo,' a pause, then a mellow resonant long-drawn 'hoo-oo-oo!'

And the female's response, 'Kee-wick! Kee-wick!'

The tawny owls hunted the rides of the woodland and along the edge of the fields, not poaching on the open-country preserves of the white owls. The male, sleeping by day in deep cover in the trees, where later in the summer the female joined him, would begin the night's activity by calling – to announce his whereabouts. I could not determine if he brought his wife food while she was incubating – this is rare in owls. But later he was busy sharing the task of feeding the owlets with her.

After an hour or so of hunting, the adult owl retired to rest and digest at one or other of several perching sites. There was a further period of hunting before the light of another dawn showed in the sky. These day roost and night perching places were easily re-cognisable from the droppings, and numerous pellets, beneath them. The pellets were of typical shape and composed of the indigestible remains – bones, fur, feather and chitinous parts of insects – of their normal prey, which are commonly vomited by owls, hawks and some other gross-feeding predators. Usually two or three pellets were ejected nightly. These neat, fluffy bundles could be teased apart with needle and pincers, or separated in water.

From their contents it was clear that the Orielton tawny owls were feeding principally on all three shrews, both bank and field voles, wood (long-tailed) mouse, occasionally a house-mouse or a mole, twice a very young rabbit, and once a red squirrel. Bird feathers and skulls were not numerous: I identified those of house-sparrow, blackbird, song thrush, starling, dunnock and chaffinch in the pellets. Remains of insects and worms could have come from the stomachs of the larger victims although the tawny owl is known to pounce on moths, beetles, frogs, newts and even small fishes.

It was a good year for voles and mice, and the pair in the American Garden reared four young. There seemed to be a large number of these wood owls (as they are often called – also known as brown owls) in my first two years at Orielton, judging by the nightly hooting. Approximately eight pairs were then breeding in the 150 acres of woodland. But in later years, with the rodent cycle at a lower population level, tawny owl numbers fell to half, and even these four pairs seemed to have small success in rearing owlets. The ratio of predator to prey remains fairly stable in order to maintain the food chain; if one link is weak numerically, the other links are forced to adjust in order to survive.

In a good season, with abundant plant and seed food, the voles and mice and shrews may build up to a considerable density – perhaps up to 1,500 individual voles per acre. Then adverse weather, such as drought, or severe frost or flooding, will cause a great mortality, gradual or sudden, through competition for the scarce, palatable foods, and the subsequent semi-starvation or at least malnutrition, followed by those viral or bacterial diseases which attack overcrowded and under-nourished communities of any species, from plants to man.

Studies of communities of voles, mice and lemmings have shown that the number of individuals which survive such a 'crash' can be as few as two per cent of the highest maximum. For instance, on Skokholm Island the only rodents are rabbit and house-mouse; both can build up to 10,000 individuals in a summer of good feeding, but there are periodic 'crashes' in the lean days of a long severe winter. The late-born young are first to die, driven from the better feeding areas by hungry adults. Then the old adults die, not of age (almost no wild animals die of old age), but of exhaustion and because they are unable to compete with the younger, more vigorous, adults born early in the spring which have had time to fatten over the summer. The rabbit has its own birth control device which slows down production of too many young in any bad season, and its crashes are less severe and occur at longer intervals. But in the house-mouse at Skokholm (accidentally introduced there over half a century ago), which occupies unchallenged the outdoor niches of the absent wood mouse, a crash occurs every winter in this short-lived rodent. From an estimated population of 10,000 by the autumn, it is reduced to only about 150 by the following spring; these, can however, reproduce so rapidly when the vegetation shoots in the spring that they can be the progenitors of another 10,000 young mice by the ensuing autumn!

At Orielton the tawny and white owls, their whole economy geared to prey on small rodents in their respective hunting grounds of woodland cover and open fields, suffered correspondingly when this food supply periodically crashed. They reared no young and the number of pairs diminished by natural losses over the winter. Of those which survived and were strong enough to mate in the spring, unless the food supply of small rodents bounded upwards (as it often did after a crash), the female would lay a small clutch, but she might give up incubation (or, rarely, starve to death on the nest) because the male, finding it difficult to procure food, ate what he caught instead of feeding her. So the density of our resident owls depended on the availability of their rodent diet; the pendulum of population swung between years of plenty and scarcity.

In mild autumns, when the small rodents and shrews were plentiful, other owls moved in to share the feast. The short-eared owl, which nests on moorland and open, remote islands, was a winter visitor. But it did not compete in working hours with the resident owls. It hunted in daylight, its splendid golden wings flapping with a leisurely, silent grace, its brilliant binocular yellow eyes staring down into the withered grass of the fields and marshy corners.

The little owl *Athene noctua* – the foreign owl, as it was called locally – preferred less open country, with a few old trees in which it could perch and study the ground, alert to pounce on insect or small mammal. It began hunting late in the afternoon, rested most of the night, and made a further sally at dawn. One pair had settled in the dismantled fireplace of the first floor (only there was no floor left) of the southern gatehouse or gazebo. These charming birds, no larger than a dove or blackbird, are named after Athene, Greek goddess of wisdom and, with their neat coiffure, and golden eyes staring fixedly from the pale facial disc, ringed finely with the sepia spangling of their plumage, they seem to portray a timeless sagacity and dignified calm.

They were almost tame, or perhaps they hoped to escape observation by their very stillness. They did not object to my quiet movements a few feet below their retreat. I was not altogether warm-hearted about their presence; on Skokholm they had fed too exclusively upon the storm-petrels which I had been studying. They could easily catch these dainty little sea-birds which came in from the ocean at dusk, and fluttered vulnerably a moment or two as each alighted at the narrow entrance to the crevice in which it nested – just long enough for the little owl to snatch it up. Athene developed the calamitous habit of beheading each petrel and storing the carcase in its 'larder' in a rabbit-burrow. One such larder contained the fresh bodies of more than a hundred beheaded petrels. Yet so beautiful were these owls, when I captured them at their larder, that I could not kill them. After all, it was not their fault that Lord Lilford had introduced them a hundred years ago, and they had spread over southern England and Wales. I asked a friend living in Bath to release this island pair in that salubrious neighbourhood, and I am glad to say they never returned.

Here on the mainland there were no storm-petrels and, although little owls are commonly accused of taking the chicks of game birds, their diet is innocuous and possibly beneficial, on balance, to man. At Orielton in winter their pellets contained up to 50 per cent remains of small mammals, the largest of these a mole and young rat; in the summer bird bones and feathers, identified as chiefly those of very young individuals, made up less than five per cent; at all times their diet includes of a great variety of insects and earthworms.

When in April a cock starling took up residence opposite the owls' roost in the Folly, and began to chuckle and wheeze his invitation to a female to join him, the little owls appeared to take no notice of this vulgar noise, in which the cries of curlew, cuckoo, lark, even of the owls themselves, to say nothing of a very accurate imitation of a human 'wolf-whistle', were included. Doubtless the owls had long noted the ravens which by that month had fledged children hopping out of the nest twenty feet above upon the parapet of the Folly, wide open to salt wind from the sea – birds too large for a little owl to tackle. When a female starling appeared and the male redoubled his vocal blandishments, and wooed her to take possession of the joist-hole in the wall which he had already untidily stuffed with straw and grass, the owls still remained aloof. So I have seen a sparrow nesting unmolested, in the edge of the stick nest of an eagle – in Spain; and jackdaws nesting in fissures of a Welsh cliff, hardly one metre below the open eyrie of a peregrine falcon.

Predator and prey were too busy about their own domestic

affairs; perhaps familiarity breeds indifference, rather than contempt, in the world of nature? The owls were now nesting themselves – in the dark hollow where once an Adam fireplace had been. Taking a ladder there one day in May, I found Athene sitting close on four dull white eggs. She slipped away on silent wings when I gently pushed a stick towards her breast.

The young starlings were ready to fly during the week when the owlets hatched. And now, in the hour of need for extra food, the attack was launched. For five days, early each morning, one by one the five young starlings were dragged screaming from their nest, killed and fed to the owlets. The parents put up a good fight (as I witnessed one morning), stabbing, leaping around the raider and cursing. But the owl, swivelling its head (owl eyes are fixed, and unable to move in their sockets) to face the anguished starlings, was not intimidated; it proceeded calmly to collect the daily ration from the live larder in the joist hole. In five days none was left, and the adult starlings wisely flew away, brave but beaten, before their turn came to be eaten.

Feeding largely on pasture grubs and pests, starlings are useful to the farmer, but in summer they were not plentiful in this sparsely inhabited western land. In winter immense flocks invaded Wales, moving south and west from the frost and snow of the Continent, seeking our mild shores. At dusk the chattering multitudes of immigrants settled to roost in large reed-beds and rhododendron coverts, and many flew out to the safety of uninhabited offshore islands, where there are no four-legged predators to disturb their sleep.

These were foreigners, however, and although our resident, stay-at-home, starlings might join these regimented squadrons sweeping across a local pasture in a concerted feeding movement during the day, the locals returned at sunset faithfully, to roost at home. A favourite site was the thick ivy, virginia creeper and clematis clinging to the tall walls of the manor.

4

I think I could turn and live with animals,
  they are so placid and self-contain'd,
I stand and look at them long and long.
They do not sweat and whine about their condition,
They do not lie awake in the dark and weep
  for their sins,
They do not make me sick discussing their
  duty to God,
Not one is dissatisfied, not one is demented with
  the mania of owning things,
Not one kneels to another, nor to his kind that
  lived thousands of years ago,
Not one is respectable or unhappy over the
  whole earth.

WALT WHITMAN
Song of Myself

'I will meet you anywhere in Pembrokeshire you care to name. I am trying to locate local starling roosts – just a holiday pastime.'

Thus Max Nicholson (whom I had never met) on a winter holiday from his normal occupation, which at various times has included a secretaryship to the Privy Council, co-founder of PEP (Political and Economic Planning), and of the British Trust for Ornithology and the Nature Conservancy. He had reviewed my first research paper (on the life of the Manx shearwater) with praise. I knew him by repute as an amateur naturalist and writer. I had greatly admired his early book, *How Birds Live*.

'As I have never been to the top of Pembrokeshire's highest mountain, although I have lived most of my life in the county, I suggest we meet there at the trig. station, at noon on Boxing Day. Presceli Top is exactly one-third of a mile above sea-level, so it won't be too strenuous. We might even see snow-buntings at this time of year.'

'Feeding on molinia roots?'

'Ah, you know those birds?'

'I've studied snow-buntings in Greenland.'

'Splendid, I'll meet you at Presceli Top, but only if there's no mist – and there often is!' I put the phone down.

There was a thick sea-mist, and I did not go. However, Max wrote that he had climbed the mountain and on the way back had traced starling flight-lines converging at dusk on a roost in the vast rhododendron coverts of a 'secret' place – a valley he was stopped from entering. This hid an underground arsenal of the War Department, so hush-hush that it was well-known to everyone living locally (many nearby residents worked in the catacombs. It was a tribute to the Nazi spy network during the war that Lord Haw-Haw used to announce in his English propaganda broadcasts from Germany the details of the building of the tunnels of this hidden arsenal as each was completed!).

A few months before I bought Orielton Nicholson was appointed Director-General of the new British Nature Conservancy. At the stately headquarters in Belgrave Square he invited me to undertake a field study of the wild rabbit. Myxomatosis, an epidemic non-fatal disease of the Brazilian rabbit, had proved almost one hundred per cent lethal in hutch-bred European rabbits imported into South America. A certain doctor had obtained the virus and introduced it to his rabbit-plagued estate near Paris, and it was rapidly sweeping across western Europe. If it crossed the English Channel the disease would result in tremendous vegetational and other ecological changes in the British countryside, notoriously overrun at present by rabbits. There would, of course, be joy among the farmers and foresters, who would doubtless try to spread the disease, but there would be alarm and despondency among the shooting and poaching fraternity, deprived of their principal quarry. Also, it was such a horrible-looking disease in its final stages of blindness and deafness, that there would be a great outcry from the humanitarians . . .

'My concern is with the changes which the virtual disappearance of the rabbit would cause to the flora and fauna of the many new nature reserves the Conservancy is setting up,' said the far-sighted Max. 'As you have knowledge of the disease from the pre-war experiments with the virus which Sir Charles Martin carried out for the Australian Government – on your island of Skokholm – part of your rabbit research will be to ascertain the facts about its introduction and progress in France.'

'It was, of course, a failure twenty years ago, at Skokholm. I had hoped it would – as Sir Charles Martin promised – exterminate the island rabbits, and so I could keep more sheep there. But although all the rabbits which Sir Charles inoculated with the virus at Skokholm died, the disease did not spread. Quite inexplicable, since the same highly lethal strain of the virus had just wiped out the wild rabbits in small experimental enclosures Sir Charles had set up at Cambridge.'

'You will have to try to find out why, and what the vectors of the disease are. Just now the mass media is becoming hysterical about myxomatosis and its likelihood of reaching Britain. No one seems to know much about wild rabbits and their habits. The Conservancy must get busy, quickly, on a serious scientific study.'

'Difficult. How do you study an animal which is largely nocturnal, and lives underground?'

'As you have successfully studied shearwaters and storm-petrels, which are both nocturnal and live underground, at Skokholm, I imagine you'll find a way.'

In a flash of inspiration I had the answer – Orielton!

I told Max of my new opportunity to buy an old walled estate in Wales. It was overrun with rabbits. The only way to study them would be to keep a group of marked individuals under reasonable control and regular observation in large enclosures. In fact, isolate them as if they were confined on small natural islands, but where there was space for them to find enough food and behave as normal free individuals – except that they would be unable to escape altogether.

The idea grew rapidly, even as we talked. I was excited. It was all possible – if I bought Orielton. Here was a further incentive . . .

'It's up to you,' said Max. 'Orielton sounds ideal. In any case, prepare your plan for a field study as soon as possible, and I'll consider it while you go off to France at once, and report on what is happening there at the moment. A conflicting situation by all counts: the rabbit is considered not a pest but the principal beast of the chase and is protected by law for most of the year!'

It was – by a nine-months' close season, as I found when I interviewed Dr Armand Delille at his vast medieval Chateau Maillebois. He had introduced the virus of myxomatosis with spectacular, lethal effect within the walls of his estate, twice as large as the walled estate in Wales of which I was about to become owner.

The doctor, well-known for his research on the bacteria of tuberculosis, was a troubled man when we walked and talked in the beautiful wooded grounds, now virtually free of the rabbit pest. He was being prosecuted by the hunting clubs of France, and praised by the few landowners anxious to improve agriculture and forestry.

'I am damned, with faint praise, as we say. The French Ministry of Agriculture is secretly pleased, yet financially worried because it derives a large income annually – well over a million – from gun licences, and as hunters obtain licences chiefly to shoot rabbits, this revenue will drop very low. But I am not guilty of spreading the disease throughout France, as the Press say. I have refused to allow any sick rabbits to be taken from my property. All the same, people have come by night, scaled the walls and carried off infected rabbits.'

The prosecution was to fail on this technicality: Delille had not himself allowed the diseased rabbits to escape. Later he was awarded a gold medal (depicting a sick rabbit!) by the French Academy of Agriculture.

It is relevant to mention here the study which I undertook for the Conservancy (which has been published in book form as *The Private Life of the Rabbit*) because the grant I received over four years of observation was a considerable help in the difficult period of financing Orielton and building up the small farm to that state of profitability which would, I hoped, allow me to continue solvent thereafter by private enterprise.

Myxomatosis spread so rapidly through Britain, chiefly by way of infected rabbits deliberately introduced the length and breadth of the land, that it appeared at Orielton soon after I took possession. In a few weeks it was difficult to find a healthy rabbit anywhere. This was awkward for my life history study. I had to obtain a nucleus for my enclosures from my old home, the disease-free island of Skokholm. And in due course I was to discover why Sir Charles Martin's experiment of introducing the virus there failed. For some unknown reason there are no rabbit fleas on that remote island. And the rabbit's own specific flea *Spillopsyllus cuniculi*, as I was quickly able to prove in the first few months of my Conservancy research, is the principal vector of the virus in Britain, carrying the virus in its saliva after biting a myxomatous rabbit. Lacking these fleas, Skokholm has remained free of the disease, a useful reservoir of healthy rabbits, much studied subsequently by scientists.

*　　　*　　　*

The Lily Pond at midsummer was crowded with white water-lilies. In the deeper open centre, young coot swam and dived and cried querulously to their parents in the sultry noon. Families of mallard were already well-grown. In the Japanese Garden the water had sunk to a marshy bog in which the lovely variegated mimulus dominated the centre, with cohorts of purple loosestrife, yellow flag and bur-reed a vivid backdrop lively with the songs of sedge-warbler and reed-bunting.

From the little observation hut we built high up in a decayed elm, the small events of the wood, water and meadow enclosed by the high netting of the rabbit fence provided entertainment for the watcher perched there, hidden from the watched ones. Not only did I and my relief helpers put down on paper every activity of the rabbits, each identified by a numbered ear-tag, in the several enclosures around the old elm, but we also made notes on the birds and other wild creatures. The recording pencil scribbled steadily after each bout of observation with eye and binoculars.

The bustling rabbit activity was most visible at dawn and attracted the attention of other than human watchers then. There were predators: although buzzards could not carry off a full-grown rabbit, they would pounce on a young 'kitten' when it first appeared above ground at about three weeks old. The buzzards would make a sudden silent sally from a perch, far more effective than the clumsy hunting technique of the ravens, which hopped about near a nursery burrow, too slow to capture a healthy baby rabbit – in fact, they were searching for sickly and diseased ones, of which during the late epidemic of myxomatosis they had had more than they could eat. Birds were a natural acceptable predation.

Often in the dawn watch I would see a fox slink along outside the netting, or sit for a while gazing longingly at the enclosed inaccessible rabbits. But some of the local tame and gone-wild cats learned to claw their way up the support posts and spring down inside. I regarded this as an artificial, and intolerable, source of predation. To shoot these unwelcome cats would cause too much disturbance. It was easier to make my counter-attack with a weapon which for years had lain idle in the shed in the Decoy Wood, and which the decoyman Greenslade said was an otter-trap. It was quite simple, a large wire cage with a trigger upon which a piece of fish was firmly tied. One tug at the bait released the spring door which was then locked by a falling wire bar. For otters this trap would be set on the edge of the pond, chained to a stake pegged below the water line; before the victim could bite its way out, its struggles would topple the trap under the water and drown the otter.

This trap was successful – the fish bait was irresistible – and caught most of the cats which had started this habit of climbing into the rabbit enclosures. All except one – a vivid ginger tabby with pale goat-eyes.

You had to admire that feline visitor not only for its intelligence in avoiding the trap, but also for its perfection of form and fitness for survival; it belonged to no one, but only its superb sleek slinking self, sublimely indifferent to my efforts to capture it. Yet I had begun to hate it. It was decimating my supply of young rabbits in the study enclosures; and I was extremely angry one day to find it eating a beautiful cock bullfinch in the American Garden, one of its favourite haunts. In the midst of my daily communion with nature, enjoying those small phenological events – perhaps some newly-arrived bird or wild flower – which diverted my mind from the pettiness of financial or other problems, my composure would be shattered by an encounter with Madame Goateyes. She would watch me disdainfully, not allowing me to approach her, yet not scurrying away if I kept my distance. Little heaps of feathers told of her latest meal.

There is always a scattered population of gone-wild domestic cats and their descendants roaming the countryside. These originated in, and from time to time are augmented by, cats and kittens callously abandoned by their owners, often on the excuse that they were moving to live in another district. I frequently found a kitten too young to hunt food successfully, starving and too weak to crawl, and no doubt some of these waifs were put out of their misery by dogs or foxes.

But Madame Goateyes was in splendid condition, on her diet of small mammals and my cherished wild birds. At first I had thought that golden cat was male, it ranged the woods and enclosures in such a lordly way; and perhaps I had rather identified myself with the footloose slinking creature, for I too had been incorrigibly restless, seeking to explore, longing for new horizons, to be reaching to the stars and living free. Until one winter morning I saw that her ginger-striped belly was swelling in the family way, so after all she was a queen cat, the worst sort to be, with her potential for populating Orielton with more bird-eating progeny.

Days later I saw her crouching near the bird table in front of my study window, half concealed in the aromatic plants of the miniature herb-garden I had planted there. She suddenly sprang upon a sparrow, too late for me to intervene. I don't particularly welcome the greedy vulgar sparrows which will often clean up the food before the shy finches, nuthatches and woodpeckers arrive. But when, on the following day, I saw her creeping towards a handsome cock greenfinch which was feeding on the ground on wheat spilled from the bird table, I flung up my window and yelled her away.

Soon after, Victoria brought my morning coffee, and looking out of the window, said casually: 'Don Ronald, Victoria see lovely gold cat! She soon be having babies. She ver' hungry. You like Victoria give her bowl of milk?'

'Victoria! If you succeed in enticing that cat into the house, I'd be glad. For I shall at once drown it, I warn you! Be satisfied you've got your Mr X – though I admit you have so pampered and overfed him that he's too lazy to go and look for a bird, or even a mouse any more.'

Victoria, like most domesticated women, adored cats. She had managed to hide a young kitten in her bedroom for a while; when I discovered the deception and said it would have to be drowned, she burst into floods of tears. Jesus was furious with me and said untruthfully that the house was overrun with mice. I had to let her keep it, but I made sure it was neutered. It soon became very fat and lazy. She called it by some incomprehensible Andalusian term of endearment, which we translated into 'Mr X'.

Mr X developed into an oversized black and tan with long fur and a white bow-tie. He was so much indulged by everyone for his friendly, aristocratic ways, that even I accepted him – when he leaped upon my lap as we sat in front of the evening fire. My sons were soon deeply attached, and bought him a handsome fireside basket, a bargain at a local jumble sale. Victoria was jealous when

Mr X was elevated to the fireside basket – she regarded the cat as her property and tried to lure him back to the warm kitchen where she reigned supreme. Fortunately Mr X had never been known to catch a bird; as I have said, he became too supine too early in life.

Madame Goateyes, however, continued her depredations. One morning, after a clear winter night sleeping on the flat roof or, rather, not sleeping, for I had been too conscious of the immeasurable sighing of the white surf on the rocks five miles distant, brought by an almost warm sea breeze, while my mind tried to calculate how it was possible for a migrant bird to navigate by the almost imperceptible motion of the stars against the chimney silhouette; that morning, I say, excited with this celestial communion, I got up, intending first to stroll to the Gazebo Tower. The ravens, early beginning to refurnish the old nest for the coming season, would be indulging their raucous dawn discussion on the day's possibilities of a carrion breakfast . . .

Soft-footed through the rough track to the quarry in the American Garden, I was annoyed to spy Madame Goateyes crouched near the entrance to a low mound, formerly occupied by rabbits – before the epidemic of myxomatosis had wiped them out. But what astonished me was the presence of two small weanling rabbits nibbling grass beside some overgrown blackberry vines. I had supposed that the last wild rabbit had vanished in the great myxo plague! Not only had one fertile doe survived, she was now breeding. . . .

Madame Goateyes, engrossed in stalking, had not noticed me, as I studied the scene for a few seconds. She was very close to her time: I saw that her teats were swollen with milk under the bulging belly. But I hardened my heart, as I tip-toed back to the house, thinking; 'Great Heaven, another damned pack of wild half-starved kittens will soon be feeding on my cherished chaffinches, goldfinches, bullfinches, buntings and summer warblers!'

Opening the armoury cupboard in my study, I sought among the heaped-up books and field equipment for Alf Hitchcox's twelve-bore, and a couple of cartridges. I could hear Jesus busy stoking the furnace in the basement; I hoped he would not hear the blast of the gun I had told him I never used. I ran back, still on tip-toe. I was just in time.

There was Madame Goateyes, only the tip of her tail tweaking (could this be a cat's device to fascinate and temporarily distract the attention of its prey from the rigid menacing face of the predator?). Her back towards me, crouched low in the woodland grass, she was ready to leap as she studied the innocent movements of the nearest of the two little rabbits grazing, probably for the first time, close to the runway under the brambles.

Cautiously I raised the gun to the firing position at my shoulder, but I saw that a shot at that angle would spread to cover the innocent kittens beyond Madame Goateyes. I paused . . .

It often happens that in a moment of crisis I have the most irrelevant thoughts, and just then I wondered why nobody I knew had ever eaten cat (except I think my friend Jim Henderson when he was a gunner with the 'Desert Rats' Regiment besieged at Tobruk in the last war. He told me he had eaten cat, and was hungry enough to enjoy it, disguised on the menu of his mess under the nom-de-plume of desert rabbit), and if not, why not? Would it not be one way of keeping unwanted cats down, to eat cat pie, or devilled domestic kitten now and then? While I was thus wondering and wandering in my mind, my eye, trained along the gunsights, caught the sudden leap of that golden cat and my finger reacted on the trigger, quite involuntarily. There was a loud bang and a violent kick-back to my shoulder.

I am no good at shooting. I wish I could cure myself of the cowardly habit of closing my eyes at the moment of pulling the trigger, and it always surprises me that I ever hit anything on those very rare occasions in the past when I have used a gun. But my trick is to hold the gun absolutely steady on target, as last sighted before shutting my eyes. This practice is quite unaudacious, but it could be a form of insurance against the loss of one or both eyes if, as in this instance, the gun is not yours, but on permanent loan from Alf Hitchcox, and known to be around eighty years old, and its worm-eaten stock is bound with sticky tape because of its history of falling apart when fired.

There lay Madame Goateyes, apparently stone dead. Momentarily a primitive surge of pride swept me. Man is essentially a hunter who misses most of his targets in life, so when he makes a bang-on hit it does rouse a burst of elation. Mine was brief: I always feel some remorse at killing anything, even a pestilential cat which, after all, was only behaving with the superb craftsmanship she was born with and had developed so successfully; secondly, I knew I would have to bury the corpse quickly, in case the ever inquisitive Jesus or some other busybody came nosing around to see what the shot portended (there was recently a suicide in this lonely district); and, lastly, one baby rabbit was staggering around in a tight circle, screaming its whiskers off! The other little rabbit had darted into cover.

I rushed forward and picked it up. Blood was streaming down its face from one ear, through which two lead pellets had passed. In my arms, it stopped screaming, and presently half-closed its eyes. When I placed it on the grass it did not move – just sat hunched up, evidently suffering extreme shock and possibly fatal wounding. I dragged the body of Madame Goateyes into some bushes, intending to bury her later.

The wounded baby had not moved. I carried it back to my study and put it in a shoe-box under my desk. I cleaned, oiled and put away the Hitchcox gun. Breakfast with my two sons was ready. For half an hour I forgot about the kitten rabbit; I had decided that if it recovered I might find it useful to supplement the Skokholm-born rabbits in my study enclosures – I had not noted any fleas on its ears, which might be carrying the virus of myxomatosis – but in any case it would have to be isolated and deloused in quarantine for three weeks.

Meanwhile that weanling rabbit recovered sufficiently to push open the shoe-box and wander from the study – and she encountered Mr X in the lounge.

Thus confronted in his own territory even the supine Mr X had felt obliged to snatch up the weanling. Martin rushed to me, screaming that Mr X had caught a baby rabbit and was about to kill it.

'Save it, Daddy!' Tears of despair were in my son's eyes as he stamped his feet, scaring the cat long enough for me to grab the little rabbit, which flopped sideways, now indeed apparently dying – from this second attack.

That Rabbit (as she became known, or TR for short) was kept alive only by Martin's determination that she should not die. She was barely breathing, but he hugged her close for most of that day. When at last she woke from her coma, she stayed hunched up, refusing food of any kind. In the evening we force-fed her with milk laced with glucose and brandy, through a rubber ink tube from an old fountain pen. Martin remained beside her that night, watching her uneasy breathing as she lay wrapped in a doll's blanket in Mr X's basket. Mr X was furious at this indignity, but Martin sensibly made him remain in the room, determined that the cat must be taught never to harm again That Rabbit.

Victoria's demand that Mr X be allowed, as was not unusual, to spend the night in her bedroom, was overruled. The insulted cat retired to the corner of the settle farthest from the hearth where Martin lay covered with a rug, his arms cradling the cat-basket containing TR.

His vigil was successful. At breakfast Martin yawned hugely, satisfied: 'TR's going to live. She actually preened her whiskers after the last milk and brandy.'

Mr X had learned his lesson. He accepted TR as yet another part of the household not to be touched – like not stealing food from the table. But he sulked when TR came close and stalked away when she, later realising he was harmless, attempted to play with him.

How quickly TR wormed her way into our affections! In her first few weeks she was excessively playful. After tea – she liked hers weak, with a lot of milk and a little sugar – she would start some game or other. A favourite one was Upstairs Downstairs. She would hop up and down the great whitestone staircase, playing hide-and-seek at the corners and the landings. She would try to efface herself behind the Regency wrought-iron uprights of the balustrade as the finder approached, crawling on all fours so as to be fair – that is, as near level as possible with a rabbit's world. But her whiskers would be detected, twitching in anticipation, as they protruded from her scant hiding place. As with children, one had to pretend not to have seen her immediately. When cornered she would give a little grunt of affected surprise, or possibly it was her genuine pleasure in our participation, then leap up or down the stairs away from her pursuer. If two people approached, one from below and one from above, she sometimes made a triumphant escape by springing exuberantly from between the banisters to the floor below.

From the beginning TR was instinctively clean when indoors – as the wild rabbit is at home. At first she used a tray of earth we placed in a corner of the room during her brief convalescence, to deposit her pellets and urine. But as she learned to follow us out of doors she quickly established the routine hygiene of wild rabbits, by passing all waste matter then. There was no need to teach her to use the little cat door we had cut for Mr X in the basement entrance. Even Mr X had given up using this – it was too far away, down the basement stairs. It was at last nailed up, to keep out the rats. TR slept all morning – in the cat basket. She was most lively, as might be expected from the crepuscular habit of rabbits, late in the day. She would then begin to prowl about the house, where she had complete freedom. But she avoided the kitchen, with its heat and cooking odours and the active displeasure of Jesus, who was loyal to Mr X. When the boys were not in school they would take TR for a walk. At first she was nervous in the open, keeping close to your heels, avoiding strangers, seeking refuge in your arms if a dog or other large animal appeared. She seemed glad to be back indoors, after each stroll. She would hop to the fireside basket and if Mr X was there, he would rise up and stalk away in a pronounced huff, his tail swishing in disgust.

TR would seek my company in default of younger playmates. I would hear a gentle tap of claws on the stone flags of the hall as she hopped to the study door and nosed her way in. If I took no notice she would sit at my feet, at first with an appearance of smug satisfaction at finding me there. Soon she would place her fore-paws on my ankle and scratch gently, silently asking why I was ignoring her, why couldn't I play with her? So I might have to throw her a wooden reel on a string and jerk it occasionally to keep her amused. This would absorb her interest for a while but, soon bored, she would give me a sly glance and bite through the thread. Seizing the reel in her teeth she would scutter away tri-umphantly through the furniture, dodging like a rugby three-quarter, and hoping I would try to tackle her.

If I did not appear to notice her, she would creep back and begin to scratch and nibble my footwear. She gnawed holes in my favourite slippers and ruined several pairs of socks. If she could not get a response by all these signals of her frustration, she would adopt her last trick to force attention. She would leap straight into my lap and from there on to my desk. And so in the end she would sit on top of the letter I was writing, or the book I was reading, even perhaps strike at the keys of the typewriter if I was using it.

And then what could I do? I would have to pick her up and solemnly kiss her soft whiskered face, and look into her bold black eyes, and tell her she was an intolerable nuisance. That she simply must learn to amuse herself while I was working. Or else I would have to banish her to solitary confinement – a hutch, or an en-closure I was planning for her on the lawn.

'Don't you know what I mean when I say NO, silly TR?'

But even as I talked, and held her close to my face, she would utter faint wheezing, grunting sounds, as if telling me she was at last happy, and appreciative of the notice and affection I bestowed on her. And to prove it she would lean forward and give me a rabbit's kiss – a rub of her chin against my cheek. Her breath was as sweet as a cow's – a faint scent of wild thyme was left from the imprint of that kiss.

From the continuing study of the enclosure rabbits I knew that TR was developing the special scent gland under her chin which the rabbit uses on ceremonial occasions. I knew too that this intensely sociable mammal needed company and, at her age, play-mates, the more because my young sons had just gone back to school.

'You are a nuisance, TR. I would put you into the big pens with all the other ear-tagged rabbits, if I had my way. But Martin has forbidden me to. He says, and I daresay he is right, that the older rabbits would bully you. I agree, you would have no status there. You have to be born into a warren to be acknowledged. So for the present, we have to put up with you. But I do wish you would stop teasing everyone, especially poor Mr X.'

Having quickly forgotten or forgiven his intention to murder and eat her, TR sought to play with Mr X if no one else was available. If the cat was stretched out asleep on the hearthrug, hitherto his custom and privilege when the fire was lit in the evening, TR would hop towards him and begin pawing his long elegant tail. Hissing his disgust Mr X would retire to his basket, wrapping his tail around him. If TR followed, determined on a game, the cat would leap on to chair or settle. It was not long before TR learned to jump up beside him – it was the old game of hide-and-seek to her, but it infuriated Mr X. Outraged, he would run to the door and if it was shut he would miaow for it to be opened, so he could escape to the kitchen, and Victoria's loving care.

Mr X was safe nowhere in the house save at the back of the kitchen stove, a spot too hot for a little rabbit. Mr X's splendid long fur gradually assumed an ochreous tinge – he was partially roasted some evenings.

*   *   *

If cleanliness is next to godliness, they were a godly pair. Both attended meticulously to preening every part of their fur, sometimes sitting near together, as if it were a competition, as if preening were contagious; as it surely is, like scratching and yawning in humans.

Well fed, and with leisure to rest, most fur-bearing animals keep themselves clean by licking every part of their bodies, except those the tongue cannot reach. These places (the face and the neck) are carefully brushed with saliva placed upon the forepaws, which press and squeeze these parts. Dirt and moulting hairs are thus removed; clinging lice, mites and ticks which irritate are nibbled loose by the teeth and some are disposed of by swallowing. The anal-genital region is thoroughly washed with the harsh brush of the tongue, an action which stimulates a copious saliva for the purpose; the toilet is completed by swallowing any deposit collected by the tongue.

73

Sexless and grown lazy with too much food, as neuter cats are, Mr X preened less often than TR. He conserved energy by washing himself, and arranging his sanitary hygiene, at longer intervals, and gladly allowed Victoria to groom him. Before she went to bed she would take Mr X to the back door in her arms, drop him at the threshold, and invite him to do his duty under the stars. But if the night were wet or windy, the craven cat might shudder and run back indoors. There was always the tray of clean dry earth which Victoria kept for his needs, in the passage behind the scullery door. I would hear an affectionate curse in Spanish afterwards as Victoria bolted the door (quite unnecessary – I never bolted the front door).

TR's sanitary arrangements were different, more effective, and certainly unique and interesting. As a small kitten she had used the earth tray already mentioned, but subsequently gave it up, except to attempt to dig a burrow there when her claws needed exercise. I would wake her after my breakfast and invite her to accompany me to inspect the weather outdoors; she would run around my feet on the lawn, nibble grass, make water and rapidly evacuate the firm, perfectly round, black pellets containing the dry indigestible cuticle of her vegetarian diet. So long as she was indoors she dropped no waste matter. But from time to time she would bend her head down between her forelegs (her ears falling forward and decently masking from our gaze this personal duty), then, raising her head erect again, she appeared to chew or swallow what she had licked away from her back passage. I knew that she was swallowing whole, and without cutting with her teeth, certain small clusters of glossy black pellets, which are in fact a unique source of nourishment, a form of cud. Unlike the large balls of cud produced by ruminant mammals and passed from stomach to mouth for mastication, the little black pellets are obtained from the rear by the rabbit and re-ingested, but they serve a similar purpose. They are sticky and probably irritate as they cling to the muscular cloaca, which is slightly everted during cleaning and evacuation. With deft movements of the tongue, hidden from human view by the inner folds of the side lips, the rabbit then passes the liquorice-like pellets unbroken down the throat. In the high temperature of the upper stomach the clusters are 'incubated' for a few hours, swelling in size as their nutritive contents of vitamins, lactic acid and bacteria develop. Finally the capsules

74

burst and, mixing with the secretions of the stomach walls, help to break down and digest the coarse raw matter grazed during the intensive period of feeding outdoors at night.

This is surely an admirable device and adaptation for survival in a wild animal which, having so many surface predators, needs to graze fast and fills its stomach full over as short a period as possible while at risk above ground, so that it can digest – and re-digest (that is, re-ingest) its food at leisure – and evidently enjoy this indoor meal, in the comparative safety of its burrow. This habit incidentally enables it to keep its home perfectly clean and dry. For while its stomach is full on returning home from grazing, the large hard pellets are yet unformed; instead the small soft capsules, so rich in nutritive matter, developing lower down in the intestinal tract (in the caecum or blind gut), will by several hours precede the normal tough pellets of indigestible residues on their way to the rectum.

I confess I enjoyed studying the little rabbit, which paid me more attention out of her loneliness now that the boys were at school. She grew rapidly, became less kittenish, and teased Mr X less often. But he, too, had lately discovered that he could keep TR at arm's length – safety distance, as the animal observers say – by repelling her too intimate approach with a thrusting paw and unsheathed claws. After one or two scratches from these TR learned the unpleasantness of this response and, although no coward, would desist, unless his tail was lying unguarded in the open and he himself asleep – she could not resist a poke then. Thus roused, Mr X, remembering our command to him that the little rabbit was not to be hurt, might prefer to slink away in undignified retreat, when she might follow, vainly hoping a game of some sort would result.

Undoubtedly TR was lonely. She still sought my company, continued to scratch at my legs and leap on to my lap or desk. Again I would find myself talking to her, instead of dealing with letters, accounts and the telephone.

'How d'you suppose I'm going to finish my work, TR? It's all very well for you to sit there, looking smug, but I've my living to get, and you're forever interfering, and not a single bit of help. If you'd only discuss my problems and offer some advice, I wouldn't mind so much. As it is you distract me, and as I am naturally lazy, I tend to put off urgent matters . . .'

Mostly when I talked aloud to her she was well-behaved. She developed the habit of sitting quietly as close to my face as possible, listening with the nearer ear directed at me, the other ear limp (as if my talk was loud enough half-heard). She obviously got some satisfaction out of the sound of my voice, because when I was silent she would flip up both ears and move restlessly, as if to say: 'Well, go on, let's hear the rest of this nonsense you're talking. If you won't play, at least talk to me, please.'

Focusing her ass-ears upon me and raising those long black eyelashes, she would gaze at me with soulful eyes, making her silent plea. Not altogether silent, either: increasingly she uttered a low wheezy grunt. It was her way of saying 'please', or alternatively, 'yes'. We were gradually establishing an understanding of each other's language, or at least how to communicate by sound. For instance when I said loudly NO and stamped one foot, her ears would fold back and, literally crestfallen, she would desist for a while from what she was doing, generally bothering me, or nibbling a valuable plant in the flower border. She in turn used her feet to warn me of her displeasure, or fear; a short stamp indicated a warning, or disapproval of what was happening. Several repeated loud stamps indicated, 'Help, come and defend me!' If she wanted a door opened she would scratch at it; but as she learned to realise that I disapproved of this habit, she would first of all hop towards the door, uttering her wheezy 'Please!' and politely wait for a second or two to see if I would come and open it. If not, scratch, scratch, scratch! She was impatient also.

Of course I was pleased by her seemingly intelligent behaviour. But I was wary of reading more than learned responses into her attitudes towards me. The ethologist Konrad Lorenz insisted that it was because my appearance and voice had been imprinted on her unformed mind as a kitten, that she appeared to love me; I was the one creature who had consistently and reliably fed and protected her. In her eyes I was her mother (my teasing sons were merely temporary playmates), and she would be happy, Konrad would say, to be my mate for life. Very likely she would accept me as a husband, as his hand-reared geese had accepted Lorenz; in the spring the attachment she had for me would turn to lust – if I allowed her to dote on me too long, or if I cuddled and stroked her body then, as a buck rabbit does in courtship of the doe.

It was a possibility I ought to consider. But it was not yet another spring, and all through that summer TR remained a simple virginal companion. There were times when I was away, or otherwise too occupied to deal with TR's daily routine. Perhaps a temporary secretary, or one of my rabbit-enclosure student-watchers, would attend to TR, and place her in a small movable wire-netted enclosure which I built for her, which gave her enough space and grass for a day's grazing. Often Victoria would attend to this routine – secretly she doted on the young rabbit, her maternal instinct roused by the appearance of TR's baby face and wistful, helpless look.

TR had hardly had time to see and recognise her own mother, who had given birth to her in the dark nest hidden under the earth, I had saved her from the ginger tabby almost on the first day of her emergence to taste grass. But rabbits live chiefly by their keen sense of smell. I felt sure that her baby mind had already stored the olfactory memory of her mother's body odour, associated as it was with the delights of the nursery nest: abundant milk supply, warmth and security. I must be a very poor substitute mother, which she recognised less by the sight of a giant figure, than by my peculiar sort of human smell: molecules of tobacco, old clothes, soap and sweat. This mixture of smells had become the dominant factor assuring her, by way of her sensitive ever-twitching nostrils, that she was safe. Certainly she did not have to see or hear me to recognise me. Even at night she instantly knew me as a peculiar, evidently endearing, smell.

Towards the other grown-up members of our household TR behaved differently – she avoided them. Victoria had her special odour, which even my indifferent nose instantly recognised: a kitchen smell, overlaid with mothballs, and inadequately disguised with cheap deodorant. You grew to tolerate, even to like the mixture, because you liked the forthright Victoria – for her simple honest vigour, reliability, and comeliness. But TR seemed to find that robustness, coupled with the powerful smell, too overpowering, and would hide or sneak away when she encountered Victoria. Perhaps she remembered Victoria's early unfriendliness over the rabbit's usurpation of Mr X's rights; so now, when Victoria tried to catch her and place her in the grazing pen, she would try to escape from those arms willing to forgive and cuddle her. Victoria had complimented me on having house-trained TR, who deserved the credit herself, from a rabbit's natural instinct to keep her home as spotless as Victoria tried to keep ours.

If TR barely tolerated Victoria, she ran away altogether from Jesus; maybe because his scent molecules were too strong or she sensed his antipathy to wild life generally. Jesus smelled of strong tobacco during the day, and when he put on his evening clothes to serve dinner it was a mixture of mothballs and brilliantine. A peasant out of place, he was happiest out of doors, though excessively clumsy with fine machinery. He liked to roam the estate in his spare time, seeking edible wildlife: snails in the wall, large grasshoppers and mushrooms in the meadows, berries, nuts and herbs in the woods, and it remained a grievance that I would not allow him to use a gun or keep a sporting dog. At last, to satisfy his restless energy, I consented to his restoring a garden I had discovered, a triangular plot containing a ruined hothouse, screened by high walls, abutting Hitchcox's four acres. It was completely overgrown, but Jesus tackled it on the understanding that he could grow early potatoes (the favourite cash crop locally in this mild climate), in his own time, at his own expense. Sadly I watched while he drove out the warblers and little birds in this quarter-acre sanctuary, and dug to great purpose and profit. But it made him more content to remain in my employment – an individualist I grew to respect and admire in the end.

*   *   *

On our little walks together, TR was timid at first. She would explore in a radius of a few yards around me, nibbling here and there; sniffing like a dog to identify and remember objects and scents in her world of smell and black-and-white vision. I had the feeling that she was longing for the company of other rabbits; when we strolled towards the rabbit enclosures she would run ahead, and peep and sniff along the edge of the pens, savouring the rich odours of pellets, urine and chin-scent deposited by the ear-tagged community inside the fence. But she seldom saw these inmates – they ran to cover below ground at the approach of humans.

As for the natural burrow in the American Garden in which she had been born, there was no sign of any of her brothers or sisters or parents there. They had vanished with the shooting of the ginger tabby, probably accounted for by the hungry foxes.

TR would inspect the site, sniffing casually at the overgrown entrance, but not attempting to go below.

By July TR was six months old and almost full-grown. She still had the run of the house, but from midday until evening she had to be confined to her movable grazing pen, assisting in this way to keep short the grass of our weedy croquet lawn in front of the house. She could not be entirely trusted not to eat the petunias and other flowers which Jesus and my secretary were endeavouring to maintain in the beds against the walls of the manor. But every fine afternoon Victoria would take the tea-tray to this lawn and TR was then permitted to run free, under observation.

She still enjoyed weak tea, with milk and a little sugar; and would accept a plain dry biscuit. She would frolic around us, happy to be able to make little jumps in the air – impossible while confined to her grazing pen. Sometimes she would run to the flowerbed and, with what I considered to be a sly look, bend down to nibble a petunia. I think that she did so out of sheer devilment, and to draw my attention; for she would desist and droop her ears at my loud NO, and run back obediently towards the tea-tray. She liked to lie in the sun in the sweet-smelling herb garden here.

Mr X, on these occasions of tea on the lawn, would seldom venture farther than the sunlight beyond the pillars of the Grecian portico, where he would find the warmest spot to lay out his great bulk. He liked to be sociable, but with TR prancing on the grass, the cat was satisfied to be part of the human group at this safety distance of a dozen yards.

One warm afternoon, on being set free, TR darted around as usual, with little leaps and pirouettes of joy. Then she made for the herb garden, where she hopped along the miniature paths I had laid down, twitching her nose at sundry herbs – mint, thyme, sage, chives, wormwood, bergamot and hyssop – strong smelling plants which are normally distasteful to rabbits. We took little notice when she presently began to scratch at the base of a clump of catmint. We were watching the little fishes in the shallow concrete pond I had not so long ago constructed here, where it mirrored the sky, pleasantly reflecting light into the rooms of the manor.

TR was using her claws much now – no doubt at this adolescent age they needed wearing down more. When next we looked towards the herb garden we found that she had dug quite a deep hole – only her brown rump and white scut were visible. As I strolled over to remonstrate with her, she backed out, flinging the soft dry soil beneath her body with her forepaws, spraying my foot. She turned to look at me, then grabbed a mouthful of the tough catmint roots which she had exposed, and wrenched them to and fro.

'No, TR! No!' I warned with a stamp of my foot.

As if annoyed by my command, TR desisted, and hopped rapidly towards the house. She seemed to be in a huff. As she neared the portico she encountered the prostrate Mr X. I saw her study him for a moment, then creep nearer warily, perhaps resentful and intent on some mischief to relieve her frustration.

Mr X lazily raised his head, sniffed towards TR, then slowly got up, and to our astonishment and delight, began to lick the rabbit's face!

TR settled on her haunches with the utmost complacency while the cat continued to groom her ears, neck and shoulders. A complete reversal of his attitude to That Rabbit!

It was some moments before I realised why. The pungent whiff of catmint on the rabbit's foreparts had broken down the last of his resentment and distrust. He even followed her a little way towards the lawn, comically attempting to lick her head when she turned to face him with a playful movement. He was, however, too lazy to indulge in childish games. Nor had he ever been as far as the herb garden since I had made it. When TR hopped back towards the tea-tray, Mr X made a dignified slump back to his basking position in the sun.

Nevertheless an armistice had been entered into, in the form of the olfactory bond of catmint. Thereafter Mr X accepted TR and even attempted to move back into her basket and sleep beside her at night. If relations ever cooled down, I believed I could engage the cat's tolerance again by rubbing catmint leaf over TR's fur.

*   *   *

Perhaps I was becoming too fond of a mere rabbit, but it seemed to me that, despite the continuing study of the groups of individually-marked wild rabbits in the three separate compartments of the enclosure, which was revealing much that had hitherto been little understood of the nature of their intensely social and matriarchal behaviour, I would have learned nothing of the soul of a rabbit if, by accident, TR had not impinged on my daily life. For she was exhibiting a degree of apparent intelligence (or discernment) that I had never suspected possible in this fast-breeding, short-lived mammal. Most animals are playful and, from their need for security, often affectionate, when young; but TR, now almost mature, continued to seek my company, and show a deep attachment to my person that was not only flattering but gave me every opportunity to study the working of her mind, at least as far as I was capable of interpreting her behaviour. No doubt I was prejudiced by her interest in me, and I was able thereby to admire her burgeoning natural beauty: her gleaming well-groomed coat of grey and brown, overlaid with long jet black hairs, her spotlessly white undercarriage, those liquid black eyes, and those amusingly mobile white whiskers of cheek and eyebrow, so sensitive to the touch, and useful in cover or in darkness as a tactile guide. The ever-twitching nose suggested intense awareness and wisdom, and a sense of humour, which I had almost come to believe she did possess – in her rabbit fashion.

The habit of talking aloud to That Rabbit, of emptying my mind of little worrying problems, chiefly as working owner of this rambling ancient manor, grew. It had begun when TR was quite small. I had inadvertently overheard Martin talking to her alone on the evening before my sons were going away on holiday. He was saying good-bye after his fashion, genuinely grieved at leaving her.

'Ah, you wouldn't understand, TR, but I've got to leave you tomorrow. Perhaps you do understand? Why are you licking my face? I only wish I could take you with me, but anyway, you'll be safe enough with the old man. He's quite a kind sort of bloke really; and I've made him promise he'll never put you in the enclosures with those big bossy rabbits. Like putting you in a lunatic asylum! What's that you're saying? You'll miss me? Rubbish! With everyone spoiling you! What's that you're whispering? Speak up, TR, you're a dreadful mumbler. And stop smearing me with your chin scent. Yes, yes, I know we've had lots of good games together. But not just now. You can come and help me pack if you like . . . What? You're worried you'll have no one to play with? I'll be back in a couple of weeks . . . Why, I do believe you really know I am going away . . . Do you, TR?'

It was all make-believe, but somehow, like the child Martin, who had hardly ceased talking to his woolly-dog pyjama case yet, the grown-up man could still enjoy a one-sided conversation with a pet rabbit, as you would with a loved dog – only just now I had no dog. And as one talks to a dog and gets its full attention, so too as I talked to TR she would gaze steadily at me, giving me the moment of acceptable suspension of disbelief that she understood what I was saying.

The profound wisdom of nature seemed to look out through those gleaming bulging eyes, as if she was trying to convey to me that of course, she knew all about everything, the whole world and its man-made problems, that she understood all my fears and hopes, that I was foolish to be worried, that I should live as she did, taking joy as she flies. 'Tomorrow never comes,' she seemed to say. 'Look at me, I'm perfectly happy in being a rabbit, and trusting in your love and company. But what are you? A poor puzzled creature with an over-inquisitive mind. Oh, I understand you well enough! I can read you like a book. I can always fool you because you are lazy and soft-hearted and when no one is looking you love to talk and play with me. You like to think you know what is going on in my rabbit mind! Let me tell you I know just as much about the workings of your mind too. Just now you are wondering why at my tender age of a few months I am perfectly equipped to live the free life of a wild rabbit, with all its many perils, when at my age you were still a sucking and defaecating babe at the breast, without a thought in your head, or power in your limbs, to do more than just that! Yet, though I am so well equipped to go forth and live wild and free, when you leave the door wide open I do not run away and leave you, old man . . .'

'I confess you have read my thoughts, TR,' I whispered humbly.

5

My heart leaps up when I behold
A rainbow in the sky:
So was it when my life began;
So is it now I am a man;
So be it when I shall grow old,
  Or let me die!
The child is father of the Man;
And I could wish my days to be
Bound each to each by natural piety.
WILLIAM WORDSWORTH

As far as one woman can forgive another I forgive thee.
JOHN GAY

The inexorable dawn rose, whether misty or clear, over the eastern hills which stretched beyond our woods and walls far into the brooding mountains. There never seemed time enough to accomplish all I had set out to do, rise as early and go to bed as late as I might. I would find each day had slipped away below the Atlantic horizon into that ocean of eternity from which its uniqueness, sweet or sour, could never return; leaving my heart a little heavy because I was making such slow progress with my task. Ah, if only I could have followed the warm sun, the rosy cloud and the sea wind each day into tranquillity! Too often my sleep was troubled with the nightmares of impending disaster as my tired brain ticked on, planning to meet and solve tomorrow's problems, in order to survive at Orielton.

Yet there were moments of glory too. There were heights of blissful enjoyment, of living on a sunlit day in that splendid natural and historic environment, every fibre of body and soul stretched to capacity – that capacity for intense joy I often experienced at such moments in the burden of work I was able to carry. No time to be bored, so eager was I to live, to study and admire nature in all its myriad manifestations around me: the wild and free in park and wood, the growing domestic farm and its fertile

83

fields, the fascinating story of the ecology of the rabbits and associated animals and plants revealed in the enclosures.

All mine – to do as I pleased – up to the point that nature herself permitted; a challenge to the imagination and my ability. Of course much had gone awry with my calculations, which were too sanguine, too optimistic, even grandiose. But I needed, I was determined, to make the little estate self-supporting as quickly as possible. This required far more money than I could muster. In taking over the hundred acres of the farm fields from the present tenant, who grazed and fattened livestock for his local business as butcher, I was dismayed to discover that despite his airy promise when I first met him that he would gladly give up, as he was retiring soon, and despite his apparently cheerful acceptance of one year's statutory notice to quit which my lawyer had served on him, he now claimed every penny, and more, of compensation which the law allowed, including not one, but three, years' rent for disturbance, He informed me further that he would not quit unless I bought all his machinery, implements and crops at valuation, pointing out, quite truthfully, that he would have no further use for them but that I would – if I was to farm the land as successfully as he had.

His bill seemed to me exorbitant:

To R. M. Lockley, Orielton Manor:

	£
Two tractors and all farm implements	1,300
Hay in stack	270
Twelve acres standing oats	360
Eight acres standing barley	240
Unexhausted manures	240
Fencing materials	80
Three years' rent	210
	£2,700

The old butcher, with a lifetime of local business experience, knew well how to exploit my ill-concealed eagerness. Yet until I had sold my late home of the Old Rectory near Tenby I could not meet this bill. Nor would the bank advance another penny of overdraft; in the current financial recession the government had forbidden any extension of credit, and even required banks to reduce their lending.

I told the butcher that he would have to wait for his money, but I relied on him to give me possession of the fields that coming Michaelmas, as he had first agreed, although legally I knew I could not enforce possession for another twelve months. Meanwhile I was buying all our growing meat requirements for the Manor from his butchery – quite a large sum was paid to him weekly on this account, and I could see this was important to him, at least until he retired.

Thus arose a curious, legally irregular, situation in which neither wished to offend the other, yet each was determined to have his way. No agreement was signed about his outgoing valuation, which I showed to my land agent Charles in Tenby, who agreed with me that it was exorbitant. Meanwhile the butcher asked me to harvest his oats and barley, and it was tacitly agreed, as between gentlemen, that I would do so. His man was leaving him and he lived too far from the fields to be troubled any longer with employing and overseeing labour. He pointed out that he had allowed for this by putting a generously low figure for the standing corn in his valuation, and of course I would need the grain as winter feed for the stock I was now getting together . . . We were standing beside the field of barley.

'Go right ahead, it won't be long before this barley is ripe. You can do what you like with it, stack it where you find it convenient. You can use my tractors and implements. I see you've got plenty of young people to help you gather it. I haven't anybody. And if you're as short of cash as you make out, I shan't mind if you thresh and sell what you don't need for stockfeed. . . .' He put on his most genial smile. 'We can settle up when I quit, later.'

Did he take me for a fool, putting me under an obligation to him in this way? He did – and I was! He knew he had me in a cleft stick. He knew I wanted him to quit this Michaelmas, in a month's time. But what was the legal position if I threshed his corn? And no agreement signed?

'I'm certainly not paying you that exorbitant figure you've valued the crops at!'

'You will – when you thresh it and find it will yield a couple of tons to the acre. Lovely stuff – see how heavy the heads are! Well, I must be away.'

He drove off in his butcher's van, leaving me alone with the 'lovely stuff'.

The field of barley, embowered, like all Orielton fields, in trees, was beautiful to behold, the golden near-ripe heads bowed and tinkling in the summer breeze. Close above hovered a vivid shimmering pattern of birds and insects: red admirals, peacocks, white and yellow-winged and small blue butterflies, and fritillaries fluttering in from the woods. All were seeking the nectar of late summer's little flowers thrusting up as the barley ears bent steeply down. Red poppy, lesser stitchwort, scarlet pimpernel, corn cockle, hemp nettle, woundwort, corn marigold, buckwheat and the little nonsuch. Gold and green finches prattled as they robbed the ripe heads of barley. Beautiful, yes, to the naturalist, but to the farmer? Two tons to the acre, my foot! Far too many weeds; the old rogue was overcharging me heavily at £30 an acre!

Yet even as I watched a migrant humming-bird hawkmoth hover before a knapweed plant, and insert its long proboscis into the purple thistlelike flowers, I knew I would be too impatient not to agree to pay the butcher what he demanded, in order to get possession in a few weeks' time. I dare not wait another year. Once more I walked the length of the barley field, uneasy, trying to assess its true worth in terms of yield and cash. Willow-warblers were beginning their autumn trill – a delicate modulated sub-song – as I passed through the belt of trees and into the twelve-acre field known as Baker's Mountain (all fields had local names, derived from their use or ownership centuries ago). A red squirrel scolded me from a hazel bough.

From the gate I studied the feeding behaviour of a family of pheasants; six poults and a hen were tugging at the black seeds in the tall bluish-white panicles of the oats. Give the crop perhaps another fourteen days before it was fit to cut?

The farmer in me frowned at the sight of wild oats and other tall grasses ripening amid the cultivated heads. Surely I ought to be able to control weeds better than this in a future crop? Would I have to use chemical herbicides? Not if I could help it.

In one corner of the field badgers had flattened a space where they had played games and relieved the itch in their thick fur coats. On the edge of this clearing were little sanitary pits, open shallow slots in which they had neatly deposited their scats. These were heavily sprinkled with undigested oat grains. They had eaten their fill, digesting some, but their stomach juices had failed to cope with the rest. Quite a bit of damage altogether; and what did I (as an aspirant efficient farmer) intend to do about sharing my profit with all this wild life which helped itself so liberally? The naturalist in me answered that some of these living organisms were only claiming wages for services rendered; the badger ate small rodents and noxious grubs and beetles, some butterflies fed on weeds during their larval existence, the weeds themselves were cover for armies of insects of many kinds which maintained a balance preventing any one species destroying the crop completely. I had read about certain organisms (bacteria, fungus, insect or bird) which, in large fields where monoculture was practised, had been able to multiply excessively in the absence of their natural predators which had been destroyed by spraying the crops with a chemical formula to which the organisms had become resistant. Leaving behind a soil blighted for years with poisonous residues.

No, I thought, I would not use poison sprays. I would copy the sound practice of Friend Sykes, who produced lush, weed-free disease-resistant crops by feeding the land liberally with humus, ploughing in green crops and enriching the soil with liquid manure from the stockyard pits.

It was all very well to idealise. The plain truth was that if I really did harvest these crops, and set up a farm, I would be taxing my resources to their uttermost limit. But surely now was just the opportunity? The Nature Conservancy grant was a great help financially; it was scheduled to last for four years only, in which time I was supposed to produce a complete life history of the wild rabbit. This research in the field was deeply rewarding in the discovery of new facets in the behaviour of *Oryctolagus cuniculus*, but there was one disadvantage – it involved frequent time-consuming visits to London, to attend meetings and discussions at the Conservancy and at the Ministry of Agriculture headquarters. (For already I was considered to be what I was not – an expert on rabbits.) Then I was serving on far too many voluntary councils and committees, concerned with the protection of nature and the environment. My diary frequently records that I was experiencing frustration – man's 'sublime right of sorrow and anger' – over these hindrances to enjoying life in the freedom of this gracious home.

Nevertheless I believed it was possible to realise this dream of a model self-supporting estate if only I planned wisely and delegated sufficiently; that is, if I found the capital and spread the work-load over a sufficient staff of responsible persons. As to helpers, the people whom I met on those London visits and through some published work, resulted in a steady stream of offers. But here, too, a natural capacity for helping lame dogs over stiles (was not I one myself?) did not always have the results I had hoped for.

'You suffer fools too gladly.'

Thus my wife's valid criticism when, all too frequently, a crisis arose following the arrival of some of these helpers. My wife had loyally co-operated in settling in, after her first refusal to live in such a vast barn. Her solution was to take over the former nursery quarters at the top of the house. This had a marvellous view over the estate, and it was commodious enough to be converted for family living, separate from the coming and going of visitors below. There were three bedrooms, a bathroom, a kitchenette and a large living room, opening to a broad gallery which commanded the top of the great stone staircase in the well of the house, lit by broad windows. In itself this forecourt to the nursery wing was larger than the main entrance hall at ground level. In the roof close above, the bees still hummed, invisible, inviolate. (My sons were delighted with a bedroom each. Martin satisfied some of his appetite for drawing and painting by inscribing neatly on each of the doors of the dozen or so bedrooms of the manor the names they bear today, from the list of waterfowl recorded at the duck decoy: mallard, teal, wigeon, gadwall, golden-eye, etc.)

Was it such a great fault that I suffered fools gladly? Among these who came to Orielton were many wise and delightful, and some odd, persons. Those older people, who could afford to, contributed to the upkeep of the house, by paying a modest fee for the privilege of sleeping in the large old-fashioned bedrooms on the first floor, eating home-produced food superbly cooked in the Spanish style by Victoria, being waited upon by Jesus (wearing his clip-on bow-tie), and enjoying our intelligent (I hoped) conversation. Music, billiards and bats were available indoors in the evenings, and outdoors the freedom of 260 acres of wood, water and farmland.

Some younger people applied to come who could not afford to

be other than working guests, paying nothing, being paid nothing. 'Fools on trial', as my critics had said. But how do you recognise a fool without trying him out? It is true that Orielton became something of a target for parents who wished to place a son or daughter to grass cheaply – for health or other reasons: 'he is prepared to work for his keep (or perhaps a small wage if you find he deserves one?) in return for living with you in your beautiful house close to nature and the sea.' I quote from a typical application.

The majority of these trainee helpers spent their days happily, usefully, at Orielton and I was glad of their cheap and generally enthusiastic assistance in rabbit-watching, or on the farm, and some in the house. It was a sad moment when they left. Let me thank them here, especially those who came from afar, certain young people with interesting names: Aino Eskola (Finland), Klaus Dapp (Germany), Lars Fellander (Swedish Lapland), Annemarie Jenny (Geneva), Pierre de Bonald (Provence), Orsina von Planta (Basle), Kes and Marguerithe (Holland), Eithne Latt (Estonia), and Georgetta (Italy). They left an indelibly happy memory of their stay with us.

The high-spirited twenty-one-year-old Georgetta was an ugly duckling with a beautiful swan-like body. Her English mother, married to an Italian count, had written to ask me to give her daughter house-room in return for 'any job outdoors, such as helping on the farm or with your interesting rabbit study. She is mad about animals and wild birds, and takes them seriously. She is exceptionally intelligent, has been to a finishing school, but just now has broken off her engagement (to a quite unsuitable person), and does not know quite what she wants to do. She is frightfully energetic, and has spent part of last summer helping to look after cattle, milking and making Gruyère cheese in the Alps. You need pay her nothing, she has an allowance.'

As I had begun to build up a herd of pedigree Jerseys, I admitted Georgetta on trial to help with the cows. I admired her at once, despite her overlarge, somewhat twisted nose. She had deep-set enigmatic eyes, fair hair and a beautiful carriage, moving with the gliding grace of the trained aristocrat, subtly, unostentatiously, showing to advantage her perfectly-proportioned body. She proved marvellously efficient and enthusiastic in carrying out her dual assignment as relief milker in the new cow parlour and relief watcher of our enclosure rabbits.

She told me in her quiet, assured voice that she loved birds, particularly swallows, martins and swifts, and was pleased to find a pair of swallows nesting in the hayshed, and three house-martins' nests in the eaves of the stables. Best of all she loved swifts; she had studied *Apus melba*, the Alpine swift, in Switzerland . . .

'They are so beautiful, the mad way they fly, so fast and so high! They nest in the old tower in the centre of Lucerne. But here I see only the common swift *Apus apus*. I suppose they are nesting in the roof of your house?'

'I don't think so. I wish they did. They breed in the limestone walls of Pembroke Castle, three miles away, and come and visit us most days. They fly high on the thermals over our Lily Pond on fine days, and low over the water when there's a hatch of lake flies.'

'But surely I've just seen a couple visiting your eaves?'

'I think that when they fly close to the eaves at this season, without entering a crevice, they are just prospecting. Probably they are young birds only a year old, which return too late in the summer to lay eggs. They are merely checking on possible breeding sites for next year – what I call sweethearting – and very natural too, as well as necessary in such an aerial bird which, when it has no nesting cares, hardly ever alights to rest or roost but flies for days and weeks non-stop. At night these birds go far into the sky.'

'They say swifts can sleep on the wing.'

'Impossible. They would fall out of the sky if they did. Try going to sleep standing up, and see what happens! But possibly, the swift's ceaseless wing-beat at night is somehow tuned in to, and is as regular as, its heart-beat. Its wing muscles are large and strong and with this equipment it can fly – at least I believe it may – for months, quite comfortably, needing no more than a daily intake of flying insects to build up its energy – that is, its fat reserves sufficiently to last through the short night. Quite probably the swift does not alight or roost normally for eight or nine months of the year when it is not breeding. For the common European swift has never been reliably recorded to rest with wings closed in any part of its winter quarters in tropical and southern Africa.'

'Always and forever on the wing! Heavenly birds!' exclaimed Georgetta, smiling with quiet joy at the thought.

A few days later she told me triumphantly that she had seen two swifts one after the other enter a crevice under the eaves above the high north wall of the Manor. 'And they did not come out all the time I watched in the dusk!'

Two evenings later I saw two swifts enter where Georgetta had indicated, after some chasing and screaming around the Manor with other swifts. But it was already early July, and none were seen there again that summer. Even the adult swifts leave during August.

Despite her docile demeanour Georgetta was full of life and restless as a swift. She was the last to leave the drawing-room at bed time, if she was present at all, for she often wandered in search of badgers, foxes and owls, on a fine night, or would volunteer for a spell of night duty in the underground rabbit-observation hut. She was popular with men, but roused a certain antagonism among our womenfolk, who hinted to me that the wild life she preferred walked on two legs, and was male. I soon found occasion to believe this – that like her beloved swifts she indulged in sweethearting – might be true, but as her employer and a mere male myself I could not but consider this apparent jealousy rather amusing and typically female – although I was careful to make no outward comment.

One conquest at least I knew of: the son of a local farmer who had come to help set up the bound sheaves of oats behind the reaper-and-binder (inherited by valuation from the old butcher) in Baker's Mountain. Georgetta lingered with him 'to tidy up the stooks' (as she declared) in the cool of the evening after the other workers had gone home. Walking there to assess the value of the crop by the time-proved method of counting the number of stooks, each of six sheaves, I noticed a pair of buzzards wheeling and mewing above the far corner of this field. Expecting a hare or other small animal killed during the harvesting, I walked over and stumbled upon the happy pair entwined amid a wall of sheaves. I withdrew unnoticed, leaving the buzzards more annoyed than I. For the presence and antics of the human couple were preventing the birds from feeding on the voles and mice, whose homes and runways had been crushed by machinery and trampling feet.

My neighbour's son returned to college soon after. Undismayed, Georgetta turned to another candidate for her undoubted charms.

*   *   *

It had been hot sleeping on the roof that night, even under a cloudless sky and a full moon. The calm sunlit July morning promised another day of stifling heat. Full and new moon brought the lowest spring tides, and so I consulted the nautical almanac.

The West Wales Naturalists' Trust had lately appointed me honorary warden of its island nature reserves, and I had command of the Trust's fast new launch *Mayflower*, which had been specially built to provide access to coastal sites, and for scientific work such as seal-marking and biological studies generally. I had great joy in this opportunity to return at intervals to the wild lonely islands, and shores inaccessible under sheer cliffs.

Georgetta had seen few sea-birds, and longed to visit the colony of twenty thousand gannets nesting on the remote, twenty-two-acre Grassholm which lies on the sunset horizon beyond Skokholm. As it was Sunday, and other enthusiastic nature-lovers were holidaying with us, including an American physicist, the British ambassador to Siam, and their wives, I announced at breakfast:

'Ronnie Pearson has asked me to capture him a dolphin, which he intends to train in his lake at Baynton Hall, in order to ride it across the English Channel. I am not sure that this is strictly a scientific purpose, justifying the use of the Trust's boat, but it would be interesting to confirm Pliny's story of the young boy riding a dolphin to and from school at Puteoli over "the broad arm of the sea at Lucrinus". I don't have much faith that we shall be able to net a dolphin, but we can try. And if not, then I have a spare project which might be of interest, possibly of national importance . . . Be ready in half an hour, and bring the Sunday papers.'

'A mystery tour, a mystery tour!' chanted Georgetta (my sons had told her of some previous ones).

Mayflower cruised westwards over a silken sea. Near Skokholm we sighted and gave chase to porpoises and dolphins. But even at full speed of fifteen knots we could not get close enough to throw the big seal-net in which we hoped to take one. The school of porpoises ignored us; the dolphins, which have an affinity with small boats, cavorted joyously in our bow-wave, or mockingly brushed their sleek bodies against the keel. The net fouled the propellor. Georgetta, magnificent in a new bikini, slipped overboard and cleared it.

Before noon everyone was ashore at Grassholm, from which the tall finger of the Smalls lighthouse marked the horizon due west, eight miles towards Ireland. It is possibly the loneliest inhabited rock in Europe. I had landed there but once – twenty-one years ago. It lies at the edge of a submarine ridge extending through Skomer and Grassholm, with many hidden reefs and shallows dangerous to navigation before your boat reaches the lighthouse. This was at first a wooden-legged structure, completed by private enterprise and lit in 1776. It proved highly profitable, but was nearly blown away in the first winter, and had to be strengthened. In the stormy winter of 1800-1, one of its two keepers was taken ill and died. The other was obliged to make a coffin out of the wooden bulkhead of the living room, and as no one answered his distress signals, he lashed the coffin to the gallery rail.

'And there it remained until relief came at last – three months later,' I concluded, reading from an old book I had brought with me, as *Mayflower* threaded a way through the dangers marked on the chart. 'It says here that the present stone lighthouse is 126 feet tall, and was completed by Trinity House in 1861 at a cost of £50,125. But the Trinity Brethren were obliged to pay the owner of the wooden structure compensation to the tune of £148,430, representing sixteen-and-a-half-years' revenue from the huge shipping dues which he had enjoyed!'

We delivered the Sunday papers (on day of publication) to the three surprised and pleased keepers, and brought away their letters and watched seals lying at ease on the laminaria-covered rocks extending for a quarter of a mile around the landing place. The sawn-off stumps of the oak legs of the original lighthouse were rigid in their basalt sockets, steel-hard yet, after two hundred years of salt gales; at high water a violent tide-race covers the base of the lighthouse.

It was not yet low water. Our party seemed impressed and satisfied with my arrangement of the sea-adventure – so far. By afternoon the air of expectancy had subtly changed to a bemused enjoyment, sun-induced and somewhat somnolent. As *Mayflower* nudged her way homewards, fishing lines trailed in the deeper channels above the hidden Hats reef. Ahead of us a seaweed-draped rock had emerged, occupied by two Atlantic seals reclining, their hind flippers lapped by the gentle surf.

'We shall drop anchor in the eddy south of the Barrels Rock, and have tea,' I announced. 'I want to make a survey. No one has ever landed on the Barrels – weather and tide have always made it too difficult. Anyway, who would want to land on such a desolate rock?'

There was an unanimous cry of 'I do!'

'But it's a no-man's-land. It's outside the three-mile territorial limit, and belongs to no one – except the seals!'

'Can't we land and take possession?' cried Georgetta, throwing off her jersey, to reveal once more her glowing, tanned body where it appeared between the segments of her bikini. 'I can easily swim there.'

'Gee, I guess I'd like that!' agreed physicist Dr Murray Gell-Mann.

'It would hardly be politic,' whispered Ambassador Douglas Rivett-Carnac in my ear. 'These people are, after all, foreigners...'

'Don't worry!' I whispered back; then aloud: 'We'll take turns to go in the dinghy. Someone can hold the dinghy off while I land. I must first of all claim this virgin land in the name of Her Majesty Queen Elizabeth the Second... Give me that flag!'

This was done in all solemnity, accompanied, however, by rousing cheers from the observers in *Mayflower*. We drew a plan and measured this dromedary-shaped rock: approximately twenty-five yards east–west, by six yards north–south, of hard basalt surface were added to Her Majesty's dominions, at no expense of money or blood (save scratches to clumsy legs and arms when scrambling ashore). Specimens of rock, weeds, mussels, limpets and barnacles were collected.

A small shark – or a large tope – deterred Georgetta from swimming to the rock. It had been savaging the mackerel and pollack hooked by our lines at anchor, before we could lift the fish into the boat.

The spring tide rose rapidly. Soon Her Majesty's newest possession, ten feet above the sea at lowest water, would disappear for about eight hours beneath the racing waves of the seven-knot current.

'Will you be informing the Queen?' asked the physicist, as he helped raise anchor. 'Would she be interested?'

'I must refer you for protocol to our ambassador in attendance,' I nodded sagely. 'I'll be sending the specimens to the Natural History Museum at South Kensington. I must write a scientific report for *Nature in Wales*, and possibly a more general one for *The Times*.'

(In due course both were published – with no obvious response from Buckingham Palace.)

*   *   *

To return to the financial battle with my grazier tenant, the old butcher. (May his soul rest in the peace he sought on earth. Like many another successful business man, he grew more stout than ever in his retirement, and died suddenly within the year.) As I still had no ready money to pay for the ingoing I had once more told him I could only settle up when my former home, the Old Rectory near Tenby (for sale, but with no buyers, at £5,000) was disposed of. Michaelmas was a few days away, and no agreement on the valuation had been signed. But I had gathered his harvest in anticipation of making it my own. I had used some of his machinery in doing so, and now the barley and oats were built into stacks ready for thatching – or threshing. My diary notes: 'Take care these stacks don't overheat. The oats were a bit green here and there.'

Legally nothing on the farm was in my possession, except the eight-acre home meadow rented, along with the walled garden, by my tenant Alf Hitchcox, who had kept his plough horse (now retired) and a couple of milch cows there; but Alf had cheerfully sold the cows. ('They're almost as old as I am, and practically dry for the last ten years, but the missus loved them. You need the field, so take it. Just allow my old horse to end his days in peace there, please.') The old horse was to live for a year in perfect amity with my Jersey cows, before it passed away.

With this field available, I had spent every penny of my research grant, and some book royalties, on buying the nucleus of the herd which would, I hoped, be a major source of revenue in the future. I had engaged a young cowman, and Georgetta was already helping him in the milking parlour now being completed by adapting the substantial stone buildings of the old timber mill as my farm centre. (The great wheel was still there, rusting to its slow dissolution in spite of my dreams of making it work again; except in heavy rains there was not enough head of water to drive it for more than an hour or two.)

All these operations had been spied upon by the butcher with deep interest and concern. He reproached me with spending money in this way while owing him so much, when, the day before Michaelmas, he asked me for settlement by cheque dated for the morrow. I explained that the cow parlour was an investment, not yet paid for.

'In any case I am not satisfied with your figure of £2,700. My agent in Tenby . . . '

'My agent went to see him yesterday and I have agreed to knock off £500. Your agent said he was going to recommend you accept the adjustment of the valuation figures between our agents – yours and mine – at £2,200.'

'Splendid! Thank you. Excuse me, I'll phone now and confirm with him. Perhaps he's also sold the Old Rectory?'

'No such luck,' came Charles's voice over the wires. 'The best offer I've got is £4,000 for the old Rectory, seventy-five per cent to be left on mortgage for two years at three per cent. Can't recommend that! But don't worry we'll win yet! Take a strong line with the old butcher; doesn't do to show weakness with a man like that – he's well lined with more than his fat. Yes, I did get him down to £2,200 for his outgoings, but it was a hard tussle, I can tell you. Can't the bank help you?'

'No, they want me to reduce my overdraft by about that amount! New government restrictions.'

I returned to the drawing-room where I had left the butcher. Victoria had brought him some coffee.

'I am extremely sorry, but at the moment I cannot settle in full. You must see how I have invested every penny of my capital and more on trying to upgrade the farm to make it pay with a milking herd. I hope it's going to be very profitable. You yourself have boasted how fertile the land is – under the many years of your farming it. And when we first discussed my taking possession, you said we wouldn't quarrel over a settlement, that you were in no hurry . . .'

'But I was talking about days, not months and months for a settlement! You shouldn't rush into farming without adequate capital. I warn you I'm not quitting until you've paid up every penny due. I need the money. I'm building a new house for my retirement.'

'The best I can do is to pay you a deposit of ten per cent.'

Without much hope that the bank would honour it, I gave him a cheque for £220. I felt suddenly unutterably depressed, and anxious to get rid of the old Shylock. He immediately departed, shaking hands in haste – and I knew he was going to rush to the bank. Hang it, hang the bank, if it bounced that cheque I would ... well, what would I do? I had never had a cheque bounce yet.

My misery increased all day. After all, the old butcher was only asking for what had been agreed was his just due. He wasn't really a Shylock at all – it was I who was a stupid impetuous fool. Why hadn't I waited a year, and consolidated in other directions – writing, for instance. I was two books behind on contracts with publishers, but there never seemed time to settle to authorship at present, between work on the burgeoning farm and my obligation to maintain the rabbit study.

Thank heaven, there was no unfriendly ring from the bank; they must have honoured that cheque!

With a lighter heart, I went out after tea, crept into the little 'underground' hut, and studied the enclosure rabbits in the artificial burrow which I had built, against a plate glass screen, to record behaviour below ground. Mostly the rabbits did nothing much when at home in the burrow. Under a red light (which they had ignored from the start) they slept, yawned, re-ingested faeces and, as soon as twilight came, went outdoors to graze. Really therapeutical behaviour, restful for both observer and observed, but rather boring once they had departed to feed outside. I fell asleep on duty, in the comfortable camp-chair, my mind, unable to struggle any longer with the financial problem, as blank as the burrow.

On the following morning, Michaelmas Day, a young clerk, sent by the butcher's agent, suddenly walked into my study just before noon. He demanded immediate settlement of the £1,980 outstanding on the valuation, or his client would re-possess everything, including the corn I had laboriously harvested. He began to talk about writs, and summonses to the debtors' court, if I did not comply.

'You didn't knock at the door? Do you usually rush into private houses with your bits of paper?'

'The front door was open – I mean, it was not locked. Your office door was on the latch . . .'

'The front door is never locked at Orielton, day or night. But we expect all visitors, welcome or unwelcome, to knock. Just a courtesy.'

'I had to be sure of catching you in.'

'You mean you were afraid I would sneak away if I saw you? In my own house? I must ask you to leave at once.'

'Are you, or are you not, giving me that cheque? I have a receipt ready, but also a writ. You can choose . . . '

It seemed to me, in my angered mood, that behind that youthful face, with its neck-pimples restrained by a public school tie, his first cocksureness, his contempt for my ragged appearance in soil-smeared corduroys, fresh from outdoor work, was fading. Poor chap, doing his wretched duty under compulsion from his employer. For a moment we stared at each other. No doubt he was pitying me in his tidy suburban-trained mind – as the penniless, near-bankrupt owner of this shabby old mansion. But his air of triumph on first bursting into my room, and complete lack of courtesy in making his request, had outraged me.

'Get out – and stay out!'

I rang the bank. 'Thanks for paying that cheque yesterday. Now I want further credit of £2,000 – today – to pay off the gentleman concerned!'

The bank of course knew all the details of the transaction. I had already discussed it with the manager, and had been refused credit. He reiterated his refusal.

'Look here, I'm desperate. I've never let the bank down yet, and you've got to help until I can sell the Old Rectory.'

'But that's mortgaged too. Where is our security for a new loan – which headquarters won't give you anyway?'

'You've got the title deeds of both Orielton and the Old Rectory, and you can have a lien on the farm machinery, cows and crops if you like.'

'Hardly the best collateral if we had to realise on second-hand machinery and weedy stacks of corn!' He laughed, politely.

'You're about the rashest customer we've got, not a notion about business. Can't possibly be done.'

'Is that an ultimatum? If so, here's one from me. If you don't find me that £2,000 by the close of business today I'm removing my overdraft altogether from your bank! I am asking you to ring up your head office straight away and tell them what I have said, and you can add that they will lose a customer who's very cranky, no doubt, but one who has been helping them by paying heavy overdraft interest for nearly forty years. I want my answer before your closing time today.'

'Don't talk nonsense! You'd better come and see me, and we'll work something out . . .'

'Much too busy at home. Good-day for now.' I put down the phone.

Hours passed. I pictured myself in a debtor's court, then in a debtor's prison (were there such places today?), then an enforced sale of Orielton and its contents . . .

Suddenly the phone rang. It was Charles, the agent in Tenby.

'I think your immediate worries are over. At least I've got a firm offer of £4,000, cash down, for the Old Rectory. I know you will drop £1,000 on the property, but the market is too depressed for words, and I've failed to get a better offer in six months of advertising. He's in the office now, got an American accent, I think an expatriate returning from the USA. I might push him a bit higher, by asking him to pay the conveyance expenses. He says he loves the Old Rectory, the thirteenth-century church next door, the view, the warm springs. Wants immediate possession. What do you say?'

'I say, bless all expatriates from America. I accept, I accept!'

'I think you're wise. Cash is mighty scarce just now. Where are the title deeds of the Old Rectory, by the way?'

'In the clutches of my bank, of course!'

'Righto, I'll send them a deposit and get them back, if you'll instruct them to release. All the best . . .'

Almost as soon as I put the phone down, it rang again. The bank manager had some good news, too. Headquarters had authorised the increase of overdraft I had asked for, not above £2,500, for the purpose specified . . . repayment over one year.

'I had to argue quite a while with the assistant manager in

Swansea. Said that your threat was absurd. He wouldn't budge. Then the head manager came through, said he knew you a long time ago, had been at Cardiff High School with you during the First World War. He was quite genial, said he was rather a fan of yours, had read one or two articles and books you had written. Liked your enterprise, you were an exceptional case, a bit idiotic – I mean idealistic – and in spite of the new lending restrictions, etc., etc.'

Splendid! Now I could buy some more of those beautiful fawn-eyed pedigree Jerseys!

*   *   *

The new cowman rejoiced in the name of Rudolf Valentino Cortez. With him he brought his newly-wedded wife Dulcinea, cousin of our redoubtable but loveable Victoria. The emigration of this couple from Andalusia to Orielton had, in fact, been engineered by Victoria, with my full support. Victoria had talked glowingly of the skill of Cortez with cattle: he had been a cowherd from boyhood.

The Cortez couple were a handsome pair, and somewhat to Victoria's envy her dainty little raven-haired cousin was well advanced to becoming a mother a few months after her arrival. Rudolf was likewise short in stature, but as strikingly good-looking as the film star after whom, as was fashionable at the time of his birth, he had been named. Fortunately he was transparently modest, a humble young peasant preoccupied, like Victoria and Jesus, with an ambition to earn enough money to retire as soon as possible to the beloved Andalusian village where he belonged, and start his own herd of milch cattle.

My Jerseys prospered under the skilful care of Cortez, aided and abetted by the intelligent Georgetta as relief milker. It was a partnership of love – both doted on the gentle-natured golden-coated Jersey cows, whose huge black eyes with long lashes, and small dished faces, indicate an aristocratic ancestry, a cross in the distant past with the dainty fallow deer has even been suggested. In fact the Jersey breed originated in Normandy, where the Normandy cow today is similar in appearance, but white-faced and red-coated. Transported to Jersey, fifteen miles distant, in medieval times, the island cow has by line-breeding become the small fine animal of the present day. As in all cattle

developed for milk production, the females are perfectly docile, but the bulls are highly temperamental and addicted to attacking humans on sight. I had no intention of keeping a Jersey bull; artificial insemination was convenient and inexpensive, and one could obtain the semen from a choice of pedigree bulls, the sons of dams with high milk records. You could even obtain the semen of a valuable bull long dead – it remained viable indefinitely in the deep-freeze of the local cattle-breeding society.

Alf Hitchcox had always taken his cows to a neighbour's bull. He told me a tale of this neighbour, to whom he had complained that his bull had become sterile: for lately Alf's cows had failed to conceive. The neighbour decided to be in the fashion and adopt artificial insemination. When the inseminator arrived to impregnate the first cow to come on heat, he asked the old farmer if she was quiet at such a time . . .

'Aye, she loves it!' answered Alf's neighbour. 'Stands to the bull without even stoppin' chewin' the cud,' and watched with fascination the preparations – the instruments, apron, rubber gloves . . .

But when the inseminator thrust his arm in the cow's rectum, in the usual way, to feel for the position of what he called the 'ring' (the entrance to the oviduct lying beneath, at the end of the vaginal passage) in order to guide with the other hand the ejaculator or plastic penis towards the womb, the cow knew that she was receiving the wrong sensation. She turned her head, gave a great bellow and kicked the operator into the dung-gutter. He picked himself up, bruised, filthy and very angry.

'I thought you said that the cow was quiet!'

'Aye, but maybe she's never seen a bull afore wearing apron and cap!'

Georgetta was getting on splendidly with Cortez; and at first Dulcinea accepted Georgetta's offer to teach them to speak English properly. Many an evening there was talk and laughter as the lessons progressed in the living room of the flat under the clock tower of the stables block which I had furnished for the Cortez couple – this had been the coachman's home, in the days of the Owen dynasty.

Dulcinea was delighted with the flat, the first home of her own since leaving her parents. Also she was happily occupied earning some wages, part-time helping Victoria in the big house, and part-time in feeding the flock of several hundred laying hens which I had lately established in the vast coach-house just opposite the clock tower. I was making use of most of the hitherto empty, unprofitable compartments of the stables. These birds were pedigree Rhode Island Red stock, and their eggs were sold at above market price under contract to a hatchery.

Dulcinea was in fact very busy, feeding her man and washing his clothes, cleaning and grading the eggs, preparing for the baby, and taking lessons in English. Too busy to pay more than rare visits, which involved tramping a few hundred metres down the muddy farm lane to the new cow parlour, where, as the number of cows increased, Georgetta spent more of her time helping Cortez.

Quite suddenly the lessons in speaking correct English ceased. Georgetta was no longer welcomed at the flat. And presently I discovered why.

Spanish country folk are reticent about exposing the body. Georgetta perspired freely at work in the cow parlour, heated as it was by the summer-warmed bodies of the Jerseys, and their steaming waste matter. She wore the minimum of clothes at milking time, discarding her blouse, but often not troubling to put on overalls. I would find her wearing only a slip which showed off to great advantage a sun-tanned cleavage, slender midriff and dimpled belly-button above short black pantaloons; nothing else, save her sandals.

All very shocking to the prudish Dulcinea, but very provocative for any man working regularly so close to the half-naked Georgetta. But it was not my business to reproach Georgetta, much as I might consider it unfair to the charming Dulcinea, who (Victoria told me) had been betrothed to Rudolf when she was a child. I wondered how long Cortez would resist the wiles of such a man-eater as our Georgetta. In a way her behaviour reminded me of that of the female phalarope, which I had once watched on a Hebridean loch. In this dainty wader species it is the female who initiates the courtship ceremony. Like Georgetta she is more gorgeously attired, and when she is ready to mate she pirouettes in front of the sober-coloured male, showing off her charms. But having mated, as soon as she has laid a clutch of four eggs in the grass, she flies away altogether. She seeks the company of another male, and goes through a second performance – in a word, she is polyandrous. Meanwhile each abandoned husband stolidly does his duty as nurse and father, incubating the eggs and rearing the chicks entirely on his own. His sexual instinct or drive frustrated, he takes on willingly the substitute activity of parenthood.

Phalaropic behaviour includes jealousy and fighting between rival females, while the males stand passively by. How far the phalaropic display of Georgetta was successful I never discovered. On my visits to the cowshed I had once or twice observed what I considered unnecessary touching or fondling. On other occasions there were muffled giggles from the darkness of the hayshed. But I could detect no slackening of attention to the cows; their coats were groomed, their tails and udders immaculately washed in sterile water before milking, and afterwards the parlour was cleaned out and washed down with the hose. Often, on a hot day, Georgetta would turn the hose on her muck-splashed self – unless Cortez was available to do her this service.

One day Dulcinea burst into my office, without tapping at the door, something this shy woman had never dared to do before. Her pretty face was distorted and streaked with tears of hysteria.

'Señor Don Ronald, I kill, I kill! I kill that blutty *puta Shor-shetta*! I kill that blutty *puta mujer*!'

'Calm down Dulcinea, calm down! Give me that hatchet at once! Thank you – now sit down and tell me all about it.'

Relieved of the weapon, which was perfectly innocent of blood, she stamped her foot as she stood there, forlorn with rage, her stomach swollen with child.

'*Dios mío!* She blutty damn *puta* . . .' She poured out invective, a mixture of English swear words – perhaps picked up from Georgetta's lessons – and her Andalusian patois. I was amazed yet had difficulty in restraining a smile, as I said: 'Now please, Dulcinea, you must tell me calmly why you want to kill the señorita who helps your husband with the cows so well?'

'Sí, don't I know – her kinds of helps! She blutty damn *puta*! *Madre de Dios!* She go nakeds in the cowshed! She make – she make my Rudolf wash her down! With nudding on! Now I kill! I kill Shorshetta!'

'Oh, come, Dulcinea – with nothing on at all?' To hide my smile I got up briskly and pushed Dulcinea into a chair, opened the door, and shouted to Victoria to bring coffee for two. Oddly enough Victoria was only a few feet away. Victoria's face was very red as, with one shouted word, she hurried back to the kitchen.

I had asked her what a *puta* was (a whore)!

Dulcinea insisted that she had just seen Georgetta perfectly naked, being hosed down in the cow parlour by her husband. I agreed soothingly that it was a very serious insult to any wife. However, it was all really high spirits on Georgetta's part. She was due, I told Dulcinea, to leave next week anyway, and was probably having a last fling before she went back to Italy, a thousand miles away . . . But could Dulcinea understand what I was saying?

'My dear Dulcinea, I sympathise, but its hardly worth killing Georgetta under the circumstances. Might have serious consequences for your future. Of course, you oughtn't to blame your husband really; any man would do as Cortez did, if he was invited to clean down a naked young woman with a hose. I would, just for a joke! I mean it would be fun, not to be taken seriously, quite a common thing in cowsheds I believe...'

I was lying, of course, but I wanted to save Georgetta from imminent homicide. Besides, a murder would do Orielton no good, even if the excuse of *crime passionel* would be valid. But was it – in this country? I must hide that hatchet...

'Dulcinea will kill Shorshetta!'

It was a wail, followed by a flood of tears. When Victoria brought the coffee, Dulcinea buried her head in her cousin's ample bosom. They exchanged a rapid burst of invective about Georgetta in Andalusian, while I sipped my coffee, relieved that the worst was over.

Victoria, with her superior command of English, angrily explained to me the necessity of at least punishing Georgetta. The insult to her cousin must be avenged. I judged that it was a matter of honour.

'Thank you, Victoria. Just explain to Dulcinea that I shall punish Georgetta by sending her home as soon as possible. Meanwhile I will forbid her to go near the cows or Cortez for the few days she will remain.'

'Dulcinea say Georgetta must be punished. Also Georgetta must make apologies!'

'You may go, Victoria. I'll see Dulcinea to her flat, thank you.'

As I escorted the distraught Dulcinea, discreetly via the back entrance of the manor, to her cosy flat in the stables a hundred yards away, I tried to divert her thoughts to happier things. She continued scowling as we entered.

'How are the preparations for the baby getting on? I see the cradle is ready (it had been loaned by my wife). Has my wife told you she has booked you a bed in the cottage hospital – all free on the National Health Service? That's because your husband pays for half his insurance stamps as an employee at Orielton...'

'Sí, sí. Ver' good. We no get helps from old Franco in Spain. Your wife ver' good. When leaves Shorshetta?'

'And you'll get a special money allowance, I believe, for the first month after the baby is born...'

'Sí, sí. You ver' kind. Shorshetta ver' bad – blutty damn *puta*!'

'Georgetta is not really a bad girl. Just a bit stupid. Teaching you those bad words too. "Bloody damn" are not polite words for a lady to use.'

'She no teach blutty damn. Jesus say blutty damn all time he teach *inglés* to Dulcinea and Rudolf. Shorshetta she ver' good teacher, blutty damn *mujer* (woman). She no 'pologise, I pun'sh her. No kill her any more. Pun'sh her!'

It was a warm day when Georgetta entered the dining-room for lunch. She had changed into an attractive lace bodice and flowered skirt, directing as usual attention from her plain face, emphasising her beautiful figure. I quite failed to reproach this graceful, yet bouncingly lusty young woman, who looked so demure. Instead, restraining a desire to laugh, I thanked her for many weeks of excellent, unpaid assistance. But now, as she was due to go home in a few days' time, she must take the rest of her stay at Orielton off, a complete holiday, for relaxing – and packing up.

'But I don't need a holiday. It's all a holiday to me, and I shall hate leaving Orielton.'

'I insist you do no more work. You look pale (a lie – she looked radiant), you have overworked. That's final. You can borrow my car if you'd like to visit friends near by, or go to the beach, as the weather's so hot. Perhaps my sons might join you? Go around and say your good-byes.'

'Who's going to help Cortez with the cows?'

'I've got another trainee coming shortly. Until then Cortez is only too happy to earn the overtime money. I told him this morning that you are off-duty from noon today – for good.'

On her last day I happened to encounter Georgetta emerging from the stables flat. She had been saying good-bye to the Cortez couple. One side of her face was bright crimson.

Victoria did not hide from me her deep satisfaction that the honour of Andalusia had been vindicated. Dulcinea had landed an almighty slap on the cheek of the blutty damn *puta*.

6

'How I loathe the beastly things! No fear, I wouldn't go into that dark hole if you paid me – now you say it's full of these horrible creatures!'

The speaker was a middle-aged historian interested in the medieval foundations and cellarage of Orielton. I had preceded her into the cavernous icehouse which lies conveniently under the lawn opposite the former (basement) kitchen, an admittedly gloomy place which, approached by an alleyway open to the sky, was much frequented by small creatures of the dusk.

Using a torch I unhooked one of the larger bats hanging by its feet to the low lime-encrusted ceiling (a beautifully made stone arch). I brought the sleepy creature into the sunlight; and prevented it from biting my fingers by holding the scruff of its neck.

'Simply because they are creatures of the night, you distrust them! But they are really rather charming, and interesting. Look at this greater horseshoe bat; feel its long woolly brown fur. And look at its face, it's almost human, except for that aristo-cratic horseshoe-shaped leaf-nose, which is a remarkable device to assist it in finding its way – and prey – in the dark. Bats are the only mammals in the world to achieve true flight.'

'It's no good!' she shuddered, not looking too closely, but moving away. 'I always feel panic when I see bats near. They get in your hair – I could scream at the very thought! I don't know how you can touch them. Horrible dirty beasts; I read somewhere that they are verminous and can carry rabies!'

'But this is one of the finest and most interesting bats in Britain, and only found in any number here in the southwest.

Horseshoe bats seem to thrive best in deep caves, evidently they prefer the cool humid climate of Welsh, and other west-country, caves, possibly because they would become dehydrated in dry, warm situations: I discovered my first greater horseshoe bat in the great Wogan Cavern under Pembroke Castle, a few miles from here. You're a historian – wasn't Wogan a medieval knight associated with that great fortress? I wonder what he or his lady thought of the bats which cluster in the roof of that vast water-worn limestone cave beneath the great Keep of Pembroke Castle. It was a secret passage giving access to tidal water in case of siege by the enemy; and many an evening at dusk must have been used by escapers or entrants using a boat . . . even perhaps by the beautiful Helen of Wales, Nesta, the Welsh princess who was abducted from her marriage bed with a Norman knight at Pembroke by a prince of her own blood, Owain Cadwgan. I can picture the lovely Nesta hurrying down the stone stairs to the cavern and being helped into the boat in the twilight while hundreds of horseshoe bats swarmed through her hair.'

'You've a powerful imagination! There's no mention of bats in the literature of that adventure, which was so long ago – let me see, yes, it was the year 1108, a stirring period . . . Nesta's marvellous beauty had reached the king's ears, she became mistress to Henry the First, and had children by all three of her liaisons: by Henry, by Gerald de Windsor (her first husband) and by Stephen, castellan of Cardigan Castle. But ugh! I can imagine that great Wogan Cave at night and your horseshoe bats flying!'

'Bats find the equable temperature of caves and stone vaults perfect for shelter by day and hibernation in the winter. It suits their unusual metabolism, which is adapted to rapid violent exercise and breathing during the short summer nights; followed by a deep sleep with lowered breathing rate and heart beat all day, and extreme torpidity in the winter, when the body fat, accumulated in feeding all summer, is conserved by reduced temperature and inactivity. A bat can turn down its thermostat much as you regulate the temperature of your central heating at home to suit your requirements; only the bat does the opposite to you. It uses up its fuel – body fat – reserves very slowly all winter, when no supply of food is available to replenish this but turns up the thermostat when fuel is abundant in the summer. It's rather like the hummingbird which lives at such a rate (of respiration and heart-beat) all day that it would die of hunger if it kept it up all night, so it slows down as soon as it goes to roost at night and becomes almost rigid with cold, and deeply unconscious, every night of its life. I have had difficulty in lifting a hummingbird from its night-perch; it seems semi-frozen as it grips the roosting branch. A bat goes half-dead like that, but only in its winter sleep; in summer it remains fairly lively during its daytime rest. This horseshoe bat tried to bite me as soon as I lifted it from its perch.'

'Well, look out! It's still trying to bite you! You'll get rabies!'

The bat tried to bite again as I spread one of its leathery semi-transparent wings to show off its wonderful structure.

'I've often been bitten by a bat, and the horseshoe can draw blood. But they don't carry the rabies virus, simply because they don't suck blood at all. Dogs, foxes and other meat-eating canines are the carriers, and the tropical South American vampire bats which suck the blood of rabid terrestrial mammals. Open your hand, please.'

Reluctantly Miss Historian spread her hand parallel within one foot of the extended wing. I demonstrated the comparison:

'See, the bat's wing is merely two skins with connecting tissue, and a network of fine blood vessels activate the whole. It looks fragile, but is strongly attached to the body all the way from the shoulder to the heel of the foot. See how the webbing continues, joining tail with body and legs. A marvellous flying machine! Look at the thumb or first finger, free and adapted almost solely as a hook to hang by, or pull it forwards when not flying. The second finger is fairly short and supports the outer edge of the wing, while the long bones of the third, fourth and fifth fingers stiffen the whole like the ribs of an umbrella. Really a giant webbed hand is what it flies with – imagine how nice it would be if we could fly with our hands!'

'I must admit it's marvellous, but also gruesome, and weird . . .'

'Look closely at the webbed tail. It has several valuable functions. Apart from assisting flight as an extension of the wings, it is mainly used as a basket, to hold a captured insect temporarily, in full flight. But also, when giving birth at the roost the female bat turns right way up – I mean she reverses her normal head-down sleeping position – and curves this interfemoral or tail web upwards and inwards to act as a cradle to receive the child as it struggles to be born. Sometimes she has been seen adopting a horizontal attitude, on her back, like a hammock, holding on with both thumbs and leg-claws, head up and femoral web extended. Otherwise the baby might slip to the ground before it's able to crawl to and cling upon its mother's breast.'

'That's fascinating. I've never thought about bats and babies, and how they manage it!'

'Well, think of it now! The new-born bat must at once cling to its mother, for she has to take it with her when she flies out to feed at dusk each summer evening. But its claws are well-developed before it is born, and it usually emerges feet first and is already grasping the mother's skin and fur before its head and infantile wings emerge.'

'Nature is marvellous!'

'Look at this bat's knees. See how, unlike human knees, they turn outwards and backwards. If they didn't the tail and its membrane couldn't be brought forward effectively as a food basket – or cradle.'

'I always supposed a bat caught food with its mouth?'

'Mostly it does. But it also scoops freely at flying prey with one wing or the other; it will hit at a large moth or beetle in mid-air, so that it tumbles against its body and falls into the interfemoral basket, which is turned inwards to catch it. This is necessary, since it couldn't go on flying with one wing holding a large insect! High-speed photography of bats captive in large cages has shown exactly how the bat seizes and pouches an insect in flight, bending down its head to grasp and adjust the capture in its mouth. And this explains the jinking acrobatic manoeuvring in bats hunting in the open, as we see them at dusk.'

'Carrying a baby at the same time? Must be a handicap! I see no baby with this one; evidently the lucky sort – a male?'

'No, she's a nursing mother, or at least recently lactating. Her mammary glands are obvious – there, in the normal position, low on her breast. Her baby is either weaned already or only suckled at intervals; it's probably hanging up near where I unhooked this mother, which can't carry the child when it gets too large and heavy.'

'I should think not! Doesn't the baby fall off now and then?'

'Not often enough to have fatal consequences for the species. In these horseshoe bats and many others there are special arrangements for the baby to hold on. If you look closely at this female you'll see a pair of false teats close to the tail. The new-born baby anchors itself to one of these dummies with a firm mouth-grip, using its clawed feet to grasp the fur and skin higher on the mother's chest or abdomen. This gives the baby a pretty secure three-point grip while mother is busy catching food in mid-air. When Ma returns to roost the hungry baby lets go and crawls its way to suckle at the breast.'

'You amaze me. I never thought . . . well, now I do think about it, if I were a bat baby, I should be thoroughly airsick, jinking about with mother!'

'As for your fear that bats will get entangled in your hair of their own volition, that's almost impossible. I was discussing this popular myth lately with that enterprising amateur naturalist, Lord Cranbrook. He described an experiment he made in front of a television camera. He released a bat in a small room, in the centre of which sat a young lady combing her waist-long hair. As she wafted her tresses upwards, deliberately so that the strands floated in mid-air, the bat, forced to remain flying in the confined space by Cranbrook dislodging it whenever it tried to rest, nevertheless successfully avoided the swinging hair. This it was able to do, by using the echoes of its own voice, by what is called sonar. It located the objects in the room, both under artificial light and when the lights were turned off, by listening for the echoes of the continuous squeaks of its own cries against those objects, bounced back to its ears in split seconds. Even the girl's hair produced echoes.'

'Quite amazing. I understand very little about sonar, though I knew of its existence and use in the Navy – I was a Wren in the War. I remember how flocks of high-flying birds appeared on the receiver and confused the evidence of enemy activity. Just moving dots or splodges which we feared might be enemy squadrons approaching thousands of feet high – they were known as "angels" because they behaved so strangely, so erratically, in flight.'

'Sorry, you're confusing radar, which is the reflection of radio waves (which have the speed of light), with sonar, the much slower echo received from sound, which has a speed of under twenty miles per minute. Bats don't have radar, but only sonar or echo-location, which is essential to cave-dwelling night-flying bats; but incidentally not present in bats living in the open. They have large eyes and normal, often keen sight; for instance the giant flying-foxes of the tropics.'

'Good heavens, I've seen flying foxes in the parks at Singapore! Enormous creatures. Never thought they were bats!'

'There are well over a thousand bat species in the world, of many very different habits. Some live on fruit, like the flying foxes; some sip nectar from flowers, like hummingbirds; the vampire bat sucks blood. A Brazilian bat raids wasp nests by night and feeds on the grubs inside the paper envelope, which it tears open. Our British species are unspectacular compared with a giant tropical bat powerful enough to live by hunting and eating other bats on the wing, and pouncing on mice and small birds – this is the false vampire which crushes the head of its prey the moment it seizes it, conveniently immobilising the victim during the flight of the predator. At the other end of the size scale there is the minute bat which sleeps in the hollow centre of a bamboo. There is the pallid bat of North America which hunts on foot in the desert, and kills and eats poisonous scorpions without getting stung itself. Perhaps the most interesting is the bat which lives on fish, actually catching them with gaff and net.'

'Oh, come!'

'Fact. At least three sub-tropical bats are expert fishermen. I was shown a remarkable series of colour photographs of the bulldog bat, as its called, *Noctilio leporinus*, taken in a large aviary containing a pond supplied with small fish. It is not yet known how these bats locate a swimming fish at night, since echo-location signals from above do not easily penetrate below the surface of water. But catch them this bat did. Its technique is to plough the surface of the pond with the forward-directed claws of its long legs. Possibly the nearest lurking fish is attracted to the disturbance, as small fish will rise to the splash of a fisherman's hook, supposing in their dim fish's mind, or just by pure reaction, that an insect is drowning there. The fish is expertly gaffed on one or more of the ten long sharp claws of the bat's feet, and immediately transferred to the mouth. In the same sweeping forward action the tail membrane is used as a landing net, into which the fish is dropped or contained momentarily while the bat kills it with hard bites before taking it into its mouth, chewing it, storing chunks of fish in its cheek pouches – all while still in flight. An astonishing feat, for at the same moment it continues to emit the sound pulses by which it echo-navigates in flight.'

The lecture finished, I released the female horseshoe bat within the icehouse, and stood in the entrance to prevent it escaping into the daylight, while it might still be dazed by my handling it. It settled to roost at once, preening for a few moments after it had expertly landed with a little somersault, feet first, upside down. Presently the tail membrane was folded as a lid over the top, and the wings closed around the rest of the body, including the head – a neat pear-shaped capsule in the beam of my torch.

'I am amazed, and humbled!' exclaimed Miss Historian, as we returned to the house.

*   *   *

Bats have ever been a symbol of death, doom and darkness. When Ulysses entered the Underworld he was pursued by demoniac bats. In his *Vision of Death* Gustave Doré depicts a cloud of bat-like souls trailing after the Reaper. Shakespeare's references are a little happier: in *A Midsummer's Night's Dream* the bat is quaintly charming . . .

> Come, now a roundel and a fairy song;
> Then, for a third part of a minute, hence;
> Some to kill cankers in the musk-rose buds,
> Some war with rere-mice for their leathern wings,
> To make small elves coats.

The furry coat of the bat, and its ability to fly on leathern wings gave it the colloquial name of rere-mouse, or flittermouse. In *Macbeth* there is a recipe which contains

> Eye of newt and toe of frog,
> Wool of bat and tongue of dog.

In *The Tempest* Ariel sings the well-known song:

> Where the bee sucks, there suck I,
> In a cowslip's bell I lie;
> There I couch when owls do cry.
> On the bat's back I do fly
> After summer merrily.

Miss Historian forbore to scream when two horseshoe bats suddenly flew into the salon that evening as we were taking coffee. She was even amused when one of the men guests got up, in response to his wife's shuddering and cowering, and began swiping at the bats with a walking stick.

'Let them be,' I said presently. 'You'll never hit them. They'll go away when they've completed their very useful work of clearing the room of the moths and the midges, and the mosquitoes you complained of when you strolled by the lake earlier this evening. Look how that one caught that moth just then – probably a pestilential clothes moth. Just as it can catch a fluttering, zigzagging moth or a tiny midge so expertly in mid-air, it can easily flip aside from your large and obvious weapon. And by the way, it doesn't locate its prey, or your stick, by sight but, as I was explaining earlier to Miss Historian, by sound . . . Listen, can anyone hear these bats squeaking, a very high, in fact ultrasonic, note? I am getting rather deaf to their cries as I get older . . .' To prove to my guests that sight is unimportant in a nocturnal hole- or cave-roosting bat, I turned off the light and closed the curtains. The bats continued to hunt the midges and moths in the darkened salon. I had merely demonstrated Cranbook's experiment in a mild form.

'The night-flying bat carries a sonar screen in its head, even more effective than man's comparatively recent invention of electronic equipment, during the Second World War, for measuring the distance and locating the precise direction of fixed or moving objects unseen by the naked eye – as from aircraft or ship. Nothing is new under the sun: man's sonar devices are but clumsy copies of the instantaneous echo-location computer in the brain of a bat.'

The air space above and around Orielton on an average warm summer evening was nicely shared out by six species of bat, without obvious competition. The highest flier was the largest British bat, *Nyctalus noctula*. Hidden by day in hollows of decayed beech, elm and oak trees, the noctule was the earliest to emerge, spreading its wings (spanning about 350mm) often before sunset and climbing upon the last thermals of warm air where the winged insects were swirling. Its eyes are comparitively large, and evidently more efficient, than those of more nocturnal bats. Its size and rapid level flight, with frequent sudden zooming dives upon prey – especially the cockchafers active at that hour – high above the trees and lawns, were at once recognisable.

Most numerous and smallest of the bats, the pipistrelle (Latin, pipire, to squeak) *Pipistrellus pipistrellus,* lived by day in at least five large colonies, each of several hundred adults, in the roofs of the various buildings on the estate. About thirty minutes after sunset the pipistrelles would start to leave the eaves in a steady flow, lasting for half an hour. This little bat sometimes appeared in the day time, and individuals might be seen far from known roosts, occasionally on remote, windswept islands such as Skokholm and Ramsey, where it certainly does not remain or breed. Its normal altitude for hunting was well below that of the noctule, just above the tree-tops or lower, depending on the weather which in turn affected the flight levels of insect prey.

Hardly larger than the pipistrelle – both species have the same wing-span of about 220mm – the whiskered bat *Myotis mystacinus* was much scarcer, or at least was seldom obtained in the hand. It probably roosted with or close to the pipistrelle colonies, although I only once found it in such company. Two were brought to me by boys bird-nesting who had found them roosting separately in hollows in trees. Studying their flight on release, we learned to recognise certain peculiarities of gentle fluttering in slow circles close to the ground, lacking the restlessness and rapid wing-beat of the pipistrelle. We could be surest of finding a whiskered bat near the Lily Pond, where it commonly circled and twisted low over the water. Here, too, other bats came to hunt and to drink, sipping water in one swift pass, wings held high.

Sometimes, when I was working late at night, my desk lamp close to the window, moths and numerous other flying insects would accumulate on the outside of the glass, dazzled by the strong light. Often then a very handsome bat would appear, with immense rabbit ears. This was *Plecotus auritus*, the long-eared bat, more strictly nocturnal than the others, and with a different hunting technique. It was delightfully easy to observe as it fluttered from the twilight up to the glass of the window, and deftly collected in its wide-open mouth a juicy moth or bumbling beetle. It hovered with broad wings (span 250mm), ears switched forward to detect and amplify the buzz of the insects and the echoes of its own voice; and I could see the fine lines of the blood vessels of the muscles which held those wonderful semi-transparent ears erect. Presumably the enormous development of these appendages is associated with a selective orientation to and echo-location of its normal prey – insects close to or at rest upon the leaves and branches of the woodland terrain this bat seems to prefer. It is also known to echo-locate and pick up, in near darkness, flightless insects such as leaf bugs from foliage, despite the ambient sound-clutter from this background.

One evening a large house spider – a black nocturnal prowler – suddenly crawled over the paper on my desk. In brushing it thoughtlessly aside I crushed it accidentally. I opened the window, and gently stuck the spider by its own juices to the centre of the outside of the glass. Soon the long-eared bat, which had been feeding there earlier, fluttered up to the splayed corpse and collected it with a dainty snatch of its broad mouth. Spiders are probably a normal part of its diet, captured as these rival fly-catchers spin their webs by night across vegetation. Perhaps many a moth, or other nocturnal winged insect, buzzing in the new snare of a spider, has attracted the hovering long-eared bat to seize both the snarer and the snared as they grapple in the web – a juicy bonne-bouche for a hungry bat.

Our beautiful long-eared bats were opportunists whose expert hovering technique was akin to that of the Central American *Leptonycteris* species, which drink nectar with their long tongues as they hover in front of tropical blossoms; and incidentally perform the useful function of pollinating these. One evening an entomologist visiting Orielton set upon the tree trunks his moth-catching devices of sugared boards and mercury vapour lamp. As darkness closed in, hundreds of moths and other nocturnal flying insects were drawn to feed on the syrup, or buzz around the intense light of the mercury vapour bulb. To his annoyance, and our amusement, some long-eared bats arrived, and began feasting on the larger moths, neatly picking off the finest specimens he had hoped to secure for his collection.

These graceful bats had one of their roosting places in an almost inaccessible spot, not far from the corner where the honey-bees had their immemorial and totally unreachable apiary – where a maze of short rafters and cross-beams supported the parapet roof of the manor. There they slept away the bright light of day, becoming active and squeaking only at dusk; but in winter the colony was silent, hibernating safely. Always when sleeping the sensitive ears would be folded back snugly beneath the arm, leaving the curious long spike of the ear-lobe, known as the tragus, erect. (The function of the tragus is not understood, but as it is present in other bats with large ears – but not in the leaf-nose species – it seems likely it assists hearing in some way.) They were also safe from humans crawling about who sought to catch, mark and study individuals, but who gave up the attempt in the end and emerged from the dim tangle of rafters with bruised head, covered with dust and scale from timber and slate, and smeared with bat guano which, in such confined quarters, produces an almost lethal stench when an accumulation of a hundred years is disturbed!

Strangely enough this colony had one rare enemy – snow. When the crust of a sudden heavy snow, which fell one Christmas night, melted during a few hours of sunshine next day, the lower layer remained frozen, preventing the escape of the meltwater. This lay on top of the snow and trickled steadily under the slates of the surrounding parapet roof, thoroughly wetting some of the bats hibernating underneath. Normally a few drops of moisture falling on a sleeping bat is repelled by the oily surface of its skin and fur, but this deluge soaked a few. It was also crisis for the human occupants. We learned too late on that occasion the danger of snow lying on a flat lead roof shut in by slated ridges (these were about five feet high and ten feet wide at roof level, and were useful wind and safety barriers, making the flat centre of the roof a sheltered private place for sleeping, sunbathing or hanging out the washing). The first sign was the seepage, soon followed by a flood, through the topmost ceilings. It was many weeks before the manor dried out completely; meanwhile in the course of mopping-up under the roof some very wet long-eared bats were found, chilled to death.

*　　*　　*

My sons had become involved in the lives of the bats which were such a feature of their home surroundings. They were small enough to crawl and explore with a torch under the roof after the snow. Stephen was moved to tears by the sight of the corpses of the long-eared bats, and would not allow them to be thrown away. A solemn funeral had to be organised. In the soft soil by the lakeside Martin dug a grave, next to the fenced plot where Emma's spaniel Sancho lay. Stephen prepared a cross of two sticks nailed together. Their mother composed and read the funeral oration:

> The north wind did blow,
> And brought us deep snow
> So what did poor long-ears do then?
> 　　Poor things!
>
> All asleep in their roof,
> So snug and aloof,
> They hid their ears under their wings.
> 　　Poor things!
>
> When the north wind next blows
> And bring us deep snows,
> We'll sweep the roof clean for our bats.
> 　　Poor things!

There was a pause for the poor things, their long ears still folded neatly under their wings, to be lowered into the grave. From the prayer book was read: 'Earth to earth, ashes to ashes, dust to dust . . .' as Martin shovelled soil; and Stephen planted a jam jar of wild snowdrops.

The verses were slipped into an old photograph frame, and hung as a warning on the wall of my office.

Martin was old enough to be interested in and to comprehend a little of my story of the fascinating nature of the mechanism of echo-location in bats and of the background of its discovery two centuries ago by the Abbé Spallanazi in Italy. I had just received news from Donald Griffin who had studied orientation in birds with me, that he was investigating the strange oil-bird of Central America, finding that it also used sonar to locate its nest in the total darkness of deep caves. So apparently did the esculent swiftlets of tropical Asia, breeding in deep limestone caverns, whose saliva nests provided the famous birds-nest soup of the Orient . . .

But Stephen soon grew bored with long words. Action is what these young men demanded. They wanted to explore caves and roofs, helping to catch bats for our marking studies, placing a light aluminium band – a tiny bracelet – on the forearm, and entering its serial number in a register.

It was strenuous, adventurous and grimy work. We had to use the longest available ladders to reach the high roof of the vast Wogan Cave where in winter large clusters of adult greater horse-shoe bats *Rhinolophus ferrum-equinum* clung in limestone hollows, located by mounds of droppings on the muddy floor below. The drowsy lesser horseshoes *R. hipposideros* were easier to reach and handle in their hibernaculum of the icehouse and underground sites.

In the summer both horseshoe bats were harder to find. Most of them had taken up dormitories in hollow trees. Early in the autumn we endeavoured to round up and band the young bats, born about midsummer and left behind at the roosting place at night. It was inadvisable to disturb the colonies earlier, while the babies were still attached to the maternal breast; baby and mother could become separated, or the mother might escape into the sunshine – an unnatural thing to do – where by day the swift hawks were ready to snatch up slow-flying bats, especially if encumbered with young.

Pipistrelles were abundant enough for us to test their homing powers. One afternoon we collected a hundred adults from the roof of the North Lodge, banded them and set them free the same evening some ten miles away near Tenby. They were all lactating females, with well-grown young hanging independently on the rafters; so these mothers had an adequate incentive to return.

The experiment involved a second visit a few days later to see how many had returned to North Lodge; and yet another crawl through dust and guano, carrying a wide board – necessary for laying across the joists in order to avoid placing one's full weight on the flimsy batten-and-plaster ceiling of the bedrooms below.

On the first visit I had proved too substantial and far from agile in such cramped quarters, and so I enlisted the smaller of my sons to wriggle into the corners with the torch and capture all the bats his lean arm could reach. I reassured him that pipistrelles were too small to be able to draw blood when they bit you, as assuredly they would. Martin was stationed to recieve the bats as Stephen caught them, and store them in a pillowslip, the folds of which are ideally soft and comfortable to imprison the fragile creatures temporarily.

Presently: 'I can see a banded one! I've got it!' came Stephen's muffled voice after some preliminary groans as he bumped his extremities upon unyielding rafters and beams. 'Oo, it's dusty, it's stinking . . . and stinking hot, too! Ah, I've got another banded one . . . here, take it, quick, Martin! Oh, damn . . . it's biting me! It's gone! I thought you said pipistrelles wouldn't draw blood, Pa?'

'Perhaps you've got a tough old lady bat – they're rufous brown, browner than the little grey babies.' I encouraged Stephen from my comfortable seat at the top of the stepladder, my head just inside the attic trap-door. 'Keep it up, you're doing fine! How many in the bag, Martin?'

'Twenty, but only four with a ring.'

'Here's another!' yelled Stephen. 'Take it quick, it's biting, but I'm getting used to that – don't really hurt. Coo, this corner stinks! There's a few dead, babies, lying in the guano! No wonder Pa funked it second time! Say, Pa, you're cunning! Ah, there's another one with a band on its wing . . . if I can reach it! Ugh, gotcher . . .'

There was a triumphant note in the running commentary now, as Stephen warmed to the chase, forgetting the discomfort and stench for a while.

'Getting on for fifty in the bag. How many left up there, Stephen?'

'Heaps!' came the half-choked reply. 'But most have crawled

away into corners and under the slates. Can't reach many more. Can't breathe in this dust and heat and stink! Just one more and I'm coming out. A beauty with a bracelet on! Ah, would you! I got her by one leg! She's stuck in a crevice!'

Then suddenly: 'Help, help! What's happening? The board's giving way!'

There was a grinding tearing noise and to the accompaniment of heart-rending groans Stephen descended, in a cloud of dust, battens and lime-plaster, between two ceiling joists, to bounce, battered and a little bloody, upon the voluminous patchwork quilt of my tenants' double bed in the room below.

Fifteen per cent of the marked pipistrelles had been recaptured, seven days after release ten miles away. The experiment was never repeated. It had proved too exhausting (and too expensive in repairs) to justify the meagre results.

It was, however, rewarding to sit quietly and study what was happening in the colonies, as far as a torch permitted one to see into their cramped roof quarters. On a warm summer day there was a lot of activity at the roost, chiefly preening movements.

Despite the general belief to the contrary, bats are meticulous about body hygiene, constantly grooming their fur and leathery wings. Each mobile foot is used in turn to comb and preen every part of the body it can reach. The tongue supplies an oily saliva which assists in removing skin scale and loose hair, at the same time coating the body with this water-repellent. As much of the body and wings as possible is licked or passed through the lips, which are equipped with sebaceous glands; and a well-licked foot is used as a brush and comb to apply the oil to the back of the head and other parts which the tongue cannot reach.

After clearing up most of the moths, craneflies, beetles, mosquitoes and midges which, attracted by artificial light, entered the house in summer, our horseshoe bats would some-times hang up on a picture rail or a chandelier and, swinging by one foot, use the other in cleansing gymnastics. The free foot with its five separate toes would be applied to the inside of the ear, and to every part of the curious projecting nose-leaf – an instinctive action and habit prompted by that same itchy feeling we humans experience when irritated by dust, sweat or crawling insects. The mobile clawed toe of the bat is a highly efficient nose, ear and mouth probe.

Strict hygiene is essential in a crowded bat community. I noticed that even when suspended upside down in the normal roosting position, each bat, before it passed waste matter, was careful to adjust its position so that this was voided without soiling a neighbour. Normally waste falls to the floor of attic or cave, a guide to the position, size and state of the colony; much of it is subsequently reduced by scavenging insects and bacteria. Nevertheless, in spite of copious preening and oiling, bats are seldom free of ectoparasites. Roosting close together for long periods and in dark places they provide food and cover opportunities for the survival and dissemination of their specific fleas and mites.

There is also a curious wingless fly, related to the winged, flattened hippoboscid fly which is commonly found sliding agilely around beneath the body feathers of birds in summer. (This lively fly lays its egg or pupa in the nests of birds, ready to hatch in the following spring and infest the next generation.) Both wingless bat fly and winged bird fly have strongly hooked claws on the six legs, enabling them to hold firmly to the fur or feathers of their host; but without wings the bat fly looks more like a spider as it moves nimbly on long legs over the fur, easily avoiding the preening movements of the bat. It is one of the *Nycteribiid* family, which are said to do very little harm to the bat, although they are blood-suckers. They never leave their host save briefly when the females give birth to their young, in the form of already pupated larvae, which they fasten to the cave wall or roof nearest to the roosting bats.

An increasing confusion seemed to reign in the crowded roosts of pipistrelle, long-eared and lesser horseshoe bats after midsummer when, instead of carrying their babies, the mother bats left them hanging up while they foraged for food at night. It was difficult to prove that each nursing female on returning to the roost found its own infant among the scores of hungry children, so hard was it to sort out the activity as seen under cramped conditions of observation, and in addition the adults behaved unnaturally when disturbed by a torch beamed on them. But the young ones were less sensitive – probably near-blind as yet – and at night, after the adults had flown, these half-grown children would be discovered actively preening their fur and stretching their wings, one limb at a time.

The well-grown youngsters were more restless and would move about (perhaps they become more photonegative at this age – that is, able to see more clearly, and seeking the protection of darkness). Horseshoe babies often used their leg claws to hook themselves along, but pipstrelles turned around, head up, and pulled themselves forward with the hooked thumb, freely clinging to the bodies of neighbours en route. A neighbour so disturbed might show resentment by biting or opening its jaws towards the trespasser. However, this aggressiveness seemed more like the play of puppies, and it is possible that young bats do play limited little games together while hanging up, games which must usefully serve the purpose of exercising and strengthening their muscles.

Does each mother, returning from the night's hunting, recognise its own child by its individual cry, or by its particular scent which her own body odour would have imparted at birth and during the suckling afterwards? Sight-recognition is impossible, in that dark bedlam of hundreds of tightly-packed squeaking children; but it is known that the adult bat invariably returns to its favourite roosting position and there, in normal conditions, a mother would find its child waiting. This would be less difficult in British colonies. They are not so vast and dense as some of the tropical and sub-tropical bat nurseries, where it has been proved that in some species the lactating female, returning home after the evening flight, is suckled indiscriminately by any one or more of the babies nearest to her roosting niche. She acts as a general milk supply to the overcrowded nursery; as soon as one infant is satiated and releases a nipple, another hungry baby grabs it.

Because of this difficulty of observation of bat colonies, the fascinating picture of maternity in bats is still not complete but it is being pieced together by the study of bats in captivity, and of their curious histology. Dr Leo Harrison Matthews has been foremost in the latter study, and I am grateful for the opportunity to extract information from his numerous papers to supplement that of other writers.

The single young bat (twins are rare) is born around about midsummer after a gestation period of approximately sixteen weeks. But this does not necessarily mean that mating takes place sixteen weeks earlier, which would date the courtship and copulation to a period in February – in Britain a very cold month when bats are usually still hibernating. Odd as it may seem in view of the known gestation period, mating usually takes place in the autumn, when the adults are in optimum health, and often enormously fat after feeding well all summer. The sperm from this mating (most likely involving several males during what is believed to be a long period of oestrus in the female) remains stored and alive in the uterus of the female during the several months of winter sleep.

Normally, in most other mammals, sperm dies within a few days if it cannot reach and fertilise the egg. But the uterus of a mated female bat examined in the autumn and during hibernation has been quite distended with active sperm. However, there is some variation in the method of storing this. In our horseshoe bats the sperm does not travel as far as the uterus, but halts when it reaches a special pocket in the upper part of the vagina. Here it remains alive throughout the winter in the centre of a plug of coagulated mucus, secreted, apparently during mating, by the urethral glands of both sexes. From this store is drawn the sperm which will fertilise the ovum in early spring, during the latter end of hibernation, sixteen weeks before parturition.

Delayed fertilisation of the egg is a convenient device to ensure that mating takes place at the optimum state of health in the adults, and at the most convenient moment when the sexes can come together. It occurs in various forms in several other animals, including wasps and bees, also some fleas. In certain mammals the egg is fertilised at mating but the resulting blasto-cyst (ovum containing sperm) remains dormant and is not implanted in the womb until months later – as in some seals, mustelids and bears.

In the horseshoe bats the female becomes pregnant from, and afterwards expels, the stored plug of sperm during the early spring awakening; if by chance she fails to become pregnant, or was too young to mate the previous autumn, she becomes oestrous, and is mated again. But here is another remarkable phenomenon: the male, having lost much of his autumn fat over the long fast of winter, is in no condition to manufacture fresh sperm in the spring. In fact, the testes have regressed back into the abdomen and no spermatogenesis is possible. Instead the sperm with which he impregnates a female in the spring is drawn from the considerable reservoir of autumn-produced sperm which has remained quiescent in the long coiled duct of his genital region (the epididymis) throughout his deep winter sleep! Yet another form of insurance of procreation in bats.

The courtship of bats has been observed occasionally, but only in captivity. The sebaceous glands become enlarged at mating time and, as in other nocturnal animals during the rut, male and female come together through olfactory clues. A compliant female responds to an ardent male's gesticulating approach and squeaking with the same. They soon embrace, the male manoeuvring to copulate from the rear; the penis is proportionately long in order to reach under her interfemoral membrane.

The new-born bat is blind and naked, and about one-fifth as heavy as its mother. It clings at all times to the front of its mother's body, as already described, holding tightly to one false or real teat during the night flight, until it is about six weeks old, when it becomes too heavy to be carried on hunting expeditions. Near this stage the considerable load has to be finely distributed so as not to throw the mother off balance when in flight; if the baby mouth holds by a false teat below her abdomen, it throws its legs around its mother's neck; if it grips one breast then the legs embrace the mother's thigh on the opposite side.

As far as is known very young bats which fall accidentally to the floor of cave or attic and are too feeble to climb back, are never rescued or fed by their dam. This at least eliminates the weakling; the strong remains firmly attached, first to the mother, and later to the site where she roosts. Until it is able to fly it clings here, as we have seen, growing fat on a rich milk diet, exercising its wings, preening, even indulging in mock fights with neighbours. At last it makes short flights within the dark cavity of its birthplace. It is never fed by the adult with solid food, although I have seen a female return to roost with her cheek pouches full of crushed insects – to masticate these at her leisure.

The young bat is well covered with a layer of fat which serves to sustain it over any fasting period between weaning in late summer and its first successful aerial hunt in the open. On first emerging the weanling hovers for a while, to memorise by sight or sonar – or both?) the surroundings outside, and this facilitates an accurate return to the nursery well before dawn, for while immature it will spend its first hibernation close to the adult females. In the next summer, if it is a male, it will be segregated with adults of its own sex, occupying either a separate part of the roost, or separate male quarters elsewhere.

On the occasion when Stephen fell through the ceiling at North Lodge, he was far less concerned about his bumps and bruises than his discovery of baby bats dead below the roost. 'And some were still just about alive, Pa. I tried to hang them up again, but they dropped down each time . . .'

I explained that this was a natural mortality, that he need not worry, bats were far older than man, and from their origin as ground-living mammals millions of years ago, by clever adaption of their limbs, had taken to the air . . .

'Millions of years? How long does a bat live?'

'It must live longer than a mouse, rat or rabbit, simply because its rate of reproduction is so slow. Not more than one baby a year; so it takes one pair of bats two years to reproduce themselves. But you must allow that on average a female bat may not breed until she is two years old. Then you should reckon she must produce. at least one more baby, three altogether, to make up for infant mortality such as you have seen in the nursery, and bats killed by owls or from some other cause. Supposing a female bat must produce four babies to keep up the numbers of her species, then she must live at least six years, on average. And as some will suffer accidents and death earlier, many individuals will live longer.'

Consulting my library, I could report that the published results of marking bats showed that some individuals had lived at least seven, and one above seventeen years – one of these was a greater horseshoe bat.

'But why do bats fly at night anyway? There are millions of insects in the air all day long. Look how swallows and swifts chase insects, from near the ground to as far as you can see in the sky!'

In the literature several reasons are given. One is that fur-covered mammals in flight would find the heat of the sun too dehydrating. Another explanation appeals more: bats never fly at high speeds, like the swallows and swifts; they flit about at well under twenty miles an hour and therefore would be extremely vulnerable to fast-flying diurnal predatory birds. I have seen the dashing hobby falcon take swifts on the wing, and a bat would be easy prey – in fact hobbies will take bats which emerge too early in the evening.

'So you see, Stephen, those bats which were foolish enough to fly by day have been eliminated in favour of night-flying individuals. Owls will take bats occasionally, but as they too fly very slowly and prefer to pounce on prey on the ground, they are not a serious menace to bats. Again bats, as the only mammals that can fly, are able to exploit a rich food source in the vast volume of night-flying insects. Only a few birds do this by night, notably the nightjars which nest in our woodland in summer.'

*　　*　　*

One day a speleologist asked me to identify a young full-grown greater horseshoe bat which he had captured in a cave he had been investigating in the limestone cliffs a few miles south of Orielton, caves which had yielded many bones of prehistoric animals: mammoth, hippopotamus, woolly rhinoceros, bear, reindeer, elk, and others now extinct which once roamed the great pre-glacial plain of what is now the Bristol Channel.

Rin-tin, as she was soon dubbed, was for a while the subject of a study in captivity, and of some admiration and respect by those who came to know her. She could and did bite severely at first, until we realised that her biting was partly because she was hungry. We learned to approach her with a large insect or mealworm, which she would at once begin to eat – instead of our fingers.

Rin-tin was given the freedom of the barrel cellar, where the temperature was as constant and the air as humid as the deep cave where she had been found. During this study I kept her prisoner in the dark there all day. Towards sunset I would switch on the cellar light and observe her through a small window in the door. I would talk to her, beginning with a few high hisses (which I fondly hoped might be as near as I could get to her ultrasonic calls). If she had not already begun to fly – and she had an accurate sense of time of day, even in that dark place – around the cellar before my arrival she would respond by swinging off her roosting niche and, as I opened the little window and extended a bowl of mealworms into the cellar, she would alight and begin greedily to eat.

It was then easy to place a small kitchen strainer over the bowl as she crunched her supper and carry her safely to my study and release her. To prevent her escape I had covered the top half of one opened window with a screen of half-inch wire-netting. A 100-watt electric light bulb placed on the same level as the open window attracted numerous moths, beetles and other flying insects which could pass easily through the mesh.

By the time I had eaten my evening meal elsewhere Rin-tin would have captured and eaten hers, her second repast of the day. On my return I would find her hung up at her favourite spot, clinging to the ornate plaster moulding of the ceiling. She would be smacking her mobile lips over the remains of her self-caught supper, digesting, preening, and attending meticulously to the oiling of her fur, wings, ears and horseshoe-shaped nose-leaf. Beneath her I had provided a wide tray of dry earth to obviate soiling the carpet with her waste matter – urine, faeces and the rejected wings and legs of larger insects.

Although I did not want to domesticate her to such an extent that she would lose her ability to survive in the wild, to which I would eventually return her, I became fond of Rin-tin. She ceased to bite my fingers and even gave me a casual lick of recognition now and then. Despite her poor sight she knew me at once from any strangers who came to watch her aerobatics of an evening.

It was amusing to note how smoothly and neatly she would fly up to her resting niche, at the last moment executing a turn over so that she hung by her clawed feet, not her thumbs. Before taking off she lifted her head into view and opened her mouth to utter high squeaks (which older people found difficult to hear) as she 'scanned' her surroundings acoustically, head swinging in a semi-circle, automatically registering the distances of objects around her, before opening her wings wide and jumping off.

Rin-tin had a large appetite. Her movements in pursuit of flying insects were typical of a bat using sonar, but were often too rapid to follow closely. She normally seemed to grab a small insect in her mouth by a sudden swoop; and swallow it in flight. Once or twice I could glimpse her swift fielding of a large moth or beetle with a flip of one wing towards her body, and in a split second she had netted it in her interfemoral membrane and taken it in her mouth, chewing its head first.

One or two food preference tests were carried out. A small black outdoor spider, freshly killed, hung in the centre of the room by a fine thread and, swaying in mid-air, was quickly echo-located by Rin-tin, who grabbed it and carried it off (the thread had been deliberately frayed so as to break at the tie). But she ignored a large, gaudy garden spider hung in turn on the same thread, and avoided wasp and bee when these were released in the study. She eagerly hunted and crunched up large bottle flies and other noisome flies.

Research has shown that conspicuously-coloured insects, such as wasps, bees, and certain moths, and butterflies and beetles (ladybirds and burying beetles) are usually avoided by predators which hunt by sight. Their bright colours and stripes – especially yellows, reds and blues – serve as warnings. Often justifiably, as these gaudy insects are usually unpleasant to eat, some have offensive odours, and some sting when captured. Of course a bat at night cannot see bright colours (it is almost certainly colour-blind, if it sees much at all). Rin-tin's apparent recognition of the unpalatibility of such insects must have been through auditory or olfactory clues.

Yet certain insects have evolved anti-bat devices. Some arctuid moths, on hearing the ultrasonic echo-pulses of a bat's hunting trill, produce a series of high-frequency squeaks of their own which, in some way not yet fathomed by man, inhibit their being captured by the bat. It is suggested that this has much the same effect as gaudy colouring, it warns the bat: 'Leave me alone. I taste horrible!' Other moths fold their wings and tumble to the ground as if dead on hearing a bat's voice. The bat's searching sonar is then nullified against the ambient echo it receives from earth. Other moths tumble through the air in sudden loops and evasive zigzags, so that the hunter is confused and unable to beam its sonar accurately.

I was usually up before dawn, even in summer. I would carry Rin-tin back to the cellar first thing. If her stomach was not bulging with what she had managed to catch and eat all night in the study, I would see that it did by giving her a breakfast of mealworms. She invariably ate a dozen of these; and she would enjoy the gentle grooming I gave her with an old toothbrush which I kept in a jar of insecticide powder – to keep her free of fleas and mites. She was sleek and fat now, and increased in weight to 30 gm by the end of September.

In mid-October Rin-tin's appetite waned; she ate fewer mealworms, and as the study was sometimes cold from having a window open, she would become sluggish and disinclined to stay in the air long. In any case there were fewer insects on the wing. The barrel cellar retained its summer temperature long after the first November frost. But the natural seasonal (Circadian) rhythm by which animals live – the cyclic or metabolic clock in the computer of her brain – had already informed Rin-tin of the approach of hibernation, even in an individual disturbed by the restrictions of captivity. Before November began she ceased to answer my invitation of 'Good evening' squeaks when I peeped through the window of her dungeon.

Martin wondered if she would be lonely if we left her to hibernate by herself in the barrel cellar.

'Can you be lonely when you are fast asleep?' I asked, as we crept nearer the torpid Rin-tin.

As Martin moved one hand gently towards the hanging, folded bat, we saw a slight movement, an upward hunching of the leg-joints.

'She's not fast asleep, Pa! I bet you she's feeling very lonely, all by herself in this dungeon. Can't we put her with a colony of bats for the winter – to keep warm?'

'She's fast asleep, don't worry. This shrinking movement in torpid bats has often been recorded before; something to do with the sensitiveness of the wing-membranes which wrap up Rin-tin like a shroud. Perhaps unconsciously the skin reacts to the slight heat of your hand near it. I shall take her temperature to prove she is more or less hibernating. I can't even see her breathing.'

A thermometer, quietly inserted along her body beneath the tent of her closed wings so that its bulb rested against the breast and inward-bent chin, registered only seven degrees above the temperature of the cellar. Her body felt cold; but it was still plump. Again that very slight drawing up of her knees when I touched her . . .

'There, she's 50°F, just half her normal summer temperature when hunting in my study. She's deep in sleep, unconscious, safe and quiet here, much warmer than her sea-cave in winter. I promise you she shall have her freedom when she wakes next spring.'

7

What is the sense of life? What is the sense of life of any living being at all? To know the answer to this question is to be religious . . . He who feels that his own life or that of his fellow beings is senseless is not only unhappy, but hardly capable of living. My views are . . . admiration for the beauty of and belief in the logical simplicity of the order and harmony which we can grasp humbly and only imperfectly. I believe that we have to content ourselves with our imperfect knowledge and understanding and treat values and moral obligations as a purely human problem – the most important of all human problems.

ALBERT EINSTEIN

A wild raven, illegally taken into captivity by someone living in London, who had been prosecuted for the offence by the Royal Society for the Prevention of Cruelty to Animals, was sent to me for release at my discretion. It arrived in a roomy wire-netted box, complete with a tin of cat meat and a drip-feed water-bottle.

I placed the contraption on newspapers on the table. I wanted to study the bird's behaviour, to estimate if it was sound and fit to be set free. It was tame enough to look me in the eye; no frantic wing-beating when I unfastened the side door and thrust a portion of cat meat into the cage, and refilled the water-bottle.

'Come on! Come on, Bird of Odin!' I coaxed.

Daintily the Bird of Odin picked up a fragment of meat, then sipped water thirstily. It was healthy enough. Cocking its head in different directions it inspected as much of its surroundings as it could see with its beady grey-brown eye.

'Come on, Odin, have some more? Come on, Odin.'

With a deep trisyllabic croak it gulped down the rest of the portion of meat.

'Ah you're hungry, are you, Odin?' I scooped another chunk out of the tin and pushed it into the cage. 'Come on, Odin.'

The raven ruffled its sable feathers, then stropped its beak on the perch, but did not eat any more.

'Come on, Odin, come on.'

'Coom'n Od'n, coom'n!' To my surprise it imitated my words as perfectly as a raven's croak may.

'H'm, you're not so wild after all. Wonder if you've been taught many words? Can you say "Hullo"? Or "Good-bye"?'

'Coom'n Od'n, coom'n!' came the *sotto voce* croak, muffled as the great beak preened the black wings.

'Ought I to release you if you're tame? I believe our ravens at the Gazebo wouldn't welcome you. They'd resent a strange raven visiting their private territory. Pity the RSPCA didn't find out where you were stolen from in the first place . . . What?'

'Coom'n Od'n, coom'n.'

I had kept young ravens before, taken from the nest at Skokholm, at the suggestion of Konrad Lorenz when he had visited the island many years ago. Konrad was then a young little-known amateur naturalist, who had published in German some notes on animal psychology – or, as it is now called, ethology. After his visit to Skokholm I had submitted some of his writings to the *Countryman*, introducing British readers to those delightful stories of his early experiments with captive and wild ravens and jackdaws. Young hand-reared wild birds may become so attached to ('imprinted' with) their keeper and the environment of his house that they are unable to adjust to a wild and free existence. The young ravens we reared at Skokholm, on being given their freedom, skulked around close to the house, chased the chickens, stole their eggs and food at every opportunity and took a special delight in tormenting domestic animals. They would tweak the tail or stab at the eye of goat, dog and cat if they could steal upon them unobserved.

After all, the tame raven released from captivity is simply behaving as it does in the wild – searching inquisitively for food – but with the difference that it has no fear of man. I shuddered as I thought of what the hand-reared Odin might do on finding a sleeping baby unguarded in cradle or pram, if I set him free near civilisation. There seemed to be only two courses of action: either to send Odin back to captivity, where he would be safe, well-fed, unable to be a nuisance and thoroughly bored. The best place would be a zoo, where he could be useful as an exhibit, and be studied. (I was frequently asked, but invariably refused, to supply wild creatures to zoological collections.) Or to make him frightened of man before releasing him in some remote place, such as an uninhabited island, where he could find plenty of natural food, and be near – but not too near – other wild ravens. Highly intelligent birds such as ravens need to see others of their kind daily; even if rejected by a pair holding territory, the lone raven can still 'belong' as it feeds and lives within sight of the local ravens, but just out of striking range. Here it can maintain 'safety distance' from the adult ravens in possession, and after the breeding season, although the mature raven mates for life, there is a period of truce, of moulting, flocking and mingling peacefully by all ages, which admits the outsider to find its level – at first near the bottom – in the general peck-order. If it is healthy and bold enough it will work its way upwards in the hierarchy, eventually winning a faithful mate. However, I thought that Odin's fate in the end would be a zoo, but meantime I could at least try to train him to be afraid of me, and if he became wild enough I would take him to the unoccupied island of Skomer, where at this time of year I had seen a flock of up to a hundred ravens in the air together. Shortly I would be visiting Skomer to mark Atlantic seals . . .

Poor Odin! I felt mean when I carried his cage to the stables and set him loose in one of the empty compartments. Everyone had had a chance to admire his splendid iridiscent black plumage, with its ruff of glossy throat hackles, and my sons had tried to teach him to say more words; but he stuck to the trisyllabic 'Coom'n Od'n'. Now he was in solitary confinement in this roomy well-lighted loose-box, with a tub of water for his bath, a perch to sleep on and good raven food (including roughage of whole mice and grasshoppers, gathered for pence by my sons; Odin gobbled these up with great relish). But I had forbidden anyone but myself to visit him.

The training to become wild, and to fear human beings, was to last about a week before I took him to Skomer – or sent him to a zoo. Every time I fed and watered him I shooed him around with a waving stick for five minutes or so. He treated this as an amusing game at first, until I redoubled my efforts, heartily scaring him and making him hate me. He croaked his reproaches as he flipped away from the weapon, but never again said 'Coom'n Od'n'. He was miserable – and so was I.

Julian and Juliette Huxley were visiting Orielton at this time, on one of those not infrequent holidays they made to escape the busy round of their London existence. It had been one of Julian's cherished ambitions, when he was Secretary of the London Zoo, to see ravens and other large birds re-established wild in London parks. We had corresponded about this project, but the war had intervened and he had long ago left the Zoo. In fact, he had been ignominiously dismissed by a majority on the Zoo Council for overstaying a lecture tour in America, during which he had tried patriotically to convince his audiences in that great Republic of the importance of the USA entering the war to help save beleaguered Britain and the world from the tyranny of a mad German house-painter.

But that is another story. Julian was now on very good terms with the present Zoo Council and staff, and as soon as I allowed him a peep at the unhappy Odin, the subject of the restoration of ravens to London parks came up.

'Ravens with clipped wings in the Tower of London are safe enough from harm, and from harming other birds – and people,' I reminded him. 'But I am still doubtful about your plan to set them free, along with buzzards, and perhaps kites, in the middle of London.'

'But wouldn't it be wonderful – spectacular! If only we could have those splendid birds back again, soaring on broad pinions over the Serpentine!' he exclaimed, with his usual infectious enthusiasm. 'So many wild birds have reappeared quite naturally in London of late – as well as few rare new breeders, like the black redstarts which colonised the waste land left after the bombing raids and doodlebugs. So why not help this fascinating recolonisation by re-introducing the larger scavenging birds, which have a useful job to do? A century or so ago ravens and kites cleaned the rubbish and filth from the gutters of London streets and the backyards of knackers and butchers. They mightn't find the same abundance of meaty food, carrion and ordure under today's hygienic conditions, but they would help to keep down the sparrows, pigeons and even the starlings, which are far too numerous and make such a mess of buildings and parks. What about Odin for a start? Supply a few more like him and I will arrange that they are released in Regent's Park, where the zoo keepers can provide enough food to keep them going until they can fend for themselves.'

He was warming to his project again and laughed away my

fears about ravens attacking other forms of small life in the parks, including babies in prams. In a few more seconds, while Odin impudently walked about behind the wire-netting frame I had fitted to the door of his cell, unafraid of me so long as I did not enter with a stick, Julian was remembering and reciting Lear's limerick about the old man of Whitehaven who danced a quadrille with a raven. Soon inventing one of his own, which this seventy-year-old savant was apt to do on the least provocation:

> A craven tame raven called Odin
> Which Lockley supplied (with forebodin'),
> In playing mad larks
> Pecked babies in parks,
> That craven tame raven called Odin.

'Maybe you're right,' I said, 'but I can't see Londoners being altogether happy about large predatory birds, for several reasons, much as I agree they would add to the natural attractions of the great city. Once, at Lord Revelstoke's request, I took a pair of young buzzards to his private island of Lambay off Dublin. It's a marvellous place where the Baring family have a castle built by Lutyens and gardens landscaped by Gertrude Jekyll. Half of Lambay is a farm, the other half is fenced off as a wildlife sanctuary, full of sea-birds, deer and game. Revelstoke's gamekeeper was deputed to complete the hand-rearing of these Welsh buzzards and let them fly wild, as this species once did on that coast. But not only did these imported buzzards start their free careers by taking pheasant and partridge chicks, but they attacked and ate the gamekeeper's laying hens! He was not instructed to shoot the poor buzzards; nevertheless he did!'

'You don't think that buzzards and ravens could survive in London simply on the unwanted sparrows, pigeons, rats and mice? There are plenty of tawny owls which do so, in almost every park and wooded square in London, and quite a few kestrels have begun to nest, some of them on skyscraper buildings.'

'You remember last time you were staying here I had some small ducks on the little pond in front of the house? Pretty Cape teal and highly ornamental Mandarin and Carolina species, for which I provided nesting boxes? Peter Scott sent me them and other ducks and geese. He was anxious that I should develop

Orielton as a supplementary breeding ground for wildfowl. He's trying, as you know, to start up a series of waterfowl refuges around Britain – and ultimately world-wide. Well, certain wild buzzards took to visiting the pond early each morning, impudently sitting on the gatepost near my study window, waiting to pounce. Some days I would wake in the morning to the sound of a squawk – these little ducks are light enough for a buzzard to carry off whole. That, I suggest, will be the fate of many ornamental waterfowl in London parks, if you set free large predatory birds.'

So long as I had the high wire-netted fence to enclose the twelve acres containing the ponds and rabbit pens, exotic wildfowl, experimentally set free inside, were safe from prowling foxes. But, as I had feared, buzzards and ravens, as well as crows and magpies, steadily reduced these non-native ducks or took their eggs or progeny. Now and then too an otter came upstream from the Decoy, easily scaled the ten-foot wall of the lower side and, as most of the introduced waterfowl were pinioned or wing-clipped, found the birds easy prey.

'No doubt I'm lazy, but essentially I prefer to study, protect and encourage native-born birds and other animals, rather than introduce species which will need hand-feeding, and special protection from the endemic predators – at least here at Orielton, where there is a nice balance of a wide variety of predators and prey. Our native-breeding ducks, born wild and free, survive by their natural wisdom . . .'

I told Julian of the courage of a mallard duck which I had watched defending her dozen newly-hatched ducklings from an attacking buzzard – possibly the rogue individual which had taken the exotic ducks mentioned. When the buzzard glided silently from its watchpost towards the family feeding in the weedy shallows of the Lily Pond, the mother duck zig-zagged over the green surface, threshing her wings and uttering distress calls as if wounded, incapable of flight and easy prey for the big hawk. Only briefly distracted by this injury-feigning display, the buzzard soon directed its talons towards one of the terrified brood which was squeaking and scuttering behind its mother. But just as the buzzard was about to snatch up the duckling, the duck leaped into the air, falling upon the buzzard's back, forcing it down into the water. The hawk disappeared entirely for a moment, with the duck standing on its back, pecking and beating its wings savagely.

If, in my astonishment, I had not rushed forward to get a better view, the brave mother might have drowned the buzzard beneath the weedy surface! As it was I disturbed her and she resumed her injury-feigning display and distress squawks, this time to deceive me, while her brood scattered to cover or dived.

The buzzard, relieved of the duck's weight, raised its head wanly above the water. It was sodden and too feeble to resist my picking it up, its long hooked talons full of water-weeds. Back in my study I dried the hawk with a towel in front of the fire; it sat there for two hours, slowly recovering. During this time it passed substantial waste matter, indicating that it had eaten well – it was quite fat, no feeble individual which the courageous mallard mother had nearly drowned! It flew away after I had placed a numbered band on one leg.

*   *   *

On the day the Huxleys left Orielton, an unusual species of trainee helper, Lord X, arrived and became at his request Odin's keeper while the raven was prisoner in the loose-box.

In temperament cheeky bird and timid keeper were very different, yet they were alike in being isolated individuals, more or less outcasts of society through no fault of their own. A common bond of sympathy, not to say affection, soon united them and against my instructions to continue to make Odin wild and fear human society, Lord X, when I was not there to prevent him, befriended Odin.

Much to my annoyance one morning I found that the trainee had carelessly allowed Odin to escape. But instead of flying away, Odin had investigated the coach-house, a few doors away, climbed in through a window and terrified 300 laying hens and their cocks, eating a few eggs and smashing many more. I suppose his curiosity as to the source of all the daily cackling and crowing which he could hear but not see from the loose-box had grown to such a pitch that he simply had to look for himself.

As he hopped from one hen-perch to another to avoid the combined assault of the outraged Rhode Island cocks, these belligerent be-hackled and be-spurred males attacked each other in the general alarm raised by the stupid hens. They had panicked and, rushing hither and thither, were raising clouds of dust and feathers, cackling blue murder. Normally this big deep-litter house was peaceful, each cock keeping to the few square metres of his territory, with a dozen admiring hens around him. A blood-bath of cock-fighting ensued, the weakest in the peck-order of the males losing; and two were savaged and spurred to death. We fielded Odin with the aid of a long-handled bird net. But the 300 hens were off laying for several days after.

Lord X (he had a long aristocratic name which for obvious reasons I cannot reveal here) had come as a result of an arrangement which his distinguished admiral father (whom I knew in private life as a keen amateur naturalist) had made by letter. I had agreed to help his son and heir, recovering from a long mental illness, to try and find work and happiness outdoors, preferably as warden of a nature reserve.

Lord X (so dubbed secretly by my sons on arrival at Orielton because of his stutter and his favourite preface to conversation: 'ex-ex-excuse me'; but later, to avoid confusion with our cat Mr X, this was changed to Lord Y, and so to Lordy) was a wild tramp-like figure, stooping, fragile, with a luxuriant disordered beard, no teeth, and shy, bewildered eyes. He rolled and smoked cigarettes of cheap shag tobacco incessantly. Tipping the ash nervously into the breast pocket of his jacket, he stuttered in his hoarse whispering voice:

'Ex-ex-excuse me, I da-da-daresay the old man has t-t-told you what he th-thinks about my f-f-future? All I w-w-want just n-n-now is to es-es-escape into some peaceful forest, or to some rem-remote island wh-wh-where I can keep a g-g-g-oat and n-n-never be t-t-tracked down in a thou-thousand years. Where I can wo-wo-work things out myself. D-d-does that s-s-sound stu-stupid?'

He spoke with painful slowness, searching for the right words as he stuttered (I shall not try to reproduce his stutter again).

'Why a goat?'

'Excuse me, as a mythologist I'm interested in goats. They're splendid independent creatures. I would need to have someone I can respect to talk to, who won't be impatient and order me around, when I am alone in a forest or on an island,' he stuttered, getting through his sentences so slowly that I had ample time to think of other matters exercising my mind even as I considered his pitiable difficulties and explanation. 'Besides, a lady goat would give milk, and yet I wouldn't have to bother about her food. A goat will eat anything, poisonous plants, even old clothes, boots and books.'

He grinned over the next observation, as if he had made a tremendous joke: 'A goat I once had did me a good service by eating *The Decline and Fall of the Roman Empire*! Somehow I never liked it. Gibbon I mean – not the goat.'

'Why not?' It seemed impossible to conduct a normal conversation with this odd character. (Suffering fools gladly again? But somehow I was fascinated by Lord X and desired to help him.)

'Excuse me, the truth is the old man forced me to read it during the war. Said it would teach me strategy and how Hitler would eventually come a cropper. You see the old man couldn't bear the sight of me when war broke out because I said I was a pacifist. And he and his father and grandfather had been militarists – the naval variety – it's a family tradition. But me – I hated war. Excuse me, I am only explaining, in case he's said something to you in his letters . . .'

'I understand. It's quite natural for sons to kick against parental authority now and then.'

He sighed prodigiously. 'Excuse me, I suppose the old man means well. But he scares the liver out of me. He hasn't a clue about anything except war and ships, salt water and sea-birds. He forced me to join the army when war was declared. I wouldn't join his beastly navy. So he shoved me into Sandhurst straight from school – hopeless, hopeless . . .'

(The late Duke of Bedford, then Marquess of Tavistock, who supplied me with St Kildan sheep, as I shall relate in the next chapter, had told me how much he had suffered from a like pressure from his militaristic father. He had refused to fight, but had spent much of the war as a social worker in bomb-battered London.)

'Well, I've got a nice, peaceful job for you here to start with – alone in the forest, like you say. I take it you can use axe and saw?'

I intended to release Lord X, and possibly the raven Odin, on

Skomer for a test period, in the hope that these displaced souls would find what they needed to rehabilitate their disordered lives. But it would not be wise to do so until I had studied the Admiral's son at Orielton, to see how fit he might be to rough it on an uninhabited island. Our local West Wales Naturalists' Trust had been negotiating to buy Skomer for years, it was one of the finest of sea-bird sanctuaries in the world; and now we were more hopeful, for Max Nicholson at the Nature Conservancy had thrown in the resources of that new organisation. If we bought it, a full-time warden would be wanted – but would Lord X make a suitable one? We should see.

I set Lordy to work first to thin out mis-shapen, unthrifty saplings in the beech and larch wood, far from the manor. I showed him how to cut the straightest of these into lengths of pulpwood, and the crooked into firewood. He was weak, but willing. I left him wielding the axe in a manner which gave me some misgiving but, I reflected, it was not the first time his life had been in danger. He had once been a soldier in the front line, albeit reluctantly.

Two hours later, with a can of hot coffee in my hand for his refreshment, I could not find him. The axe, looking blunt, was lying beside only two felled saplings, chopped inexpertly into pulpwood of the wrong length. Had he already fled into the solitude he craved? There was no answer to my calls.

Later that day the decoyman Greenslade, in search of a drink himself, reported Lordy in *The Speculation*, two miles away.

I drove to the pub in the farm van. In a haze of tobacco and beer fumes Lordy told me the rest of the sad story of his life; he was in an expansive, almost aggressive, mood and stuttered much less, despite or because of the large quantity of ale he had consumed.

Compelled by his father to join up when still in his teens, he was stricken by appendicitis in the fighting zone. The war was going badly for Britain, and it was several days before he could be operated on during the retreat of his unit. As a result he lay moribund with acute peritonitis for half a year. For this (he said scornfully) he was considered a war hero, worthy of mentioning in despatches. On being declared fit for service again, he was made a captain in the infantry, and sent – utterly against his will, 'but you can't argue with War Lords, and my father was one' – to help recover Burma from the Japanese invaders . . .

'And there I managed to pick up malaria, which affected my spine. I was sent back to base, and lay on my back for a year. So, you see what a picnic I had – and I hated war all along. Never fired a gun at anyone in my life, and I hope I never shall. I lost everything in the war, even my teeth. But at least I could not be forced to be a soldier any more! You see me as I am, twenty years later, still a total wreck. I am nothing, less than nothing, and I like it that way now. All I've got is my disability pension – just over two quid a week. I won't take charity from the old man, damn his good intentions. By the way, I've just finished last week's pension. Can you lend me a couple of quid until I get the next?'

'You won't need any money where I'm taking you. We are going on a seal-marking trip, then I hope to dump you on a remote island where there are no shops or pubs! See if you really like island life, as you say you believe you will. Perhaps this may be the answer to your personal problems. I don't think you should blame your father, by the way. He's very concerned to make amends for your terrible experience during the war, and he's written another letter, which came today, hoping you are happy and working hard at Orielton and I am to remind you he is longing to have news of you, if you would only write to him.'

'Excuse me, I never write letters any more. But I'd like to go to Skomer. I'd like that very much. I'm too feeble just now to do much physical work, I'm afraid. Have you any books on mythology I could take to the island? I'm interested in investigating the occult through the study of myths; you know, the macabre side of mythology, heart of darkness, ghosts, the womb of night and all that. I suppose I have sunk to the bottom and I want to find out what's there . . .'

'You're just too late this year to encounter those living demons of darkness, the oceanic shearwaters and storm-petrels, which nest under the ground and nightly moan and scream at Skomer. They've all flown away to sea for the winter. What a pity – you'd enjoy that witches' concert! But there are some gone-wild goats there, which you might befriend.'

'Can I have Odin with me?'

'Not to make a pet of him. You must keep him as wild and frightened of you as possible. Otherwise I am sending him to a zoo.'

'Very well,' Lordy looked disappointed. 'What duties would I have to perform?'

'Just keep a diary of what you see, and what you do. It will be a test of your powers of observation. Make a record of birds, flowers, any natural event. There will be seals breeding and you can go down to the caves and beaches and record the birth of the pups. I'll be showing you how to mark them soon. Just note down everything and anything, even what you think about the island life, so that we can judge if you are likely to be suitable as a future warden, not necessarily on Skomer, but at some nature reserve. You may decide yourself it's not for you; too lonely . . .'

'Excuse me! It'll be marvellous!'

'A friendly rabbit-catcher will be with you, just to help you to start, and show you the domestic side. He's very experienced in island living, but he won't bother you, he's got his own job to do.'

'Marvellous! I'm sorry I'm a failure with the axe. But I'm ready to have another shot at those saplings . . .'

Back in the dark beech wood, we heard the drumming of the rare little woodpecker, which always delighted me, but which Lord X found eerie and at once connected the sound with the occult tapping of the spiritualists whose séances he had often attended. I explained the meaning of the drumming, which we heard at Orielton daily throughout the year – although bird books say that drumming is confined to spring and summer.

'They are certainly intelligent signals from another world – the magic world of the forest – which you tell me you want to live in. There are three species of woodpecker at Orielton: great and lesser spotted and green. Only the spotted ones drum, and each has one or more special sounding boards upon which it hammers out its distinctive signals. I can tell from the direction and high note of this one, which we are hearing, that it is made by a lesser spotted woodpecker, a tiny, charming creature, white-and-black-barred with a red topknot and as small as a sparrow. At the moment we can't see it, but I know it is clinging to the dead top branches of a stagheaded elm near the footpath. It is telling its mate, or any other woodpecker, exactly where it is. Hear the answer? That's from another lesser spotted woodpecker, a quarter of a mile away, a bit faint, the other side of this beech wood.'

'Excuse me, I'm rather deaf – it's the result of shell-fire during the war. Sorry.'

'I think it's probable that woodpeckers mate for life. They keep in touch by drumming or by loud calls. You'll surely hear sometime the much louder, deeper drumming of the great spotted woodpecker, which is produced by its tough beak hammering on a dead or hollow branch lower down a tree, easily recognisable, for the vibrating resonance of this base drum carries farther than the kettledrum of the lesser species. The rhythm of drumming has been measured with exactness on a sound recorder: it averages a dozen bursts, each lasting just under one second for the great spotted, and much the same for the little woodpecker. Mostly it is the cock bird which drums; he evidently patrols an area of woodland which he regards as exclusive to himself, his mate and young children and he drives away rivals and older children. Tape recordings of his drumming played back in his domain will bring him rushing to the spot in agitation. He would not, of course, recognise his own drumming – it would have a very different sound in playback compared with what he himself hears as he drums away. His agitation then is rather amusing, for the great spotted is an aggressive bird; and I don't have all that sympathy for a bully who is seeking to attack the mysterious source of his own disembodied voice . . .'

'Excuse me, I think that's marvellous – I mean, the way you seem to know about every bird and beast and plant, and what the signs and sounds of nature all around mean. How do you do it? I only wish I had a quarter of your knowledge of nature.'

'You will acquire it, and more, in due course. You're young enough to become a first-class naturalist. The main thing is to get into the habit of keeping notes. And that's what you must do at Skomer. I'll lend you some bird and plant identification books.'

All three woodpeckers roamed the Orielton district, each occupying a separate, useful niche in the ecology of the woodlands. The vividly coloured green woodpecker was the largest and most numerous, with a querulous loud laugh giving it the local name of yaffle. I never heard it drum, but it would tap wood, as if signalling. It spent possibly half its time feeding on the ground, picking up insects, ants especially. It probed their underground galleries with its saliva-coated tongue – a tongue so long that when not in use, it was withdrawn into a special recess in the top of its head! It would visit lawns in search of anthills, and the pasture grubs feeding just under the surface of the grass. All three woodpeckers nested in holes they excavated in decaying trees.

The great spotted was more arboreal, although it too would sometimes cruise over the lawn, after grasshoppers, grubs and insects. It had the unfortunate habit of peeping into the nests of other birds, including the natural cradles of the house-martin, and the artificial nest-boxes we hung up for tits, robins and flycatchers. If the parents of the chicks within did not defend the nest, the woodpecker would grab and devour the young.

The lesser spotted occupied the tree-tops, a canopy dweller heard often, seen rarely, and seldom visiting the ground, except occasionally to raid a currant bush. In the season all three extracted seeds from pine-cones, acorns, nuts, berries and small orchard fruits. Like the nuthatch – also common at Orielton – the woodpeckers had favourite 'anvils', usually a crevice at the junction of a branch steeply inclined towards the trunk of a tree. In this they would jam a nut, acorn or pine cone, enlarging the spot with hammer blows of the bill if the object did not fit firmly. Then it would be split open with vigorous stabs of the tough beak. The same anvil would be used time and again.

Lordy's health improved somewhat during his brief experience working daily in the Orielton woods. He got on well with young Stephen, who was just about as dreamy and impractical, and who sought the company of the Admiral's son and admired him as someone new and exciting in our humdrum existence.

On my return from a two-day visit to London I encountered my six-year-old son plodding along the public road near *The Speculation*.

'What on earth are you doing here at this time of day? You ought to be in school!'

'It's a school outing. Didn't want to go. Been helping Lordy.'

'That doesn't explain why you are loitering on a public road.'

'Woodbines for Lordy.' He held up a small parcel. 'He asked

me to get them for him at *The Spec*. On tick. Gave me a note to show the landlady.'

'H'm, you're not supposed to enter a pub at your age. Jump in beside me.'

'Lordy told me to go to the back door. Says he's got a 'rangement with the landlady, so I don't have to pay any money. Lordy is building a little house in the woods for me, Pa. He calls it *Walden*, after some old wise hermit he read about . . .'

'Is that so? And how is Lord Thoreau of Walden?'

'Fine! He's working ever so hard. Got a huge pile of pulpwood for you – at least I think so. Pa, I was telling him about the boy Rhys and the King. Lordy was terribly int'rested – doesn't know much about Henry Tudor. Are you going to tell me the next 'stalment bedtime tonight?'

'We'll see.' For a moment I stared at my son in wonder, as he climbed dreamily into the car, and I tried to abate my crossness on finding him trailing along a busy country road on an unnecessary errand. I must be careful not to say NO too often, or force him against his developing will – as Lordy's father seems to have done to his son. I recognised in Stephen my own impractical dreaminess. Like most young sons he was unique and lovable, interesting and precious to his parents. Stephen was left handed and in most respects fairly normal for his age, I suppose, but just at present he had begun sleepwalking, calmly getting out of bed and strolling about the (to him) vast corridors of the manor, eyes open, but with no recollection of doing any such thing when he woke up next morning. What did that portend? I hoped it had no link with the poltergeist – that other Stephen, described earlier in this book – which had haunted Orielton in the twelfth century.

As a mythologist, self-styled, Lordy said he believed absolutely in ghosts and that Orielton, like every great mansion, was haunted by the spirits of the people who had lived there. Spirits could be evil, if the people alive in the house were evil, mean or wrong-doers. But today he felt sure there were benign ghosts haunting Orielton; they had driven out all mean poltergeists, they were the spirits of brave and kindly Wiriets and Owens who were watching with approval the good work we were engaged in, caring for the old mansion, its woods and farm . . .

I warned Lordy not to alarm Stephen with fearful ghost

stories, for the boy had taken a great fancy to the hairy, tramp-like, malodorous person who lived with us at present, spluttered soup and crumbs into his disordered beard, and stuttered so badly. I had begun to explain to my wondering son why Lordy was so odd in his talk, appearance and habits . . . 'We are all different, it's more interesting that way, but some of us are more different than others. Lordy is unusual and sad, from his hardships during the war and from much illness. We must try to help him get back to normal in our sweet air and peace, so he can decide for himself what he will do in the future.'

It was the simplest explanation I could think of, but I was glad when Stephen changed the subject and pressed me for the next instalment of my romanticised story of the Welsh nobleman Sir Rhys ap Thomas who as a boy had lived in France and had befriended his contemporary Henry Tudor on his arrival on this coast from France in 1485. Rhys, riding his battlehorse Grey Fetterlocks, had taken his Welsh troops to victory and to the death of Richard III at Bosworth Field, where the Lancastrian heir was crowned King Henry VII.

'Rhys and the King' was Stephen's favourite bedtime serial. These heroes had become mighty men in my mind too, as I learned of their adventures in old books. We re-lived the stirring story of those far off times. We visited Henry's birthplace in Pembroke Castle, where he had been suckled by a Welsh wet nurse (his mother Margaret Beaufort being then but fourteen years old). We studied the splendid ruins of the castle and grounds of Carew, where Rhys had lived and held jousting tournaments after Bosworth. Stephen was suitably impressed that the squires and knights of Orielton had rallied to the Welsh dragon standard of Rhys and that Rhys, seemingly as a reward, had given his favourite daughter Margaret (illegitimate – but no need to mention this as yet) in marriage to Henry Wiriet of Orielton, the man who led a force of seventy-four of his retainers in Rhys's expedition to help Tudor's son Henry VIII in France.

Perhaps – nay, surely – I did embroider the continuing tale, in order to satisfy, as far as truth or legend allowed, Stephen's longing to hear more about these swashbuckling adventurers. He was most anxious that his hero Rhys should have visited Orielton, and slept there, perhaps in one of the rooms he knew so well . . .

'Of course, old son, it would have been an older house. But yes, Carew is only an hour's ride away; the noble Rhys would often have come to see his favourite daughter and his son-in-law. They had much to talk about. He loved them well. It is said that he bestowed many honours on Henry Wiriet for his loyalty...'

'And Rhys would have ridden his warhorse Grey Fetterlocks up our drive?'

'Of course. Now it's time to sleep old son. Good night.'

'Pa, won't you tell me just a wee bit of the next 'stalment?'

'Good night, old son.'

'Good night, Pa, old man!'

*　　　*　　　*

When we got to the wood, Stephen raced ahead of me excitedly over the yellow carpet of autumn leaves to the site of the new Walden. It was a poor jumble of roughly trimmed boughs and saplings, shaped like a log cabin, but more like a 'bog' hut – in fact the door had been robbed from a decayed outdoor earth-closet, chopped down. On a nail hung my old but treasured bird-watching binoculars. Lordy was lounging on a rough chair of boughs. He reached greedily for the Woodbines.

'Good lad, Steve, I'm dying for a whiff!' With hardly a stutter.

'Pa's come back,' warned Stephen.

Behind the hut was only a small heap of pulpwood. Lordy apologised for borrowing the binoculars without permission. Stuttering, he explained:

'Excuse me, Steve thought you wouldn't mind. We wanted to check on a rare bird. We think we've seen a cock golden oriole. Beautiful bird – I remember first seeing one in the woods – wartime in France. Getting keen on birds, aren't we Steve? And Steve's built this little log-cabin more or less all on his own; eh, Steve?'

'No, no, Lordy – you did all the hard work, be fair. I only drew the plan for you, and helped a bit after school. What d'you think of it, Pa?'

'Like the fox in the nursery story I think that if I could huff and puff enough I might be able to blow it down.'

'That reminds me, Pa. We did see a fox, didn't we, Lordy? Just when we were sitting quietly, having a billy of tea this morning, wasn't it, Lordy? A huge dog fox with a big white tip to his tail – brush, I mean. Lordy once killed a fox with his soldier's sword when Lordy was an officer in the war, long long ago, didn't you, Lordy?'

'N-n-not exactly, Steve. A farmer I was billeted with borrowed my sword to stab a fox which he accidently locked up in his chicken house when shutting them in one night. Don't think I would have the guts to kill a fox myself. I wouldn't want to.'

'It's cruel – fox-hunting is, Lordy says. Pa, did you know that hounds came through our woods this morning? That's why we saw the fox, he was being hunted. And Silver Star bolted, Pa, through the gate the hunt left open in Cow Park meadow . . .'

There was always trouble when I was away. I had agreed with the Master of the Foxhounds that they must not draw inside the walls of Orielton, or allow any riders to enter; the estate must be respected as a sanctuary for all wild creatures. Of course, hounds, leading far ahead on the line of a fox, wouldn't stop at any man-made boundary . . .

'What a nuisance! Which way did Silver Star go?'

'Nobody knows, but at *The Spec*. I was told he was seen galloping wild with other hunt horses – 'joying himself, the landlady said.'

'The old devil! Probably someone has shut him into a field by now. I'll have to phone around.'

Silver Star was a mettlesome mountain gelding with a bit of Arab in him which I had bought for Martin to ride, after my older son had complained that his first pony, Steady, a sedate small mare, wouldn't even gallop any more. Silver Star had thrown me once and Martin several times, but the boy persisted and eventually mastered the animal. Stephen had inherited the mare and renamed her Fetterlocks. He was delighted when she foaled in the following spring. He was content to amble through the woodland rides bareback on Fetterlocks, with the foal (named Margaret, after Rhys's daughter) at foot, and some intimate conversation *à trois* was no doubt enjoyed. They were a comical sight, for Stephen had borrowed my evening dress tails, green with age, and battered top hat.

'Lordy has been telling me all about woodpeckers, Pa,' Stephen announced, importantly. 'How useful they are, you know, they are the friend of the forester. Three kinds here, and we've heard them drumming . . .'

I had slight twinges of jealousy as I listened to my young son and the admiral's old son discussing woodpeckers so learnedly, for Stephen usually found my talk about nature boring – living with a naturalist father was for him commonplace and uninteresting. The way this middle-aged dropout told the tale had fascinated Stephen and he had remembered every word of the information Lordy had uttered – taken as it was direct from me. But at least Lordy acknowledged the source:

'Excuse me, Steve, anything I have told you about woodpeckers I learned from your pa. You should listen more to him.'

'And Pa, do you know that a woodpecker can tell where a wood-beetle grub is, simply by tapping on a tree. Makes a funny sound, doesn't it, Lordy, you said, if there's a hollow inside. Then the woodpecker hacks out a hole, keeps thrusting its long tongue down until it can hook out the grub with a barb on the tip of the tongue. Is that right, Pa?'

'Something like that. You two seem to have got quite bird-minded. Good for you, Lordy . . .'

The next week I set out with Lordy by boat on what had lately become an annual expedition to mark seals with numbered flipper-tags, as part of a national scheme to learn more about their migrations, longevity, age at breeding, and so on. September and October are the months in which the female Atlantic seals come ashore in Wales on beaches hidden in caves and under inaccessible cliffs, to drop and nurse their white-coated pups for the three weeks of the lactation period. Seal-marking is a vastly exciting experience, satisfying man's instinct to hunt, but without killing the quarry, in a wild and beautiful environment, where heavy groundseas, roaring tide-races, slippery rocks and powerful adult seals are a challenge to your skill, adding a spice of real danger to the adventure of landing on these hidden nurseries of this splendid animal. You had to work swiftly, for the hour or two over the low tides, exploring in a small dinghy through the low entrances of long caves, some extending far into utter darkness, where your torch might reveal a crèche of white-coated pups guarded by their menacing mothers. Now and then on an exceptionally low tide we discovered – and named – a new *ogof* (Welsh cave). I had great joy in these autumn sea-adventures.

Lordy was clumsy, and fell into the sea more frequently than

I did, while getting in and out of the light dinghy which sometimes capsized when a breaking wave swept into a narrow
beach or cave. At intervals he dropped oars, boathook, torch
and his precious tin of tobacco into the surf; but we recovered
most of these things. He seemed happier, his eyes clearer and
more hopeful, although his limbs were weary and aching with
bruises, and bites from baby seals. He was well-washed in brine
and cleaner than I had ever seen him. He emerged from the
ordeal, beard stiff with brine, like Proteus rising from the sea,
battered but triumphant after a week of handling and helping
to mark more than a hundred seals.

While at Ramsey Island we encountered the redoubtable
Macdonald Hastings, who wished to record our seal-marking
technique for the BBC. But Lordy slipped away from this publicity,
unfilmed, and my respect for his lack of vanity grew. Macdonald
Hastings had once immolated himself alone for a few days on a
tropical islet as a test of his capacity to survive; but this was
done in a glare of publicity, and cameras – a stunt. Lordy was
going to live on a cold windy island called Skomer, with autumn
gales imminent, and only his father and I and his companion to
know where he was.

My diary records: 'I left Lordy on Skomer with the rabbit-catcher. He is firmly convinced that he can be happy alone there. He intends to fight his battle against his incessant smoking, having lately experienced agonies from losing his tin of shag in the tideway. But while we were shopping on the way to Skomer, he nipped away and bought a new supply. I fear he is incurable. Moreover I fear that the rabbit-catcher, a puritan at heart (he has preached in local chapels as a layman), won't stomach L's lack of cleanliness, although I have asked him to be gentle and kind to a very sick man. I fear a complicated tale of woe may emerge. The rabbit-man has been splendidly co-operative, taking enough bread, bacon, potatoes and plain stores for their fortnight's sustenance at Skomer. For the rest they will have plenty of rabbits, and the rabbit-man is a keen shot. The woodcock will be arriving in the first cold spell.

'Odin I also let loose on Skomer, marked with a leg-ring – he vanished in a minute, croaking in response to other ravens croaking in the distance.'

A week later the rabbit-catcher suddenly returned his island companion to the mainland, phoning me to say he could no longer live with Lordy's unorthodox personal habits. He was going back to the island alone, leaving a note to warn Lordy, who had just gone up the lane to buy some shag at the village shop two and a half miles away, to return to Orielton. 'I mean,' he said into the phone, 'as far as I am concerned he can go to Orielton, or to blazes!'

Back at Orielton Lordy handed me the promised written account of what he had seen, done and thought. A very remark-able document by a crazed person – or, as I would like to believe, disorganised genius. It contained nothing illuminating about Skomer wildlife. Instead there were simple sober facts interspersed with wild, inconsequential scribblings. On one page he had written his sorrow at his companion's anger that he had accidently smashed the only (oil) reading lamp: 'I have apologised but he is very angry and that makes me sad.' There were fears at what his father – and I – would say when he returned home, because: 'I am a washout, weather windy, cold, wet, I have not seen a bird today. Yet the rabbit-man came home with a snipe and a woodcock, which he roasted – delicious they were – but we hardly speak any more.' He had soon run out of tobacco, and tried to dry and smoke 'some nettle and other brown herbs mixed and crushed – awful taste.' Also (I was not surprised to read) the ruins of the old farm, in which they were living, were 'horrible, haunted by ghosts of long dead island people . . . they moan every night.'

Other scribblings were less intelligible, but had a modern flavour, including musings in blank – very blank – unpunctuated verse worthy of a Dylan Thomas at his worst. Then, suddenly, fortuitously, in a little cave, he had come across a complete set of crayons, cached and forgotten by a visitor last summer. With these he had sketched and coloured vignettes of the scenery – bold cliffs and tortuous sea-carved bays and lichened rocks – on the pages of his diary. These somewhat childish illustrations were nevertheless promising, I thought – promising pleasure to both artist and viewer. I could recognise familiar bays, the landing place, certain grotesque but natural, weather-shaped monoliths of the island basalt.

Nevertheless Lordy would never make a responsible nature warden, and he knew it.

'Excuse me, I shan't go home,' he stuttered, with deep dejection, 'can't face the old man again. Shall take a job on a merchant ship at Milford Haven.'

'My dear Lordy, there are no merchant ships trading out of Milford Haven.'

'The nearest port then – Swansea?'

'You're much too weak physically at present. Can't fall off a tall ship and be rescued easily, like you can in a dinghy! One thing is quite plain from your Skomer adventure. You are a brilliant artist. At all costs you must keep that up.'

'Excuse me – you really think so?' He brightened visibly.

'Look at these charming, original pictures. The unorthodox style – very modern I should say. Wish I could use crayons half as well . . .'

'Excuse me – you really think so? I did them quite by accident! I mean, I was very pleased when I found those materials. Almost as if some kind poltergeist had put them there deliberately, for me to find! Perhaps you put them there? No? Pure luck then – I did enjoy using them. But when I showed some sketches to the rabbit-man he just shook his head and said nothing. He went down on his knees every night and said his prayers – probably for deliverance from me . . .'

'Did you ever see Odin again, after we set him free at Skomer?'

'I didn't. But the rabbit-man told me that he saw a raven with a band on its leg now and then, feeding with other birds at the heap of guts where he paunched his daily catch of rabbits. Odin won't starve while he is at Skomer!'

I have yet to learn what has happened to Lordy – or Odin since. Lordy wrote briefly: 'Very grateful for your help, and advice on my future, as an artist. I shall try, but I am sad at leaving you all. Give my love to Steve and if its still standing the old log-cabin we built together . . .'

*   *   *

Over the few days of the fine week-end while Lordy lingered, reluctant to leave Orielton, the log-cabin partnership was renewed. Stephen had been upset that he had not been allowed to accompany his hero on the seal-marking, and, particularly, the island trip. But he had to go to school.

Lordy consoled his admirer with exciting tales of his adventures, however, and Stephen came back from their secret talks in the woods to show me some paintings he had executed, inspired by Lordy's crayon sketches of Skomer. (No doubt I am prejudiced, but I thought the boy's first efforts showed more promise than the man's. From this inspiration Stephen was to go on to become a professional artist.)

Stephen wheedled a promise from me that he would be allowed to go seal-marking next year: 'Lordy says he is coming back specially to help mark seals – he 'joyed it so much this year.'

With no word or sign from Lordy a year later I nevertheless kept that promise – which resulted in some exciting adventures in which Stephen was the principal figure. As a trial run I took my sons early in their holidays to caves conveniently near home, under the high cliffs of Telpyn, which lie east of the wide sands of Amroth, sixteen miles from Orielton as the raven flies. I did not expect to find many seals so near a public bathing beach, but it would be good practice for the boys and I had never properly searched that wild rock-walled bay before.

Seal-breeding caves are rarely accessible except at low water of spring tide. We found no pups in the Telpyn caves, although Martin and I poked and scrambled into every likely deep dark hole. Stephen however found these dark places, slimy with salt and seaweed, too eerie for his liking. He wandered back into the sunlight, quickly absorbed in searching the glittering rock pools for their tidal treasures of little fishes, prawns and multicoloured anemones.

When the flood tide rose, to cut off the headland, we retreated in time and walked the half mile over Amroth sands to the picnic rendezvous near the ancient *New Inn* on the boundary between Pembroke and Carmarthen shires. My wife and friends were laying out the food, which we eyed hungrily.

'Where's Stephen?'

'He wandered back ages ago.'

No one had seen him. Looking towards the headland a great fear filled me. Gannets were diving in the fast tide-race already swirling around Telpyn Head. Impossible to swim back into the caves! Stephen was trapped under unscaleable cliffs!

The nearest boat-haven was Saundersfoot, three miles by road. While my wife rang from the Inn for the fastest boat to be ready and alerted the local cliff rescue and coastguard teams, I drove headlong to Saundersfoot.

At twenty-six knots the speed-boat rounded Telpyn Head within a quarter of an hour of my leaping aboard. But there was no sign of Stephen. The tide was rising inexorably, flooding each cave and fissure in the cliffs.

'Stephen! Stephen!'

For three terrible hours we searched and shouted, until our voices cracked with hoarseness. The rock wall at full tide echoed our despair with mocking nothingness. Each signal we exchanged in hope with watchers ranging the cliffs far above was answered negatively.

At last the tide began to ebb. We waited miserably for a limp body to be washed into view from the deepest cave where Martin and I had explored only a few hours earlier. Perhaps Stephen had somehow survived in a pocket of air farthest from the sea? But if so by now he would be unconscious from lack of oxygen?

When the top of the cave, a mere slit, showed briefly above a receding wave, I prepared to dive.

Then, 'Hullo' – a faint cry, but indubitably Stephen! He was alive!

The call seemed to issue from the wave-washed slit. Miserable swimmer though I am, I was about to plunge into the surf when my companion in the boat pointed to a small figure waving to us from the grassy top of the cliff.

After all the boy had acted sensibly. Tired of gazing into rock pools, he had decided to explore the farther, eastern headland while the tide was still low, and return to Amroth along the top of the Telpyn cliffs. He had not been found by the land-search party because he had blundered into dense gorse and blackthorn.

'What a fuss about nothing! I got so hot struggling through the bushes I must have fallen fast asleep. I dreamed someone was shouting my name, it woke me up.'

It had been for Stephen no more than a casual, somewhat bogus, adventure, soon forgotten. But he was to remember a genuine rescue in which he took a leading part a few weeks later.

Martin was strong enough to catch and hold a baby seal. Stephen was not, but, still hoping Lordy would turn up, he insisted upon joining our week-end expedition to Ramsey, the main breeding ground of the Atlantic seal in Wales. The hospitable Davies family, farming the island, once more made us welcome, although Phil's wife was grieving over the loss of her beloved Corgi, of the lithe North Pembrokeshire breed.

'Timmy's been missing thirty-eight days now,' Hannah said miserably, 'he was always hunting for rabbits and rats. He must have fallen over the cliffs and drowned, or been dashed to death on the rocks.'

The rest of this chapter comes from my diary:

19 September. Woke Phil early, so that by 08.30 we were going south about the island in his *Isle of Ramsey*, towing our dinghy. I was anxious to get into the caves and beaches inaccessible from the land while low tide and fine weather lasted. We did well today, marking altogether thirty-six pups of ages varying from new-born to the moulting stage of four weeks old [the cow seal's milk dries up when her pup is three weeks old, and the mother is then mated by the bull]. In one deep southern gully we marked three pups under sheer cliffs and towed out to the motorboat a fine trawler's

dan-buoy washed there, which Phil gleefully appropriated. Two adults and three children were a tight fit in the dinghy as we threaded the low-water reefs into grim Ogof Colomenal – while Phil kept the *Isle of R.* safely offshore. Here, under the great precipice where the peregrines nest each year, we found four pups guarded by their mothers. One cow was very aggressive, and would not allow us to touch her week-old child; the other three cows humped their way over tne rough boulders to the sea. Stephen retreated to a safe distance exploring the tide-line for more jetsam treasures, while we others marked the three deserted pups.

Suddenly there was a wild shout of triumph from Stephen. He had stumbled on Timmy the Corgi – lost for over five weeks! Somehow he had survived his fall into this grim prison in the cliffs, evidently by scrambling to a shelf of rock over each high tide. Moreover he was in quite good condition, his coat very rough but his ribs well covered. He smelled to high heaven of his diet! He had lived all this time on the afterbirths from the cows, as, one after another, a succession of mother seals had pupped in this wild nursery, over the period!

When we brought him back to the boat Phil received him with open arms – despite the stink. In the excitement at seeing him, Timmy sicked up a disgusting mess of placental flesh . . .

There was great rejoicing over the roast island lamb and Hannah's home-made blackberry wine in Ramsey's ancient farmhouse this night. Groomed and glistening after scrubbing in a tub scented with the best bath salts, Timmy lay drying in front of the driftwood fire, oblivious to the admiration bestowed on his sleeping form. Now and then his limbs twitched – was he still dreaming of his adventures in Ogof Colomenal?

8

Serenely far there swam in the sunny height
A buzzard and his mate who took their pleasure
Swirling and poising idly in golden light:
On great pied motionless moth-wings borne along,
    So effortless and so strong,
Cutting each other's paths, together they glided,
Then wheeled asunder till they soared divided
Two valleys width (as though it were delight
To part like this, being sure they could unite
So swiftly in their empty, free dominion),
Curved headlong downward, towering up the sunny steep,
Then with a sudden lift of the one great pinion,
Swung proudly to a curve and from its height
Took half a mile of sunlight in one long sweep.

MARTIN ARMSTRONG

Two, sometimes three, pairs of buzzards haunted the estate. They were beautiful to watch, miniature eagles, soaring on broad wings, the tips of the primaries upswept and splayed wide to filter the wind, as they glided in circles on the thermal of warm air rising from the parkland and lake bounded by forest trees and ancient walls.

Often when I was ploughing one of the fields for the early potato crop we now grew as the most profitable of our farming operations, one or more buzzards would quietly join the huge throng of birds following the tractor as it opened three furrows at a time, exposing a rich store of worm, grub and insect larvae, perhaps the nest of a torpid mouse, vole or shrew, or hibernating lizard or slow-worm. There would be at least a thousand gulls – black-backed, herring, common and black-headed species – many rooks, jackdaws, starlings, a few pied and grey wagtails, and here and there a meadow-pipit and skylark. Circling a short distance overhead, the woodlark sang its bell-notes sweetly all through the winter, although you could not hear it while the tractor roared its powerful countersong, promising production and plenty from the red sandstone earth.

The gulls were extremely bold, greedily competing to be first to grab this small life, even before the red soil had rolled completely over. Occasionally this resulted in the gull's head being trapped between two falling furrows. If I did not at once notice this, and stop to free the gull, it paid the penalty of its greed and was strangulated. The ploughman needs to have eyes in the back as well as the front of his head, for he must keep the tractor straight with the right-hand front wheel in the furrow ahead, and yet look behind frequently to see that share and coulter are cleaving the unploughed land evenly, each furrow equal in depth, width and turn-over – and this depends a good deal on how soft or hard the ground is, it can vary much in a few yards length, and he must adjust the plough controls to match. The small black-headed gulls were the greediest, and were sometimes completely buried – crushed to death – to rot and serve as fertiliser for the next crop.

In nature new life arises from death; vegetation and myriads of small soil organisms were buried along with the excreta from the thousand birds which thronged behind the plough, thus helping to restore fertility to the soil. I could not regret too deeply the accidental expenditure of a few lives of the gulls; beautiful in flight, they are scavengers by nature, rapacious, even cannibalistic, cold and calculating, with no tenderness save to their own mates and nestlings. But one should not judge animals by human concepts of moral behaviour.

The buzzards were unafraid of the motley winged assembly – they would pounce on an unwary starling or small bird preoccupied in feeding in the furrows. They lingered far behind; because they were scared of the man on the tractor. Yet that rearguard position had its reward in the chance to pick up the small life which still wriggled out of the disturbed earth after the squabbling mob had surged ahead: worms and larvae, a dazed mouse or vole. The big hawks stumbled awkwardly about the soft newly-exposed earth, their long, curved talons ill-adapted for walking. When the tractor turned, ploughing back a new triple furrow, the buzzards soared overhead, to take up the rearguard position again, at the opposite starting line.

Often the results of our ploughing were unsatisfactory, giving an uneven appearance to the furrows afterwards. Nevertheless I found deep satisfaction in this oldest of occupations, which changes the appearance of the earth's surface so dramatically, and for man's survival, preparing for the harvest by which he lives.

'A spirit dwells in earth,' I would muse to myself, as at three miles an hour three new furrows appeared as if by magic behind my comfortable tractor seat. 'Treat her with reverence and she will respond with bread sweeter to you than man-made riches. Treat her generously and you will enjoy the fruit of your co-operation with sun, rain, wind and soil. You have become part once more of the great ecology – and economy – of Earth and Heaven; a humbling yet joyous thought. But be careful, as you bury the tired grassland and last season's weeds (but is any plant a weed?), not to run over an early nest of lapwing or lark. Sometimes they breed very early. Remember that lapwing's nest last February – you saw it too late – you ploughed it in! Afterwards you grieved, but also you consoled yourself that the bird would soon lay another clutch of eggs . . .'

When glutted with food the buzzards left the new-ploughed land and climbed into the sky to play aerial games, circling around each other, diving in mock attack. At times they were joined by other pairs, until half a score were in the air together. Ravens from the Gazebo would appear, croaking a protest but enjoying the general *joie de vivre* engendered by satiated appetite and sunlight.

Although the buzzards mewed and tumbled high in the sky on every fine calm day, they were silent during nest-building and incubation in April and May. Stealthily slipping from tree to tree above the new flood of woodland flowers – primroses, cowslips, violets, windflowers and bluebells – they were evasive and hard to detect. At one tree nest, where we built a hide, we observed the smaller male bring a green-leaved branch of a flowering *ponticum* rhododendron (plentifully wild in our woods) to decorate the already bulky structure of the nest, long after the three eggs were laid, and again after the chicks had hatched. A pretty gesture – but with what motive? As a guard-rail for the growing family? It does have that result, at least.

The male buzzard takes little part in incubation, but he hunts assiduously, feeding his mate and later the nestlings. As incubation begins with the first egg – the female dare not leave her eggs exposed to those woodland burglars, the sneaking magpie, jay or crow – and the eggs are laid at three to four days interval, the young buzzards appear in the nest in different sizes. The third and latest to hatch had a poor time of it; the older siblings grabbed all the food, and hungry junior, struggling to get some, was pecked and pushed aside by its elders. We watched it become weaker and weaker and at last it was trampled underfoot. The older pair were reared to fledgling age in six weeks, during which they were fed on mice, rats, voles, moles, twice a young crow, once a fledgling magpie, several times on blackbirds, and on ducklings, frogs, earthworms, a grass snake, miscellaneous beetles, grasshoppers and some unidentified items. Only a few freshly-killed baby rabbits were brought to the nest; there were almost none available locally after the myxomatosis epidemic. Evidently these were taken from the enclosure warrens, from which, too, portions of adult rabbits were carried. We noticed the remains of the head, with metal-tagged ear, of an adult buck which had died naturally (from sickness or in fighting); buzzards feed freely on carrion.

Of other, less numerous hawks, the beautiful kestrel was a regular visitor to the open fields, hovering in search of voles and mice running in the grass. One pair adopted the old nest of a carrion crow in a tall elm at the back of the stables. The female kestrel merely scraped a saucer in the flattened platform, on which she laid six white eggs richly spattered with a chocolate design. Again the smaller, handsome, blue-headed male left much of the work of building and incubation to his large, browner, mate.

Two months later six young kestrels in russet adolescent plumage made a delightful study as, for a few days before departure, they perched in a row on the ridge of the stable roof, preening and uttering snatches of juvenile chatter. The house-martins and swallows, nesting in the buildings below, mobbed them incessantly, but they took little notice. Their splendid large eyes glittered, their wings shimmered and their voices were uplifted, only when their parents approached with food.

The tiercel and falcon kestrel continued to feed their children, principally on small rodents, for many days after they were strong on the wing. Early in autumn this happy family departed to hover and hunt in the cornfields, where at harvest time the numerous voles and mice were re-grouping beneath the stooks, as fast as we set up the sheaves to dry.

By watching for several days we traced a pair of sparrowhawks to their nest, fifteen feet from the ground, secreted in the crotch of a larch tree deep in Eastern Wood. Built of short dead twigs, evidently snapped off the nearest larches, in mid-May it contained four round greenish-white eggs streaked with brown.

The hen sparrowhawk is much larger than her mate, whose russet-barred breast, slate-blue back and brown-and-white-barred tail are far more vivid and rich than hers. I marvelled at the svelte beauty of the tiercel when one day, seeing him dash after a sparrow which fled into the hayloft, I was able to catch him against the window there. With my hands covering his wings to prevent struggling and to keep his sharp claws away from my flesh, he seemed very small, scarcely as large as a dove. Yet his cold yellow eyes glared at me with that appearance of deep disdain and defiance well-known to falconers who have tried to train the wild sparrowhawk.

'Little highwayman!' I told him, 'you are much too beautiful, aristocratic and savage, to be occupied with domestic duties. I don't wonder you leave those chores to your ponderous stay-at-home wife while all day you enjoy your hunting!'

Our male sparrowhawk had a special larder some distance from the nest in Eastern Wood, to which he carried his prey – instantly killed at the first clasp of those long talons piercing the victim's body. This was the bare flattened top of a wood-ant nest, upon which he plucked his daily capture of small birds. Here, too, he vomited pellets of the indigestible residue of bone and feathers. He tore the larger birds into portions which he took occasionally to the nest, but more often his wife collected them at the larder. The swarming ants, which have an irritating bite when they attack man, seemed to trouble him not at all; they were useful scavengers, carrying off the tidbits of flesh and other edible items scattered on top of the mound.

The female alone appeared to feed the nestlings, doling out small portions of meat with her bill at first, until they were strong enough to tear at the plucked food without help.

Because they are forest birds the sparrowhawks were less often seen than kestrel or buzzard but they had their place in the ecology, the food chain of the estate, as predators of the small birds, and like most predators they killed first the weaker, less wary individuals. I disliked them for slaying the attractive species: bullfinch, goldfinch, chaffinch, greenfinch, yellowhammer, flycatcher, titmouse, swallow and warbler; I was less critical when they slaughtered starling, blackbird, or thrush and now and then a pheasant chick or a woodpigeon; I could praise them for sweeping away the noisy sparrows, which pirated the cradle nests of our dainty house-martins.

Their usual hunting is a symphony of fast, sweeping flight, low over the ground, twisting and dodging along woodland rides and leafy country lanes, every twenty to thirty metres looping up and over fence or hedge or row of trees to surprise the small bird on

the other side. A few rapid wing-beats at the top of the loop, to reconnoitre and regain speed for the long, fast downhill glide. Now and then one would dash around the corner of the house and snatch up a small bird feeding on the scraps we provided at the bird table near my study window.

Not always successfully: when it failed the sparrowhawk sometimes perched on the table and gazed around as if surprised at its failure. But its sharp eye detecting the movement of a bird elsewhere, it would quickly depart. Less often it would rise up leisurely upon a thermal of warm air, with few wing-beats, and enjoy the sunlight with buzzard and kestrel.

This soaring is commonest in April and May; all three hawks

indulged then in aerial display and manoeuvre, preparatory to breeding. Maybe in the sparrowhawk, normally solitary, dwelling in the shadows of the woods, this is a necessary exhibition of its readiness to mate. On meeting, the pair would soar heavenwards, whistling to each other, the cock bird showing off his handsome tail by spreading it wide or, flying above the hen, he would exhibit his chestnut-barred breast. This was the graceful courtship flight, conducted over the parkland and drifting to the tree-tops above Eastern Wood, where in due course a family was reared.

In the autumn and early winter more sparrowhawks appeared; these were migrants on passage from Scotland and Scandinavia, flying to escape the emptiness of snow-bound forests where in winter few small birds dwelled.

Now and then the lordly peregrine, king of the falcons, with a loud hiss of wings swooped suddenly out of the sky. You might see first the panic rush to cover (or to dive) of the waterfowl it preferred to prey upon. The peregrine depended on surprise and speed, a living arrow flying downwards to strike its quarry in mid-air. Rarely would it bind to its victim; usually it struck with its clenched talons, the hind toe curved inwards so that its razor-sharp outer keel became a sword or scimitar, which sometimes severed the head from the quarry. I have seen this thrice: the body tumbles heavily to the ground and, ignoring the head which has fallen elsewhere, the peregrine alights close to the corpse. If it is too large (a curlew, or mallard, for instance) to carry off, the falcon plucks it and feeds on the spot.

Our peregrines nested on local sea-cliffs. Sometimes a young falcon could be watched hunting inexpertly, making swoops which were dodged at the last moment by the pursued. On one occasion there was a tragic end to the chase. Flying downwards upon a starling, a young falcon failed to evade a stone wall when the quarry flipped sideways at the last moment. It crashed into the wall at seventy miles an hour. A tiercel, beautiful in his first blue plumage, his dark hazel eyes were half open, half closed by the protective nictating membrane, when I picked him up and felt the last heart-beat under my hand.

The handsome little merlin, a miniature peregrine in appearance, which lives all summer on the naked Welsh mountainside, wandered across the sea-warmed peninsula of south Pembrokeshire in winter. Hardly larger than a blackbird, this falcon hunts in its special way, half like a peregrine, half like a sparrowhawk. Butter-fly-buoyant one moment, dashing at speed the next, it accommodates its flight to that of its prey, invariably a small bird of the open – pipit, lark, linnet, chat, wheatear, wagtail, bunting – which it seeks to isolate and keep away from cover. It does not swoop from a great height, but makes short upward loops to gain speed to fly down upon the quarry, whose every twist and turn it follows. It can flutter like a butterfly – when chasing a butterfly – which it sometimes does. It is a test of endurance, ending in the talons of the merlin, or with the hunted bird plunging into cover of bush or long grass.

One autumn day I watched an unexpected conclusion to the chase. A merlin appeared in pursuit of a swallow; evidently the hunt had been long, for both were at that moment too exhausted to continue. Predator and prey alighted a few feet apart on the top strand of a wire fence, both gasping for breath with mouth wide open. The merlin was too weary to close with the swallow. When the swallow flew weakly away after a minute's rest, the merlin watched with its fierce golden eyes acknowledging defeat and presently departed in the opposite direction.

*   *   *

The noble-looking hawks fulfilled their natural role of removing the weaker of their prey first, leaving the strong and the fittest to survive – enough to balance this predator–prey relationship and maintain the links in the fluctuating yet perennial food chain of the Orielton estate – that microcosm of the world state of nature. A global situation where nature is beautiful yet red in tooth and claw; where man, too, while perceiving that beauty, is no less subject to the same universal pitiless law of 'might is right'.

For I too was a sort of predator. Like other more famous or notorious squires, I dominated the little world of human souls which I had gathered together around the old manor. Only as long as I exercised vigilance of eye and mind and retained my physical strength would I survive and maintain the status quo of my own making. I was a very sparrowhawk or falcon, meta-phorically swooping at intervals in search of my means of sub-sistence – my quarry – the people, the animals, the estate, and all it ought to produce to provide food and satisfying employment for our community, whose survival as such depended on my making the right decisions. I confess that mostly I enjoyed this hawk-wise sense of power, this falcon freedom to scheme and act. But now and then, when plans went awry, when the bank balance was too far in the red, the burden of responsibility was heavy.

At such times a certain philosophic detachment helped. I would get outside my own skin, so to speak, and my naturalist's eye would observe me for what I was – a middle-aged, muddling-along lord of a remote manor, no more than a cog in the largely artificial treadmill of modern 'civilisation' which man has devised. Despite his vaunted superior intelligence and ability to think ahead, man only survives so long as his food supply (food chain) remains adequate. As soon as this balance is upset and he goes hungry, the structure of his elaborate tribalism is endangered and he becomes as wild as the beast. Under the veneer of this civilisation which he acquired by training as a child lies the primitive instinct which has survived through twenty thousand years of wearing clothes and making and using tools. He is genetically attuned to competitive strife, which is a stimulating force. For it is true that without strife man tends to become a vegetable, likely to die of boredom or chagrin from sheer inactivity. Man is yet an animal, must exert himself to survive, to eat, reproduce and defend himself in the brief span of his life on earth.

Abroad, I reflected, men were at war still. Hot wars in Africa and Asia where tribes of black, brown and yellow men fought for domination, often of those territories from which the white settlers were retreating. Ostensibly for lofty moral reasons, but in reality they were withdrawing because the more numerous indigenous people had learned how to use the white man's weapons of conquest – guns, brains and a superiority complex. Led by some opportunist, thus inspired, the new nation would perhaps become a despotic dictatorship, its leader well aware, from his harsh tribal training for survival, that only the strong and ruthless inherit the earth . . .

Then there were continuing cold wars between nations of different ideologies; warmer wars of terrorism, guerrilla activity, and espionage; of genocide within each country; and – it seemed to me – increasingly man was losing the fight against bureaucracy, and computer surveillance which threatened to reduce the average citizen to slave status, to an ant-like reaction to, and dependence upon, the mass media manipulated by power-drunk politicians.

Basically (I mused pessimistically) all war, hot or cold, is a form of predator–prey relationship by which man struggles to acquire enough food (ultimately, the territory capable of producing that food) to survive and reproduce, the two most powerful urges in life. But surely, after millennia of development of his brain, *homo sapiens* ought to have arrived at that state of grace to be able to arrange his future so that there is enough food and living space for all to enjoy this planet and not merely exist on it? I was depressed that in the same hour that I could marvel at the colour and design of a wild flower, the structure of a bird's wing, or the metamorphosis of crawling caterpillar into a fairy-like butterfly, I could also fear that man is allowing the beauty of earth to wither, heedlessly destroying open country and wildlife, cutting down forests, building concrete conurbations, as he uses up world resources and consumes the last fossil fuels, manufacturing poison chemicals and radio-active compounds, whose residual wastes will contaminate land and water for many decades to come.

Would we ever reach the arcadia of a stable world state, reduced populations, the land yielding plenty of wholesome food for all, without the incessant bloody fighting and the cold political assassination of small nations by nuclear-armed super-powers? How I longed for this peaceful solution, for the attainment of this meaningful goal of man's endeavour. But it would never come, not in my lifetime . . .

'You are an escapist, you are living in a fool's paradise,' said the lean Rhondda Valley miner on a holiday visit to Orielton. 'Welshmen like a good fight and plenty to struggle against! I once played rugger against the All Blacks – tough, those men and their Maori mates – but they're magnificent clean fighters! Save when I was a soldier in the war – and that was good fun – I've been a miner all my life, and enjoyed it. I'd go back to the coal face tomorrow, if I hadn't got a touch of the old silicosis. That's an occupational hazard – you sign on for it when you start as donkey-boy minding the ponies down below. But I've got fair compensation . . . I'm on a pension. I'm free as air these days.'

His calm, happy acceptance of his traditional role in life, from childhood, as the son and grandson of miners, made me wonder; and his blithe manner made me ashamed of my querulous doubts about mankind. Writing verse in Welsh came naturally to him and he liked buoyant themes. None of his work had yet been translated but he admired the simple, almost oriental, poetry of Welsh countrymen like his contemporaries W. H. Davies and Huw Menai, some of whose work I had lately collected into an anthology. A copy of this book, newly published, was in his pocket when he arrived at Orielton and in a few moments Ifor ap Rhys was quoting Huw Menai's

> Linnets and warblers throng
> Where homes the primal oak –
> Small birds have a sweet song,
> The large but quack or croak.

'There's simple, taut imagery for you! And I'm glad you start your book with that translation of the best of all Welsh poems, Dafyd ap Gwylym's *The Mass of the Birds*. What rapture there! But duw man, pity you can't read the original Welsh! As for our mutual friend, the priest R. S. Thomas, he's always moaning and groaning, and I'll tell you why. He's never been able to master the Welsh tongue, he's an outcast in Wales, a parson whose sermon is misery because he can't understand the Welsh mind. We are clever and cunning but innately a happy singing people. We distrust his sad verses in English, forever mourning his own unhappiness . . .'

'I've found him a most entertaining personality. He was here last week, studying birds. Quite an expert, and quietly enthusiastic. . . .'

'Aye, he's clever with nature. But almost as bad as dear old Caradoc Evans of *My People* notoriety. That's a wicked lampoon of the Welsh hill people. Thomas enjoys the same histrionic, almost biblical, wailing. Listen to this.'

Opening the anthology, he read in his melodious voice, now somewhat husky from silicosis, the fine poem:

> 'Listen, listen! Where the river fastens
> The trees together with a blue thread,
> I hear the ousel of Cilgwri telling
> The mournful story of the long dead.
> Above the clatter of the broken water
> The song is caught in the bare bough;

The very air is veined with darkness, hearken!
The brown owl wakens in the woods now.
The owl, the ousel, and the toad carousing
In Cors Fochno of the old laws –
I hear them yet, but in what thicket cowers
Gwernabwy's eagle with the sharp claws?

'Duw, man, he may be a bird expert, but that's pure misery!' He laughed merrily, softening the criticism.

Oddly, Ifor ap Rhys had not come to discuss poetry, although he loved to do so. His visit to Orielton had been initially for the purpose of planning with me some homing or orientation tests with the racing pigeons of his Rhondda Valley loft. He devoted much of his retirement to breeding long-distance winners, being firmly convinced that the homing ability in these birds is instinctive, that is, genetically inherited. In my view, as the domestic pigeon derived in the first place, centuries ago, from the rock dove, which is an entirely sedentary or non-migratory species, the successful long-distance navigation achieved by his line-bred racers was more likely to be the result of training. He had admitted that he did train his birds to win races, by starting them off first with short flights from the loft, gradually increasing the distances, and always (more or less) releasing them in the same compass quarter; so the trained birds, whether released ten or three hundred miles from home, knew accurately in which direction to fly home. This they were able to do from previous experience as well as innate knowledge of the (rhythmically changing) position of the sun in relation to the horizon and to their line of homeward flight. It involved the exercise of their acute sense of time, the 'biological clock' possessed by all creatures, but little understood by man and somewhat atrophied in him.

Now we planned to resolve the matter by repeating a similar but inconclusive homing test I had made years ago. Ifor would send me some of his strong young pigeons, bred from his best racers, but which had never flown free farther than around the home loft and were completely untrained. If, as he believed, they had an innate sense of direction (like the Manx shearwaters and other migrant sea-birds of some earlier experiments of mine at Skokholm), these youngsters should be able to return home if released one, or more, hundred miles away.

169

'Of course there are some complicating factors. Most of my shearwaters and petrels came back rapidly, a few even from three thousand miles away, because they had the incentive to get home to mate, egg or chick on Skokholm. Young pigeons will not have quite the same urge, but like young people released from home for the first time, maybe they'll be perfectly happy to go on adventures of their own. Very likely they will fall in and make friends with other pigeons nearer the point of release and stay around. They're gregarious by nature and could even join up with our local wild rock doves, breeding in the caves on the coast. In fact our rock doves are no longer clean-looking native 'blue rock' originals; they have been diluted through frequent matings with lost and gone-stray racing pigeons, with the result that they're as multi-coloured as your tame loft birds.'

'You suggest that we should use the older birds, which like your sea-birds will have the urge to return to their mates and nest, in the loft? I don't know that I would risk them – they're too valuable as breeders, most of them, to be sent away for release hundreds of miles in the wrong direction – I mean, opposite to that in which I have trained them. But maybe I could find a few of the less valuable, older birds . . .'

The argument went on. In the end we did release some of his young, completely untrained, birds of the year, some one hundred, and some one hundred and fifty, miles from his Rhondda loft. Again I did not regard the results as absolutely convincing. The weather was hazy and the sun obscured when I released the pigeons from the basket which Ifor sent to Orielton – conditions which will confuse and halt even the experienced migratory wild bird. None of these young pigeons got home to the loft where they had been born; most were never heard of again, but three turned up elsewhere, in various pigeon-fanciers' lofts, not less than seventy miles from the Rhondda.

I have brought Ifor ap Rhys into this chapter on predators and prey because of events I shall now relate. I was delighted – and so was Stephen – that Ifor claimed descent from Sir Rhys ap Thomas (of Fetterlocks fame). His pleasure in Orielton's gracious mixture of old mansion, forest and model farm, and its fascinating human and natural history, was such that he begged to be allowed to stay on for a few weeks, helping in any capacity I liked to name. I liked him enormously because of his enthusiasm for the very things that pleased me; also, perhaps, because he was not reluctant to admire my way of life and flatter my ego. He borrowed those of my books he had not yet read. From my biography of *Gilbert White of Selborne*, lately published, he quoted the words of John Mulso, college companion and correspondent of White, as expressing his own first hopes on seeing Orielton: 'I look for an Arcady with you, and I expect some kind whispers from the unseen genius of your woods.'

Ifor was indomitable in spirit, but in health he was a sick man, though he would not admit this. At night he would cough for several hours – a cough he courageously suppressed during the day, but his lungs were hard and concreted with the years of work in coal-dust. Every morning he was up early and away to help on the farm, or to take a turn observing from the several 'hides' in operation. He made me more hopeful that Orielton was indeed becoming an Arcadia where the bountiful land produced so much of our own food and where the forest yielded profit. I was selling some of the ripe timber before it became too stag-headed and decayed (as about 50 per cent of the older trees were), and we were making potato-sprouting boxes for ourselves and the local farmers, using the top and lop, planting to replace those felled and interplanting with spruce which served to shelter and nurse the native beech. The spruce would be sold off as Christmas trees in a few years. Ifor echoed my own thoughts, that every stick and stone, every bird, beast and plant was a delight to watch, study and 'possess in the mind's eye'.

Ifor's sweet talk and nature were as a balm to my hopes and fears; I basked in his genial reassurance, healing my temporary glooms. Perhaps I was, I had been, introspective and self-centred? On wet days we talked enthusiastically about men and books and nature, about the genealogy of Orielton squires he might be related to. Ifor could sigh with me that man was vile, that the newspapers (which he said he never read) were full of reports of wars in many corners of the globe, of murder, robbery with violence, rape, hunger, drought, starvation; that the world was rushing headlong towards a catastrophic crash of our present civilisation . . .

'But duw, Boyo (I was soon promoted to this miner's sobriquet for friend), it's all quite natural, as natural as the cyclic crash of population which the lemmings go through from time to time.

Don't worry, we'll all be healthier afterwards. You and I won't survive, of course, but let's hope your young sons will one day enjoy better living space, more wholesome food, in an environment they will rebuild on the pyre of our twentieth-century failure. Perhaps we shall learn from your rabbits . . .'

Ifor was intrigued by the birth control system of the rabbits in the enclosures. In the Intensive Pen acre, I had allowed the rabbits to build up to maximum numbers, excessive in relation to the quality of the food supply (the grazing). As a result the does were producing few or no young. Although they were observed to mate as usual at (approximately) weekly intervals during the summer breeding season, and conceived in the normal way, the embryos died before half the term of pregnancy had expired. They were totally re-absorbed into the blood stream of the female, without abortion, although the mother's breasts sometimes swelled briefly with milk.

'Duw, Boyo, if only we could find the trigger which sets off this re-absorption process! Better than this new contraceptive pill by far! I hope the histologists are working on it! You could make your fortune if you could patent the trigger for the ladies to get rid of unwanted pregnancies without messy abortion.'

'In the Intensive Pen, conditions somewhat resemble the human predicament in overcrowded lands,' I told him. 'Quite unnatural. The bucks are forever fighting or on edge, living too close together. They compete for, and harry the does. And added to these psychological stresses, there is the physical distress of undernourishment.'

'Uncommonly like the Rhondda Valley in the bad old days. *How Green was My Valley* was never all roast beef and Yorkshire pudding, like the film makes out. Tripe! I suppose Richard Llewellyn's been here, too?'

'When I last saw him twelve years ago, he was carving a smallholding in the Preseli Mountains, more or less out of solid rock. But about the rabbits; we don't know how their convenient and tidy form of birth control is triggered but it is believed to be the result of this so-called psycho-physiological insult, or shock.'

'Poor b . . . s!' commented Ifor one day, after a session watching the inmates of the Intensive Pen from the observation box in the pollarded elm. 'That community's certainly under stress! Two bucks have been fighting for control of territory for a whole hour.

And there's a young rabbit being chivvied around, and nowhere to go. What's the end of the experiment – you'll have to break it up soon?'

'The experiment has served its purpose of proving that rabbits use birth control to halt the rate of population increase under such stress. Very likely disease will be the final solution – coccidiosis is endemic in rabbits and becomes lethal when their resistance weakens through overcrowding. But I shan't let it go as far as that. Don't worry.'

'I'm not worried! I find it fascinating, studying them in that comfortable tree shelter. They're so human in many ways! And then there's all the other animals around to watch if you get bored with bunnies. You know of course that the Canada geese have built a nest not far from the Lily Pond?'

A pair of Canada geese, wing-clipped and set free in the winter beside the Lily Pond, had quickly made themselves at home, grazing the lush swamp and other grasses. They had mated and now the goose had built her nest of dry grass and vegetation in the shade of an alder near the water. She lined it with feathers and down plucked from her belly to lay bare the warm skin of her broodpatch, as is usual in waterfowl. In due course she incubated six eggs, alone; the gander spent his time parading near by, ready to drive away intruders, making a loud outcry when a human being came too near. His agitation increased as the warm spring days passed.

One hot May afternoon Ifor climbed into the Elm Tree Hide for another spell of rabbit watching. He had taken young Stephen by the hand, at the boy's request, to a spot on the bank of the Lily Pond sufficiently far from the goose's nest not to alarm the gander. And here Stephen had set up his stool, rod, line and float, and started fishing for the abundant roach and perch, a favourite occupation of small boys at that season.

Ifor fell asleep under the soporific influence of the heat, and the lack of much movement in the rabbit warrens below the tree. He was aroused by a wild honking of the gander as it suddenly detected Stephen, and dashed as fast as it could (with its clipped wings) to attack the boy. Before Ifor could slither out of the elm tree and race to the rescue, the gander had knocked Stephen flat and began slashing at the boy with sharp wings, and wrenching at his bare legs with its formidable grass-cutting bill.

Ifor pitched in, and managed to grab the gander by the neck, and fling it into the pond – from which it swiftly returned on foot to the sitting goose, yodelling its triumph.

Stephen was bruised and bleeding in several places. He was very frightened and at first revengeful, when Ifor brought him to the house. But he recovered enough to desire to accompany me to interview Canadensis, as we had dubbed the gander. He limped in my shadow as I approached the nest, carrying a long-handled shepherd's crook with which I proposed to tackle his assailant.

But the shock was over and Stephen relented, while from a safe distance we watched Canadensis honking to his sitting wife.

'Pa, don't let's hurt old Canadensis. He's only guarding his wife and nest, really.'

'You're dead right, old son. In any case I wasn't going to punish Canadensis. But I intend to catch him and clip the flight feathers entirely off one wing. Then when he rushes to attack anything he will merely spin in a circle with the other, good wing, and do a pirouette instead!'

In theory this seemed an admirable solution and I was proud to have thought it up; Ifor and Stephen loudly approved. But first catch your gander. I failed to pin him to the ground with the long crook. Instead he attacked and wrenched it from my grasp, then rushed at us. Stephen fled while Ifor did a rugby tackle, only to fall on his face and get a nasty flip from Canadensis' wings. I rescued the crook, but the gander side-stepped all efforts to hook his neck.

One had to admire his courage, that courage which enables this species to nest successfully in its native habitat of the Canadian tundra and defy foxes and other predators in the wilderness. A full time task for the gander – no wonder the goose alone incubates.

On the following day all seemed quiet when I strolled near the Lily Pond. The damp sward was brilliant with yellow cowslips, ultramarine bugle, burgeoning meadowsweet, ragged robin and cuckoo flowers. Golden kingcups and yellow iris blossomed, their roots in water; the white water-lilies were just about to open. The well-loved woodlark sang, as ever, low in the sky; occasionally it would alight and continue its anthem of bell notes in the top of the pollarded elm and marvellous it was then, if you were fortunate to be sitting in the rabbit-watching shelter, to gaze up and see so close the little brown throat and crest visibly vibrating in the ecstasy of sound. Surely the singer was enjoying himself – he was not entirely, as some behaviourists insist, preoccupied in advertising his presence and warning off rivals.

Yes, all seemed well within the main enclosure, where the high wire-netting fence protected both the rabbit pens and the several pairs of pinioned geese and ducks from ground predators. They lived in comparative peace and plenty, disposing themselves at will around the three ponds and the lush parkland . . .

Suddenly there was a loud clapping noise, and I was flung flat on my face! Canadensis had struck again! From behind the trees he had taxied at speed, despite his clipped wings! As we both sat up, sorting out wind and limbs, I was obliged to laugh and scowl at the same moment – there was a stinging bruise where he had struck the back of my neck. For Canadensis was uttering a discordant yodel of defiance as he swayed to and fro, winded, yet endeavouring to recover his poise and dignity, wobbling on his webbed feet. As I did not retaliate, but began to retreat, he toddled off to tell his wife another watchdog tale of triumph.

Retribution was at hand – or rather, disaster. A few nights later, the bitch otter, now that her pups were needing more solid food, trotted up from her holt in the Decoy Wood, climbed the wall near the old mill and, disregarding the gander's efforts to protect his mate, killed the goose as she sat on her nest.

Of course I did not witness this slaying, but when I visited the nest I could read the story in this sequence: the eggs smashed and trampled flat; Canadensis very subdued and making no attempt to drive me away; a trail, of feathers and some gruesome fragments of goose flesh, which ended at the edge of the Lily Pond, where two goose wings lay severed from the missing body; and in the mud the footprints of an otter.

Poor Canadensis, suddenly so meek and mild in his misery over the loss of his mate! All the same, for my son's sake, I was relieved that his bellicose attacks would now cease. The boys could resume their fishing without fear. I expected that Canadensis would console himself with the company of the other wing-clipped geese around the water: the docile pinkfeet, white-front, upland, Egyptian and barnacle species, all of which he had dominated in the past. None of these had bred so far, for various reasons, probably because Peter Scott had sent me chiefly immature birds; but Canadensis ignored them. Instead an interesting aberration occurred.

It happened that with the abundance of young grass in the parkland, Cortez, on the morning after the killing of the goose, began to graze some of our weaned Jersey heifers there – we were saving other pasture for hay. The youngest of these handsome animals was Orielton Duchess, darker than the usual Jersey colour and with a white muzzle. Only vaguely could she be said to resemble a Canada goose – in colour, but not in shape.

Nevertheless Canadensis fell in love with Duchess at first sight. That is to say, in his sudden bereavement, he adopted her in place of his mate. He followed her everywhere, generally waddling a few paces ahead as if to defend her when she was moving. When she stood still he would stand in her shadow, or even between her four legs. He loved her best when she folded her legs and sat down, for this brought her piebald head closer to his own black-and-white face, and he would squat beside her, uttering little complacent honks.

'What a splendid big goose you are, my darling!' he seemed to be telling her, plucking furiously at the grass in front of him. 'Come, sample this herbage, 'twill do you good . . .'

But Duchess's eyes were uplifted inscrutably towards the middle distance as she passed up from her stomach yet another ball of cud, and with a vulgar belch masticated the grass she had ingested earlier. She was totally disinterested in the blandishments of Canadensis. When he got in her way – as he frequently did in his eagerness to be close to her – she was even unkind, certainly ungracious. She would kick out at him impatiently, sometimes registering a hit on his tough plumage that sent him spinning sideways. But he seemed to regard this as some form of love-play, and would at once trundle back to her side, chattering happily.

Some of his former pugnaciousness was renewed. If you passed too close to his new woman he would honk a warning and make a brief run towards you. He maintained and guarded a movable territory around Duchess.

When the grass had been grazed down, Cortez removed his group of young heifers from the waterside meadow. Canadensis hurried to follow, pecking at the cowman's legs in his rage at this interference. Cortez booted him back, and closed the impassable gate in the wall. Canadensis rushed hither and thither, taxi-ing with clipped wings, honking his despair. For two days he was inconsolable, even at night he cried out at intervals, hoping perhaps to get a vocal response from Orielton Duchess, grazing several fields away, out of sight but not out of the gander's troubled mind.

A few days later I had occasion to introduce a flock of a dozen St Kildan sheep into the Extensive Pen known as Savanna (see *The Private Life of the Rabbit*), one acre in extent. Here only one pair of rabbits lived; we removed their progeny as soon as they left their nursery burrow to graze. This was an experiment to study the behaviour and population dynamics of the rabbit enjoying almost unlimited freedom and luxuriant grazing. One pair could not keep the pasture down in summer and at intervals I would introduce sheep to do so; this was important because by lowering the height of the grass the sheep gave us a clearer view of the activities of the fortunate rabbit pair, known as Lone King and Sheba.

The late Duke of Bedford had presented me with a nucleus of these rare sheep to breed at Skokholm. Originating, it is believed, from the short-tailed Scandinavian sheep carried by the Vikings in their raids on Scotland a thousand years ago, they are a very distinct breed, with short chocolate-brown wool, cream-coloured rumps and pale facial markings. The Duke of Bedford had obtained some in a pure state from the off-island of Soay, St Kilda, and was breeding them at Woburn Abbey; but on those lush inland pastures they grew coarse and large. It was hoped – and so proved – that on the lean windy grazing at Skokholm they would remain the fine small type of their St Kildan home. From time to time I removed the surplus from Skokholm to place elsewhere; at that moment a group had arrived at Orielton, for trans-shipment to another small island nature reserve.

Immediately on seeing the St Kildan sheep through the wire-netted fence of the Extensive Pen, Canadensis went wild with excitement. Here were living creatures which (we are entitled to suppose he believed) were even more like his beautiful murdered wife. Their markings and colour forcibly reminded him of her piebald face and vivid white rump. He rushed towards them honking a welcome, only to crash badly against the six-foot-tall netting.

177

All that day he paraded up and down outside the fence, assaulting the barrier at intervals, and being repulsed in a battered condition, feathers broken and awry. He cackled ecstatically when one sheep casually grazed close to the wire-netting. He flapped his wings at her, bowed his neck and with cooing noises invited her attention to his splendid courtship display. Alas, after a stare of distrust, or incomprehension, she ignored him completely.

Next morning all was strangely peaceful. For a moment I wondered if the otter had come in the night and collected Canadensis – perhaps the best solution to end his agonised longings? But no, there he was, content at last. His pertinacity had been rewarded: he had discovered that if he beat his clipped wings hard enough, and at the same time used his webbed feet to claw upwards, he could surmount the netting. He paddled majestically over the sunlit grass, keeping to the centre of the dozen ladies of St Kilda, grazing nose to beak with them. They were far gentler companions than the boisterous maiden Duchess. He waddled inseparably alongside the St Kildan sheep so long as they remained in the enclosure.

To conclude his story: in due course the St Kildan sheep were sent away to colonise another Welsh islet. Once more Canadensis became miserable but was a little less restless, for the sexual urge was dying down with his moult. After his moult I did not clip his new flight feathers – a necessary procedure if you wish to keep unpinioned waterfowl in captivity under an open sky. One day late in summer he discovered that his new wings would really lift him higher than six feet. In the next week, after several practice flights, he rose above the tree-tops. Espying my flock of Dorset Horn sheep, grazing in Baker's Mountain, he descended to inspect them. But these perfectly white, nondescript, not to say podgy, sheep were not to his liking – in no way could they be imagined to resemble Canada geese.

Next day he was flying splendidly above the manor and parkland, honking his farewell. Fortunately he headed away in the right direction – towards the sea-drowned valley of Milford Haven, in the upper reaches of which a farmer of many acres of tidal saltings had lately set free the nucleus of a wild flock of Canada geese. And with them on that shore I like to think Canadensis may yet live in patriarchal style.

*   *   *

One morning a shrill female voice announced over the phone that an otter had entered Messrs Woolworth's emporium in the High Street, Tenby, and could I come at once and save it from being hunted to death by a stupid gang of louts.

'They won't listen to reason! They say it's a savage brute, and has already bitten one man who grabbed its tail!'

'Small blame to it! Stop them if you can! I'm on my way!'

By the time I had motored at speed to Tenby, the otter had been cornered and cudgelled to death. I arrived in time to see its bloody corpse being hung on the tailboard of the town dustcart. Some people were admiring, others were cursing the workmen who had killed the 'savage brute'. Already, I thought, the killers were wilting under the reproaches, chiefly of women bystanders and now, in the cold light of reason, they gladly consented to my request for possession of the corpse. I told them I would send it to the National Museum of Wales, which needed such specimens for its collection.

It was a young male of good size, its body one metre long, and the broad tail measured another half a metre. What a shame! I could only admire the beautiful dark brown fur, dense and oily, where minute bubbles of air are trapped, warmed by the body heat, and so helping to insulate the otter from extreme cold. Longer 'guard' hairs project, giving the coat that spiky, rough appearance when it first emerges from the water, when the glistening drops cling to the longer hair until the animal shakes itself dry and assumes its sleek and sinuous beauty of form.

Could this unlucky brute have been one of the four cubs born to the bitch otter which had killed Canadensis' wife? Very likely, for the young otter, like the adult, is a great traveller and explorer. Part of their ecology is to roam and seek their food over a wide range of water, if they are to survive. For if they stay long in one place, decimating the food supply, especially trout and salmon in preserved waters, they are soon hunted to death by fishermen, ghillies and other enemies. They have become scarce in Britain because of this persecution and only the wandering Ishmaels of their species are able to live long enough to reproduce successfully. Even so, when the bitch whelps and stays in one place for a few months she is in great danger of discovery. But she is, perforce, cunning and hides her family well . . .

The decoyman Harold Greenslade was full of otter lore, some

179

of it accurate, some of it hearsay and myth. From childhood he had known the Decoy Pond, where otters were frequent visitors. Talking of these, Greenslade would shake his head, saying he both admired and feared the beast, for it had 'plenty of spunk, yer gotta admire 'is guts! In a trap an otter 'll fight like the devil, and if the trap ain't set so's to topple 'un into water and drown 'un, likely 'e'll tear 'is own leg off! I seen that once. Girt savage critturs, an' mighty tough to kill, they be.'

'What with?'

'A big cudgel be best. Knock uts brain out. Or a rabbut-trappin' paddle – the sharp edge.'

'Beastly cruel. Well, you know the new rule. The Decoy Pond is a sanctuary for all animals, even otters. Leave them alone.'

'Aye, aye. But us'll not catch many ducks for ringin' with them otters killin' an' scarin' 'em!'

Only once had he found an otter nursery or holt, under the roots of an alder, years ago when working the Decoy for Mack-worth-Praed and Barmy Gilbert.

'The littul Corgi dog us used to decoy ducks with smelled 'un out, one day in April it were. 'E was barking 'is 'ead off, an' I thought as Tom 'ad run a rabbut or fox to earth. Just as I comes up to 'im a girt big otter bitch rushed out of 'er den, an' attacked Tom. 'E scuttled behind me, yelpin' an' 'fraid. The old bitch stopped dead when she see'd me! But she thought better of ut, an' – no 'urry – she goes back cool as a cucumber into the 'olt. I could 'ear 'er pups whinin' an' whickerin' way back deep in the 'ole, outa sight. She wouldn't leave 'em – not likely. If I 'adn't been there she'd 'ave killed an' eaten my littul Corgi dog Tom – no mistake! Next mornin' me mate an' me come down at first light afore breakfast, to dig the litter out. Blow me, that cunnin' old bitch, she 'ad shifted the lot! Never found where to.'

The bitch otter will move her family if her holt is in danger. Not only that, she is said to be able to count, and knows how many pups she has. I remember once when, looking for eagles with Seton Gordon near his home in the north of Skye, we watched from the top of a high cliff a family of otters working along the rocky shore below. The mother otter was catching fish, with four pups close behind her, scrambling over boulders, dipping into rock pools left by the tide. The smallest pup was finding it difficult or else was unwilling to keep up with the others and lingered, apparently happily investigating a pool on its own. Presently the bitch caught a sizeable flatfish and showed it to the three pups close to her. They attempted to grab it but she held it too high, and they had to follow her some distance to a broad platform of rock, evidently a favourite site for a meal.

Here she allowed the three youngsters to tear at the fish. But now she seemed uneasy. She nosed the pups as if checking that all were present. In a few more moments she left the others to squabble over the flounder and retraced her route over the boulders, sniffing and peeping as she progressed. Meanwhile the absentee pup seemed thoroughly engrossed in its own hunting affair in a small pool, and heeded not the anxious whistle of its mother. At last she found it and, dipping her snout into the pool, she nudged it out of the water, then grabbed the scruff of its neck. Without further ceremony she scrambled with it in her mouth over the intervening boulders, to rejoin the others. 'A perfect example of the intelligence and love of a mother otter!' commented Seton, with the same satisfaction I was feeling.

'Boss, yer be too soft 'earted 'bout vermin,' Greenslade reminded me, almost apologetically. 'Otters 'ull ruin a decoy. Mr Praed and Captain Gilbert used to let me keep the skin for me trouble when I caught one. Worth a few quid if yer gets one clean-moulted in winter coat at the turn o' the year.'

It was some time before we realised that the otter which had killed our Canada goose had whelped earlier that year in a holt or den deep under the roots of an alder in the Decoy Wood. Otters had been a nuisance from time to time during the winter, killing waterfowl caught for banding studies in three self-catching traps which we had built along the shoreline of this sixteen-acre pond. These wire-netted devices were typical of so-called 'house' traps used at bird-marking stations. Certain birds which entered by way of two or three inward-tapering funnels at ground level seldom found the way out again, and remained within, often feeding tranquilly on the corn, or other bait provided, until the attendant came to band and release them. Otters, used to labyrinthine tunnels, went in and out easily; and if by chance, in the antics of grabbing and killing waterfowl, an otter rolled flat the flimsy netting funnels, it was quite capable of tearing a hole in the wire wall of the trap and escaping with the unfortunate victim.

At first we hoped we could surprise the raider of our traps by ambushing it at night, hiding somewhere near by and rushing out on hearing the duck's death-squawk. We planned then to block the tunnel exits and fling a thick sack over the otter. We intended to deport it for release too far from the Decoy for it to return that season.

We waited in vain, for four nights. If the otters were present, they were cunning to keep well away from us. But it was a mild time and early in February there were few migratory ducks left. The flocks of wigeon, teal, mallard, shoveler, tufted duck, pochard and a trio of whooper swans, which had found day sanctuary from the local gunners on the Decoy Pond, were moving towards their breeding grounds in the far north, to Scotland, Iceland, Scandinavia, some to the Russia tundra (as our marking with leg-bands proved). They were reasonably safe while they swam in the deeper water; only a sickly or wounded bird could be captured in the open by an otter. I was satisfied that the otter was an example of a predator legitimately living in balance with its prey, its food resources. By interfering with nature to the extent of trapping ducks and keeping exotic species in unnatural confinement, where they were helplessly exposed to their natural enemies, we were at fault, benign though our intentions might be. It was not fair to blame the otters, or hunt them to extinction, because they interfered with bird-marking or avicultural schemes.

On some late winter evenings we had heard the wild, thrilling whistle of otters borne on the west wind from the Decoy Pond, when evidently dog and bitch were frolicking in mating play. Otters will copulate in the water, like the seals, and remain locked in coitus for several minutes, the male holding to the fur on the neck of the female and curving his long tail under hers. The playful animals had made a slide in a steep part of the shore (according to Greenslade it had been used before, years ago) and enjoyed tobogganing down the earthen slope as a regular part of their nightly amusement, unseen by man – although the evidence was plain in the tufts of moulted fur, and the claw-marks. As the long thick tail somewhat incommodes their progress on land otters will freely toboggan over snow, wet grass and mud, shoving with their short legs at intervals, like children on a sledge.

Otters mate in any month of the year, for the female is receptive at monthly intervals. The true gestation period is believed to be about nine weeks. But as a bitch otter, taken into captivity, has given birth to a litter after a much longer period without access to a male, it is clear that the fertile egg may not necessarily develop immediately into a foetus. Implantation of the embryo may be delayed for a good reason, as in some bats, stoats, and seals, where the female is not in a condition physically to support a pregnancy and the embryo remains dormant, in the form known as a blastocyst. Free blastocysts have been recorded in female otters in November and December, but implantation in the wall of the womb has not taken place until February or later.

The mating of otters at any time of the year is thus an insurance for the propagation of the species in a solitary wandering animal where the sexes may not encounter each other over a long period. The male takes no interest in the pups; he is normally driven away from the holt by the female. But it appears that (again like their cousins the stoats, and some seals) she becomes receptive for a short period soon after parturition, and will mate then. He is best able to locate her at this time, while she is resident for two months on nursery duty (this mating behaviour, difficult to observe in the wild, is recorded of otters breeding in captivity).

Males may not mate until they are several years old, depending on competition from older, stronger rivals for the bitch's favours. This is suggested by the fact that in captivity the dog otter will savagely attack another male, or even his human keeper, during the period while the bitch is on heat.

Our Orielton Lutra was so secretive about her nursery arrangements that had it not been for her visit to the enclosure to kill and carry off the Canada goose, we might never have found her hiding place.

Ifor, Stephen and I tracked her route from the Lily Pond back to the Decoy, but with some difficulty. We argued that she had most likely followed the trickling stream between the two; and here and there, at muddy places, we found her slot marks and now and then a goose feather. She had dragged the wingless corpse of Canadensis' wife all the way, through thick clumps of meadow-sweet, flag, loosestrife and marsh willow-herb. But we lost the trail as soon as it reached the edge of the Decoy Pond. She had swum out into the blank expanse.

No sound of whistling at night. Doubtless her mate had long ago gone off on his peregrinations, bored with her savage repulse of him while her cubs were small and helpless. Days later I discovered her den almost by accident. Searching along the shore of the Decoy Pond, I noticed her slot marks and the characteristic tail smear here and there in the wet mud exposed by the summer drought. But I would have passed the hidden entrance if I had not paused to examine the freshly-killed body of a brown rat, the top half of which had been bitten clean off. As I stooped over it, I heard the whimpering of the pups from the nesting chamber far up under the roots of a large decayed alder.

Rats! I was glad that otters killed rats – to compensate for their predation of waterfowl and edible fish. In fact otters will eat many species normally harmful to man: mice, voles, rabbits, eels, pike and other coarse fish not wanted for the table.

I retreated quietly, anxious not to alarm Lutra into removing her pups. With Ifor's help I built a tent of sacking in the dead branches of an ancient oak some sixty metres away on the opposite shore of the pond. It was little more than a screen to hide us from the otters, in case we were lucky enough to see any in daylight. But when it flapped noisily in the first strong wind, we took it away. The broad bare branch with its backdrop of foliage, proved comfortable enough as a secret watchpost. We had some success in a surprisingly short time, just sitting still during dawn watches, having silently made our way to the tree through the damp woodland.

Ifor had more time to spare for this vigil, which he shared with the shy Estonian-born girl Eithne. Her father, she told us, had once discovered a lone and starving baby otter when fishing one morning by an upper tributary of the Rhine (where her family now lived, having escaped from Estonia at the end of the war). She had helped to rear it and so was more knowledgeable about otters than the rest of us. It was a dog otter which grew so large and eventually became so formidable that it had been given away to a man who owned a private zoo. Later someone called Gavin Maxwell had acquired it and, she believed, had taken it to his home in Scotland. Did I know Gavin Maxwell?

At that time Gavin Maxwell had not yet published his bestseller *Ring of Bright Water*. I had met him briefly at a convention on the conservation of seals; he was then known as a harpooner of basking sharks in the Hebrides.

With little time to spare for otter-watching, I envied Ifor and

Eithne the peaceful hours they spent in the crotch of the stag-headed oak, where – a strange partnership – Ifor scribbled his otter observations (and some poetry inspired by the beauty of the place and hour) in Welsh, and Eithne in French.

It was clear that Lutra at first had no suspicion that she was being watched, yet she remained secretive, usually slipping to and from the holt under the alder in darkness. She was recorded chiefly as a ripple disturbing the pond's surface at dawn; there was no activity during the heat of the day. Four times Lutra was seen with fish in her mouth, twice with a large eel, still very much alive, writhing around her neck as she gripped its shining head in her sharp fangs. Many mornings no otter observations were recorded, but plenty of notes on other creatures: fox, badger, squirrel, water-vole, water-shrew, brown rat, singing and water birds, including families of coot, moorhen and mallard; that these could rear their young safely so close to an otter holt was pleasing. Midges and mosquitoes were less delightful.

Then, just before sunrise one morning, Eithne saw Lutra take a sizeable fish, probably a tench for which the pond was noted, into the tunnel leading to the nursery. Presently she emerged, still holding the fish, but with four little otters trailing behind her. She lay down on the foreshore while the pups alternately chewed at the fish and played together, rolling like the puppies they were, on the mat of dwarf summer flowers which spring up along the newly-exposed foreshore in the drought.

After this news, there was competition to take the dawn watch in the decayed oak. I was amused and surprised by the clumsiness of these half-grown pups; they seemed top-heavy and when they entered the water – timidly and briefly at first – their large heads tended to make them sink, leaving the short tails sticking up sky-wards. They would drink and paddle cautiously, while Lutra re-clined watchfully near by.

The European otter is blind and toothless at birth, with short, dark, silky fur and pronounced facial whiskers, and weighs under 150 gm. The babies are kept warm by the devoted mother, who encircles them with her long body and tail, her head closing the top like a lid. The babies open their eyes towards the end of the first month, but do not leave the holt to play outdoors until they are two months old, by which time they weigh about one kilo-gram and are beginning to eat fish and other solid food. As many as six pups are sometimes born, but this is rare. Harrison Matthews writes that 'the female has six teats, but only four may be functional'. Some females have less: Gavin Maxwell records that his female clawless African otter had the unusual number of five mammae.

Otters will give birth to their young in a variety of situations, but usually in the disused burrow of another animal, enlarged if necessary by the bitch or, as at the Decoy, several metres under the roots of a tree near its fishing water. Where extensive reed-beds exist, as in East Anglia, and Mesopotamia, the bitch will build a mound of reeds and water-plants sufficiently above water level for her to make a dry den within, to hide her litter from the sight of the numerous predators of the marshland. American otters will deposit their young in a wigwam built by pulling tall living reeds together. C. J. Harris, in his book on the otter, lists some unusual sites: six feet up a pollarded willow; a drain beneath a noisy, operating cloth-mill; under the dining-room floor of a house (detected as a result of the 'uncouth cries' of the pups while a party was dining); and one bitch had littered underneath the seat of an outdoor lavatory.

It was while her children were still dependent on her in the holt that Lutra had begun raiding the waterfowl in the enclosed parkland in the front of the manor. Having tasted gooseflesh, she returned at intervals for more. At this season it was easier to obtain geese and ducks which for a short period are unable to fly, during the midsummer moult of their wing quills. This is a time when otters normally feed on waterbirds, a convenient supplement to their fish diet, especially for the nursing mother who has to provide extra food for her fast-growing pups.

Soon the track made by Lutra to reach the enclosure was plainer, winding the hundred or so yards through the head of the Decoy Wood, following the little feeder stream under the outer wall, then across a lane, via a tributary rivulet up to the first of our ponds. She had paused where the mill wheel stood, black and rusting, only a few of its buckets splashed with water from the leaking race; here, where the lumber sheds had been converted to the cow parlour and hay and corn stores, Lutra could prospect for a rat or two. Then upstream, to reach the high wall bounding the north side of the parkland enclosure. I had placed an iron grid in the waterway under this wall, to prevent the escape of even the smallest ducks, or the entry of ground predators. But the wall was well-festooned with ivy and Lutra had left her claw marks where she had climbed by this steep natural ladder. There were slot marks in the mud of the lowest (mill) pond and the middle pond (the Japanese Garden) of her hunting for the small life of the wet ground – frogs, bullheads, mice and voles – before she had tackled the piscatorial and ornithological opportunities of the Lily Pond.

The otter-watching from the stag-headed oak was to come to a sudden, catastrophic, end. Pestered by visiting naturalists ardent to share in the dawn watches, we had given permission for not more than two persons to accompany Ifor or Eithne to the tree – on condition that there was to be no talking, sneezing or other human noises (Ifor nobly suppressed his cough but with difficulty), which would make Lutra aware that she was being spied upon. There was no guarantee, either, that otters would be seen on any given day. However, lately the puppies had appeared every morning, swimming well, diving, endlessly playing, making longer forays along the shore and into deeper water, still under Lutra's loving protection.

One day early in August a well-known radio personality, Freddy Grisewood, and his wife, were staying with us. Inevitably they were delighted with Ifor's company and bonhomie. Freddy begged permission to be allowed to go otter-watching as soon as possible – he had only a few days with us. An enthusiastic countryman, Freddy was lame and no longer young. I was in grave doubt as to the wisdom of allowing him to climb into the oak, even by the ladder I would be obliged to provide for him. I tried to put him off, promising a trip by boat to a seal colony instead. He insisted:

'Ronald, I have seen badgers at home in their setts, I have often seen wild seals on small islands, but I have never, never, watched otters at the holt – only, sadly, killed during an otter hunt with hounds. I promise to be as quiet as a mouse and as silent as the grave. It's my last chance. I may be decrepit, but if Ifor can get up that tree then I make a bet I can, too – without a ladder! But of course, it's for you to decide . . .'

He grinned across the breakfast table at Ifor, who returned the smile and looked at me, one eyebrow comically arched, but said nothing. Ifor's unusual silence was hard to bear – he was leaving the responsibility of refusing to me.

'Ifor's too polite to say bluntly, as I do, that you're too wobbly on your pins, my dear Freddy, to start climbing trees at your age. I'll have to think about it, and you'll certainly need a ladder. We'd better wait for Eithne to come back and have the latest news of Lutra's family. She's taken the Williams' with her this morning.'

Eithne was very late returning to her breakfast. She appeared at last, covered from head to foot in black mud. In her accented English she explained dolefully, almost weeping:

'Something terrible happened! It's awful, and it's all my fault! You see . . . the Williams! Oh dear, how can I explain . . . ?'

I was alarmed. The Williams, a middle-aged couple, were on a caravan trip round the world, a jolly Australian pair, always smiling, deeply interested in nature, he nicely rotund, and she positively enormous, splitting at the seams with fat and good humour.

'It's terrible!' wailed Eithne. 'We've scared Lutra badly! I'm sure she'll never come back! She's swum away with all her babies! The whole family went off down the Decoy Pond like arrows! I feel awful about it. It's all my fault!'

'Explain, explain, please! Explain first why you are covered in mud!'

'Oh, that? Well, we had a mucky time of it, rescuing Jemima Williams. You see, we had hardly settled in the old oak tree before Lutra came out of the holt with her family. They gave us marvellous views as they all played together in the water, diving and splashing around – they swim so well now. Then Jemima – she had the camera – wanted to get a better view, there were some leaves in the way of the lens. So she wormed along, much farther out on that big dead bough. She was settling down to film when there was a tremendous crack! I though a gun had gone off! Jemima screamed – you know what a weight she is – but I always thought that bough was solid enough to hold two people. Well, it went on cracking . . . Jim tried to grab Jemima's arm . . . she was still screaming! But in any case he could not have held that weight of woman! The whole bough cracked clean away from the trunk of the tree and Jemima fell head over heels into the wet ground below, with her darling Jim on top of her! I was left quite alone in the tree!'

Ifor and the Grisewoods roared with laughter, and I was obliged to join in; even Eithne's face lightened for a moment.

'No, they weren't really hurt. No bones broken. It's all soft wet ground under the oak, very sticky and deep, deep mud! We had an awful job pulling Jemima out of the bog. They are safe back in their caravan, scraping the mud off . . . But it's Lutra I'm worried about. I saw her lead her pups right away at top speed. She'll never come back. I watched her out of sight!'

'You watched otters while poor Jemima was stuck head-first in the mud? Positively enchanting, you are, Eithne!' roared Ifor. 'There's dedication for you, eh, Freddy?'

'But the otters,' groaned Eithne, 'they've gone for good! It's my fault, I never should have allowed that heavyweight woman to go out on that dead branch. D'you think there's any hope of Lutra coming back to the holt?'

'Don't worry,' I tried to console her. 'It's time the otter family dispersed anyway. They'll be enjoying the change of scene, I expect. And you've solved one problem for me this morning. The Grisewoods will have to be satisfied with seal, instead of otter, watching.'

The otter family were seen no more. Eithne was inconsolable. She watched over many more dawns, in the broken tree-top. She tried to trace them along the bosky stream which carries the water of the Decoy Pond to the sea, six miles distant. The peregrinating otter, like the wolf and the wild dog, has the habit of advertising its presence by leaving visiting cards (droppings, known as spraints, containing faeces and the indigestible fish and fur residues of its diet) at strategic stopping places along a waterway, such as a conspicuous boulder, or some natural landing place.

Ifor's holiday was over; he went back to the Rhondda Valley. That autumn, soon after Eithne had returned to Switzerland, I had occasion to write to both otter-watchers to thank them for their help in the summer, and tell them about an inquisitive male otter, possibly one of Lutra's well-loved children which, in the innocence and inexperience of youth, had unwisely visited Messrs Woolworth's Emporium in the picturesque seaside resort of Tenby, a few miles along the coast east from Orielton.

9

*Puss grew presently familiar, would leap into my lap, raise himself
upon his hinder feet, and bite the hair from my temples. He would
suffer me to take him up, and carry him about in my arms, and has
more than once fallen fast asleep upon my knee. He was ill three days,
during which I nursed him, kept him apart from his fellows (for, like
many other wild animals, they persecute one of their own species that is
sick), and by constant care, and trying him with a variety of herbs,
restored him to perfect health. No creature could be more grateful . . .
Not so Tiney, upon him the kindest treatment had not the least
effect. He would strike with his forefeet, and bite.*

WILLIAM COWPER
On the treatment of his hares

In a cold snap with hoar frost migrant woodcock, snipe and ring-
dove arrived in numbers from the north, augmenting the residents
of these species which had nested in the quiet aisles and damp
corners of our woods. The bank manager and other friends asked
permission for a day's shooting, ostensibly after woodpigeons
which, bursting with fat from feeding on acorns, beechmast and
other autumn fruits, were annually accused of devouring the root
and clover crops. It was the day when local farmers and landowners co-operated in a synchronised shoot which kept the
pigeons flying from one roost to another; each time the flocks
attempted to alight they would meet with a hail of lead pellets.

Reluctantly I agreed to this annual *battue* of one day, provided
the sportsmen kept away from the enclosures and the walled
gardens and let me know the total bag. They did; they dropped a
sample on my doorstep. I confess I enjoyed the woodcock roasted
and the pigeons in a vast pie, so appetisingly prepared by Victoria. Also a young hare had been shot which, hung for a week,
proved delicious when jugged to a recipe of Mrs Beeton's.

The first Norway thrushes (as Greenslade called them) flew in
to a feast on the ripe hawthorn berries, the last blackberries and
the ruby globules of the elder, livening the overgrown hedges and
woodland verges with the whispering call of redwings and the

clacking note of fieldfares. Assisted by the Atlantic winds, the leaves fell steadily from the trees; sycamore, elm and ash first, oak and beech lingering longer. Parties of titmice, goldcrests, tree-creepers and wrens moved through the branches and under-growth, each seeking its share of insect and berry food in its special manner, at a different level, exploiting the total supply without undue competition, but keeping together to enjoy the advantage of many eyes and ears, both to discover food and give warning of predators. There was a scatter to deeper cover when a sparrowhawk appeared; but when an owl was discovered, the little birds gathered around the tall drowsy bird and mobbed it for a while with their different alarm calls. With eyes half shut, the owl remained motionless, unperturbed save for a downward flicker of the upper eyelids, and soon the small birds, tired of this collectively bold jeering of a predator, which each would have fled from had it encountered the owl alone, flitted onwards again.

The lone hare loped more frequently through our fields and woods. The virtual disappearance of the rabbits had been to the advantage of our hare population, which had at least trebled its numbers, aided by some releases from England by local sporting landowners. The tenant of Orielton West Lodge complained that a giant buck rabbit was eating her carrots each evening, at twi-light; she had failed to scare it away with bits of red and yellow cloth on sticks. Would I come and shoot the wretched beast?

'It's a hare,' I told her, as I examined the typical large droppings in her vegetable plot. 'There aren't any rabbits left around here – all wiped out with myxomatosis. Hares are immune to that disease. They love carrots; they will dig down and pull up wild carrots in winter. But as hares and rabbits are surely colour-blind, your pretty rags won't scare them away.'

'Is that so? Never thought about them pests being colour-blind. But I suppose being night creatures it's only nat'ral. Nobody can distinguish colours in the dark, after all. I wonder – is an owl colour-blind? Can a rat see red and yellow?'

I wasn't absolutely sure. Probably rats are colour-blind. But owls are so beautiful that it would be a shame if they saw each other only in dull tones of black, grey and white.

I gave my tenant some wire-netting to place around her vege-table plot.

* * *

191

The epidemic of myxomatosis had opportunely coincided with the Pests Act 1954 becoming law; this made illegal the use of the steel-toothed gin-trap, the main weapon of the professional rabbit-catcher. This barbaric device crushed the legs of every small creature it caught, including rabbits, hares, foxes, badgers, stoats, weasels, hedgehogs, cats and ground-feeding birds of many species. Birds were attracted to the bare earth skilfully spread over the trap placed in a slot in the ground, cut by the trapper's 'paddle', in the runways of rabbits and hares.

Now that myxomatosis had – at that moment – destroyed some 99.5 per cent of the rabbits, and traps had become illegal, the trapper was suddenly deprived of this profitable form of income. Even if he managed to catch by other means the odd immune survivor of the epidemic, it was unsaleable – the public had turned against eating an animal subject to so repulsive a disease. Many of the trappers returned to work on farms familiar to them where, in place of the high profits they had enjoyed while the land suffered low yields of corn and grass from overgrazing by rabbits, the farmer could now afford to pay them good wages as a result of much increased crop and livestock yields.

Many hares had been caught and cruelly maimed in gin-traps set in hedge-gaps and under gates. They had become rare in the west but, free of this vile trap now, and without grazing competition from rabbits, they continued to increase rapidly. This, despite the activity of poachers who, deprived of rabbits, set wire nooses by night where the new generations of hares were running.

It was commonly believed that foxes, stoats and other predators would become hungry, perhaps starve to death with this sudden disappearance of their normal food and would raid more often the farmer's poultry, even kill young lambs. But the truth revealed was very different. Foxes, too, had been heavily reduced in numbers by the gins – the trapper also hunted and poisoned them and gassed the earths of this rival rabbit-catcher. Foxes had actually increased since the gin-trap was banned and were living in equilibrium with their normal prey (as in pre-Norman Britain, before the introduction of the rabbit), feeding principally on rats, mice, voles, beetles, grasshoppers, even worms, and the occasional leveret, as well as on wild fruits, birds and their eggs and, more rarely, an unwary farm chicken.

A fox will now and then surprise and kill a leveret lying in its form, but it is no match for an adult hare. This was demonstrated early one summer morning when, looking down from a gate above a grassy field, I noticed a full-grown fox slinking some fifty paces behind a hare feeding there. The crouching fox progressed by little forward rushes every time the hare lowered its head to graze. But the hare was well aware of the fox, and moved steadily to the open centre of the field, where it turned to face the enemy, sitting upright to get a clear view. The fox thereupon stopped, somewhat closer now, and remained perfectly still, one paw poised, ready to leap forward. For a while they stared at each other, unmoving. Then the fox made another rush towards the hare, which dodged off at right angles, maintaining a safety distance of about thirty metres. The fox tried a circling move-ment; the hare pivoted to face it, accurately keeping a safe dis-tance. Again they stared at each other. After several minutes of this behaviour, the fox trotted away to the cover of the hedge; the hare calmly resumed feeding.

One autumn dawn, looking over the parapet of the roof where I had spent a night under the stars, I was angered to see Jesus coming towards the back door of the manor, carrying a hare by the scruff of its neck; it was kicking fitfully. I ran down the back-stairs in my pyjamas and accosted him.

'Jesus go early to dig Jesus' garden, Don Ronald,' he replied with a scowl. 'Jesus no catch hare, never! Jesus hear hare scream-ing in wire snare. Those gippos been poaching in wood ever since Don Ronald 'ployed them to pick potatoes.'

'But it's still alive!'

'Jesus bring hare for Don Ronald to see. Jesus no catch hare, never! You want Jesus kill hare? Victoria make good jug-jug for Don Ronald?'

I took the hare – a full-grown female, or jill – into the house, removed the wire (which Jesus had already loosened) and wiped the mud and dew from her fur. I set her down on the stone flags of the basement. Her head and neck were swollen from the con-striction of the snare, she was still dazed and unable to walk. But her heart was beating strongly when I squeezed some brandy and glucose down her throat from the fountain pen ink-tube I had once used to revive That Rabbit.

The jill had sufficiently recovered an hour later to start wander-ing around the living room on somewhat wobbly legs. I placed

Jill Hare in temporary quarters in an empty loosebox, where I fed her clover, grain and apples. She rested and 'chewed the cud' (as That Rabbit did during daylight hours), washed herself much and kept her coat spotless. But she remained as unfriendly as Cowper's Tiney and tried to bite me when I offered to stroke her. I could only wear down her belligerence by smoothing her fur with a stick until she was tired of biting it. She was too old to tame by kindness. I would have to release her back to nature as soon as she had quite recovered.

The hare is a solitary animal, but the rabbit is intensely sociable and the opportunity to study their relationship was too good to miss. When Jill Hare began to pace restlessly in her prison, I released her in the one-acre Extensive Enclosure. Here she deliberately avoided the wild rabbits Lone King and Sheba which lived in splendid isolation with abundant food and shelter. Although this hare was female, neither Lone King nor Sheba took any interest in a closer acquaintance during the week of observation we kept upon the trio from the Elm Tree Hide. Of course it was the neutral season, when the testes of male hare and rabbit are regressed, and even if females are receptive then – which is doubtful – the males are impotent and unaggressive territorially, during a period of at least three months' rest, until completion of the annual moult and the acquisition of a new thick winter coat.

Probably every hare is naturally content to be alone most of the year, and with abundant grass and herbage our Jill needed nothing – except complete freedom. This behaviour is in contrast with that of the smaller blue, or mountain, hare which is apparently gregarious at all times. (I have seen blue hares moving in close formation on some northern airports, for instance Belfast, where, attracted by the short rich sward, they are comparatively safe from natural enemies. In such places they become as unperturbed by the roar and wind created by passing aircraft as man is by the traffic in city streets.)

I next placed Jill Hare in the one-acre Intensive Pen, where more than twenty adult rabbits and their progeny were competing for food and living space. She was immediately agitated by this enforced proximity; from the Elm Tree Hide I watched her racing around the boundary, frantically avoiding the rabbits which, however, seemed just as surprised as she was and made no attempt to molest her. She ignored their numerous burrow-entrances; for, although the blue hare will take shelter below ground, the brown hare's only roof is the sky. Like gipsies these hares are Ishmaels; one country legend says that the brown hare was cast out from Paradise because it was forever quarrelling and it has remained solitary and savage towards all living things ever since.

Obviously so many cousin rabbits at close quarters were anathema to Jill Hare. She repeatedly leaped at and bounced back from the tall wire-netting fence, bruising her sensitive nose.

The tests were over. I retrieved her with a handnet. and marked her with a numbered ear-tag, pinning this half-inch metal disc painlessly to the lobe of her left ear close to the head; it carried a black X painted on a white background, easy to identify at long distance through binoculars. I carried her in a box along the woodland path to the American Garden. Setting the box down in the pathway, I pushed the lid partly open and hid behind a tree. Jill presently nosed the lid aside; she raised her head and stared around for a moment. Then with a splendid leap she was away to freedom.

She will come back into our tale later.

*　　*　　*

Jesus had accused local gipsies of poaching. He declared he had seen them skinning a hare during the week I had allowed some of them to camp at Orielton. Like most peasants with their roots at one spot, Jesus cordially distrusted gipsy people. He had experienced the cunning of the roaming Romanies of his native Andalusia – those I had seen in Spain were far more picturesquely attired than our drab Welsh tinkers. Jesus reckoned that all gipsies were deceitful.

'Gippos ver' bad people. Gippo men talk ver' clever, too damn clever all time – and all time gippo women steal behind your back!'

'Nevertheless, Jesus, our Welsh gipsies behave very well. Very honest – they have to be, or they wouldn't be allowed to stay around.'

Itinerant people without permanent jobs are distrusted by most property-owning residents: the citizens of our local towns persecuted and maligned them unceasingly. But because they were a useful source of casual labour in the fields the gipsies were accepted by the farmers.

At the time of harvesting our first early potatoes, which yielded so profitably, I was hard put to find the extra hands necessary to pick and sack the crop. My experienced neighbours had long monopolised the limited labour force of housewives and other townspeople, with one of their number paid as agent to enlist them and organise transport. I was beginning to be desperate, thinking I would miss the high prices of the first potato market.

Then one evening, on my way to Pembroke in search of helpers, I gave a lift to a ragged white-haired tinker, in soiled denims and crimson neckerchief. I was delighted when he enquired if we wanted help with our potatoes. Apparently he had just walked off the field after a disagreement with a local farmer employing both gipsies and housewives.

'Us likes to pick spuds together, me an' me family, sir. Can't abide them townee 'oomen an' their noisy chavvies. Always squabbling they be – puts you off work, ut do. They be poor lot, boss; they'll steal yer sacks an' add 'em to their own tally . . .'

We drove to their encampment hidden in a derelict quarry. The local Council had grudgingly allowed them to occupy it in place of the public common outside the town walls which had been their free camping site for centuries, but had now been enclosed and converted to a citizen's park. He introduced me to his wife Eliza, a lean and weathered figure in a silken shawl, who served tea in a handsomely-appointed caravan. I learned that he had been baptised Elijah, and was the proud father of numerous children, of which I was subsequently to employ – as noted in my wages book – Harriet, Joseph, Sally, Marguerita, Bronwen, George, John, Coral and Dawn; as well as several of his grandchildren, including Miriam, Ellen, Mary Ann, David and Douglas.

'Grandma'll come – she be fast picker, ain't yer, Eliza? But us daresen't leave camp empty. Townee's they be allus prowlin' round – they be terrible thieves. More than once they'm planted stolen goods on us, so us gets black name when gavver (policeman) comes ter inwestigate. Some of us'd be glad ter get away an' camp at Orielton, if thee'd be wantin' us for spell, boss?'

'Well, I'd be very pleased if as many as possible will come tomorrow. We'll see how many potatoes we can get out. I am paying the usual current rate per hundredweight bag.'

'Us never argues about payment, sir. Us knows as thee'll pay us fair, boss.'

A bit too ingratiating, this cunning old gipsy? But already my heart was warming to these people. I was pleasantly surprised at the orderliness of the encampment in the quarry, despite piles of town rubbish, old tyres and rusted fragments of cars dumped by the citizens of Pembroke. Their accommodation was four brightly-painted caravans, one converted coach, and two small trucks; some younger couples were living in tans (tents) of patched up material, but even these mean homes were neat and clean. Cheerful fires were burning in one corner of the quarry where cooking pots on tripods simmered appetisingly. A small girl was playing with a lean fox, which she led by a long chain attached to a thick brass-studded collar. I strolled over to examine the animal.

'Careful, sir, 'er don't like strangers. Found 'er ten years ago, it were, weren't ut, Cariad? Afore yer was born. 'Er were tiny cub by roadside, 'er were. 'Ere, hold tight, little Cariad!' – as the little maiden Cariad (Welsh for sweetheart), shy of men, dropped the chain, which Elijah instantly held down with his foot.

' 'Er's very tame, but yer gotta watch 'er. 'Er's bit of thief, likes ter make way wi' things, 'er'll bury 'em if yer don't watch 'er. Mostly gotta keep 'er tied up, because o' dogs. Them'll tease an' chase 'er, but 'er'll turn on 'em times, nip 'em real hard. Toddy's death on rats, too – faster 'n them lurchers.'

Two whippet hounds were watching Elijah as they lay slouched gracefully outside a tent. The vixen was as thin as a ferret, but otherwise looked healthy, except for her unnatural colour – her fur had a creamy base, streaked with a few black hairs. Elijah said she had been bright red as a cub, but was now white with age.

I had no trouble from the Elijah–Eliza clan; in truth I do not know how I could have harvested that first high-yielding crop of early potatoes without their labour, which I was to employ every year thereafter, both to plant and pick, until they were forced to leave the district by local pressures. In retrospect I remember them as a happy soft-voiced people who worked hard at all times to get their living – by casual labour and by trading: buying and selling anything they could (chiefly old machinery and metal). A few still made baskets and pegs, for which they cut a supply of hazel, willow and other wood during their 'holidays' wayfaring in late summer through the hill districts of mid-Wales. Some of the married women were skilled in clairvoyancy and fortune-telling, an art they made profitable use of when peddling baskets, pegs and tinware.

In camp and at work at Orielton they were orderly. My small sons loved to sneak away from the manor and sit for a while at their evening wood-fire in the open, listening to their lively talk and sampling the 'seconds' or small new potatoes which were unmarketable but so delicious boiled or roasted in their skins. As Elijah was religious, and forbade his clan to utter obscene words, I was perfectly happy with this little adventure.

It may well be that, as Jesus alleged, a hare, pheasant or other tasty wild creature was taken for the pot which produced such a tempting aroma in the evening; but if so the evidence was well disguised in the resulting stew. But I would not have objected to a little mild poaching; poaching was as natural to them as it was to the peasant heart of Jesus, perhaps secretly envious of their free and happy way of life. He was to learn from them that what he called our locust, the splendid great green grasshopper *Tettigonia viridissima*, was a delicious mouthful when roasted. (As it was far from plentiful I had to introduce a close season, until the female had finished laying her eggs in the summer, after which the adults did not survive the winter.)

There was only one unpleasant incident. One morning the merchant who sold our potatoes on commission phoned to ask me to 'make a superhuman effort to load an extra ten tons. The demand and price is very high because of short deliveries. Get cracking first thing tomorrow if you want to make a pile quickly.'

'I doubt I can find more labour at short notice.'

'Your problem, not mine. You'd be a fool not to try. Phone me midday tomorrow and report what tonnage you are likely to lift. I'll have the lorries with you in the afternoon as usual.'

Discussing the problem with a neighbour, he told me that by chance he had no more potatoes to lift that week, and his regular gang of town housewives and others would be glad of one or two days' digging . . . 'I'll phone my lady scout, and tell her to take her gang to you until I'm ready to lift again. They're a tough lot, but good workers if you treat 'em right. Crikey, you're lucky to have spuds ready to lift at today's price!'

The gipsy clan were already at work by the time the housewives and their children arrived. I could see that old Elijah was upset when the ancient bus unloaded some two dozen townees of all ages, but he courteously made no protest. I told Cortez, driving the tractor and spinner, to open a new row at the other end of the field, a hundred yards from the line being worked by the gipsies.

All went reasonably well so long as the two gangs were well separated in the field. The bus collected the house-wives at 4 pm – they had to go home to feed husband and kids and I could see by the huge bulges in their large lunch bags that my potatoes would feature on the menu at home for weeks to come. It is customary that pickers are entitled to take home any small or damaged potatoes lying in the harvested rows which are not up to the standard required by the market. But I was annoyed to see a few unscrupulous town women during the late afternoon surreptitiously thrusting large prime potatoes to fill the lower half of their bags, before topping off with unmarketable 'smalls'. I knew this was a hazard of employing casual labour; these townees would sell the top quality potatoes at a good price, perhaps almost doubling their picking commission that day. But 'treat 'em right' my neighbour had advised me . . .

Next day, as the long rows of potatoes were whirled out by the spinner, the two lines of pickers gradually converged. Small town children (who could not be left alone at home) were always a nuisance in the field: most of these urban brats were noisy and exuberant, having little idea how to amuse themselves in the country. Their mothers encouraged them to pick; but they would put every size of potato in the sacks, and many a stone. Soon, tiring of work, they would start throwing earth and potatoes at each other and, when they were near enough, at the gipsy workers.

Every picker is warned against putting rubbish in the sacks which reduces the value of the produce and even causes its rejection on reaching the sale-room. Each picker is paid according to the number of sacks filled; if stones or too many 'smalls' are detected when the sack comes to the weighbridge in the field, the rule is that the picker shall not be paid for that sack unless it has been emptied on the ground and refilled with potatoes of marketable quality.

After noon on the second day, when the two lines of pickers were only a dozen rows apart, matters came to a head. The gipsies suddenly stopped picking and began to gather together the sacks they had filled. Old Elijah slouched up to me and said, apologetically:

'Us'll be leavin' now, boss, soon's us 'as tallied sacks.'

'But please, you must stop to clear these last rows. You're doing so much better than the town ladies, and all clean sound spuds in your sacks.'

Elijah scratched his head thoughtfully, as if he would find an excuse hiding in his white locks. 'Aye, boss, us be leavin' thee, us gotta be 'ome early today. Them women can finish for thee.'

'Not without your help,' I insisted. I shouted across the green haulms of the rows at a couple of town children who had upset an open sack of potatoes and were pelting each other with them: 'Stop that at once, you little devils!'

Elijah was too polite to display his rage, not only at the behaviour of the town children but – I felt – at mine too, in employing their mothers. He cast around for soft words of prevarication as his clan continued to top up and bring their sacks to be weighed, but without picking the row spun out on their side of the crop. 'Aye, boss, us gotta leave early. An' I doubt us'll be able to come tomorrer,' he said mildly. 'But us ain't in no 'urry for money. Us knows thee'll let us 'ave what us's earned by number o' sacks. Mabbe us'll call for cash tomorrer – or thee can drop ut by me old caravan in th'quarry?'

'Elijah! You're worried by those townees and their awful brats!'

'Aye, boss, thee never told us they'd be comin' yesterday, nor today neither. Eliza an' me, us vowed us'd never work again in same field 'longside them sleevers an' their chavvies. Us likes workin' for thee. 'Tidden that. But . . .' he paused, gazing resentfully at the busy backsides of the town women drawing nearer, 'but, look – look at that, boss!'

'Look at what? I'm sorry I had to employ these people from the town, but it was a big rush order from my merchant. We couldn't get it done without the townee's help . . .'

'Thee should've asked us. Us'd 'ave brought thee more 'ands, rather than us'd 'ave that lot in field. Cor, look at that! Ugh!'

With a look of deep disgust Elijah turned his back upon the sight of the town gang still busy picking potatoes on the far side of the unharvested strip. I looked at the row of two dozen large amorphous female figures bending double, bottoms up, burrowing diligently after the smooth Arran Pilot potatoes as the mechanical spinner lifted and flung them in a pattern on the sun-warmed sandstone earth. At the far end of the row one stout lady was facing us, hoping or perhaps not caring to escape notice, as she squatted to relieve herself, her skirts thrown over the back of her head. Surely this natural occasion couldn't be bothering Elijah? He was looking away at that moment.

'Come on, Elijah, you can't leave me in the lurch like this. What's really bothering you?'

He hesitated again; then in his quiet, almost gentlemanly voice, he answered: 'Us just can't stand sight o' all them huge gorgio bums coming closer an' closer all day! Somehow . . . somehow ut be indecent, boss!'

It was an excuse I was obliged to laugh at, but Elijah was perfectly serious. At least, his face was unsmiling. I had been much too preoccupied with the speedy harvesting of the crop to pay attention to matronly attitudes at work. But looking again at the ragged but lean, graceful forms of the gipsy gang (one rarely or never saw a fat gipsy), it was quite a shock to compare them with the Gauguinesque bending backsides, bulging calves and massive ankles of the majority of these stout townee matrons, and I had to admit to myself that the latter were aesthetically unpleasing by contrast.

But I, too, was dissatisfied with the general behaviour of the townee gang.

'Hold on, Elijah, please. I'd far rather you stayed, and the townees left.'

I walked across the potato ridges to interview, as diplomatically as possible, the townee scout.

'Missus, it looks like rain (a fib). We'll stop now. You've done marvellously, we've got all the tonnage we need out of this field (another fib). By the time you've topped up your sacks and we've tallied them, your bus can have arrived. Go and phone for it at the Lodge by the gate. Oh, by the way, please make sure your good ladies take home only as many 'smalls' as they care to carry. All marketable potatoes *must* be returned to the sacks to make up our load. I don't want to embarrass the odd light-fingered member of your gang by examining their lunch bags, but you may have noticed one or two ladies carried home yesterday a few hundred-weights of big spuds between them? And that of course, is thieving – a notifiable offence. I'm sure you'll understand . . .'

I was quite sure the scout, a pleasant woman, helpful to work with, had never stolen a single marketable potato; but loyally she resented my accusation on behalf of those of her gang who had. She was on the point, I felt, of arguing that I was mistaken when, by an extraordinary coincidence, the local policeman, spruce in his uniform, appeared. Looking darkly at me, the lady scout shouted to her gang to finish work and hurried off to phone for their bus.

There was no need for a warning not to steal potatoes. Under the bland gaze of the constable, the townee women topped off their sacks properly, and put only unsaleable 'smalls' in their lunch bags.

Returning from the telephone, the lady scout announced loudly and angrily, in front of the gipsies, the policeman and the gathering women of her gang: 'We ain't coming back to Orielton, not ever! Spying on us with the police, indeed! Hand over our money and we'll be off!'

The constable raised his eyebrows and looked at me for an explanation, which I tried to give – to pacify the outraged scout, as Jesus paid each woman according to her tally of sacks – the usual procedure at the end of each day's harvesting. The scout heard my explanation but failed to convey it to her women – I felt in any case that they were in no mood to listen.

It seemed that the policeman had come to interview an older female of the Elijah clan. But he could not find her present in the field, nor did I feel it necessary to inform him that I had seen the gipsy woman concerned slip into the surrounding woodland as soon as he had appeared.

'I'm in no hurry, Elijah,' he said politely, as the townees departed. 'It can wait. Don't let me disturb you helping Mr Lockley finish the field. I know how urgent the weighing up is – to be ready when the lorries arrive. I'm a farmer's son myself. It's just that I have to ask your cousin Rebecca if she has any knowledge of how a box of silver cutlery, lost a few days ago, has been found under her caravan in the quarry this morning.'

The constable cycled away to his country home. Elijah and company finished off the field just as the merchant's lorries arrived. With great good will, twenty tons of sacked earlies were hoisted up and lashed down, and fetched some £1,000 on the Midland market next morning.

I gave each gipsy picker, including the female cousin (who now reappeared), a small bonus above their tally earnings. Elijah whispered to me that cousin Rebecca was the object of a vendetta – over some complicated fortune-telling incident – and some urban enemies were trying to plant stolen goods on her. The 'gavver' had not found her at home in the quarry, but one gipsy who saw the police poking around there had slipped away to Orielton to warn her to be on the alert.

The finer details of the persecution they suffered Elijah confided to me a little later, as we stood alone in the field, discussing tomorrow's plans.

'O' course, us be used ter this 'ere plant' o' stolen goods – common trick ter make us tinkers unpopular – an' police know ut by now. Rebecca's straight as th' Lord. Wudden' never steal nothin' from single soul. She's got plenty 'erself. She's rich. 'Er Romany mother left 'er jewels and gold. Got real gold ear-rings an' bangles, an' real silver cutlery o' 'er own. She fine 'ooman, cousin Beckie, real Romany blood in 'er. She rommered (married) me young half-brother. That's 'ow she came to live wi' us. Us be only posh-rats (tinkers), not real Romanies. She can dukker (tell fortunes) proper – straight out truth with 'er, an' sometimes truth in crystal ball don't suit them townees with nasty minds, 'specially when they'm paid Beckie 'er fee an' 'spectin' good forecast. Ah, poor Beckie! More than twenty year ago ut were, 'er husband were taken by p'lice for crime 'e never done. 'E were 'rested an' locked up for murder of young 'ooman – in North Wales ut were. O' course 'e never done ut, an' 'e an' Beckie only just 'appily married. 'E pined away in prison, couldn' live wi'out 'is darlin' Beckie. 'E was gentlest young man thee ever saw – just as sweet an' pure as Beckie. But real murderer, 'e planted girl's skirt, with 'er blood on ut, under Beckie's caravan, an' tipped off them gavvers anonymus-like on phone. O' course they never could prove 'e did murder, and in th' end p'lice 'ad ter release me brother. But th' shame, th' accusation, th' injustice – why ut killed 'im later. 'E was forced ter report ter p'lice, once a month, an' whenever 'e moved camp. Beckie's never forgiven p'lice, she won't never speak to them gavvers any more.'

'Ah,' I said, moved by the tale. 'It seemed to me the constable today had no heart in his task. He's a good understanding fellow – as I find him – our local gaffer. Only carrying out orders. . . .'

'Aye, I daresay. But mud sticks. Us moved from North Wales to south to forget th' injustice ter me brother. But them gavvers

'ere knows all about th' case; an' me, I'm only tellin' thee the
truth, case likely they 'ave warned thee about ut.'

'Certainly not, Elijah – not a word have I heard. Poor Beckie –
what a shame! She seems such a fine, innocent woman, carries
herself beautifully. That was her son working alongside her all
day?'

'Aye, all 'er's got left of 'er marriage, poor Beckie.'

'Well, good night, Elijah. I'm deeply grateful for your help
today. Please bring all your wonderful tribe tomorrow. I'm starting a new field. It looks fine for the rest of the week. I can promise
you I've finished forever with those gorgio backsides!'

'Us'll be there, us will,' Elijah nodded his hoary head.

*   *   *

In the year after her release I caught a few glimpses of ear-tagged Jill Hare. Plotting her positions on the map I found she moved over a definitive feeding zone within a range of about one square mile, covering the estate and farm land, invariably alone. She visited the harvested potato ground and ate some of the rejected 'smalls' lying on the surface, while they were fresh and not yet distastefully greened by the sun. As soon as the catch-crop of Italian ryegrass was sown and peeping there, I found her outsize pellets where she had eaten the succulent spears. She nibbled here and there, selecting and browsing on favourite plants rather than grazing omnivorously as the rabbit does. I saw her less often in winter, for she was almost strictly nocturnal at that season and seemed to prefer the shelter of the leafless woods.

In the spring she haunted Sink Fence Meadow, where I knew of two separate forms she used, in low clumps of winter-withered grass. I had not seen another hare with her until, one early March day, I spotted three hares together in the sedge at the bottom of the meadow. One was our Jill; the others were evidently jack hares. All three cavorted in a crazy dance, standing on the tips of their hind legs and boxing with forepaws in a ludicrous manner, seldom striking each other, and then tumbling and crouching instead, twitching their hindquarters as they prepared for the next antic. Between bouts of boxing the jacks chased Jill. She dodged them, never running away, but turning in a circle around them. The grass became quite trampled, in two or three mornings' madness.

This behaviour is typical of the so-called mad March hare meetings – the only time the sexes consort together. In the promiscuous hare, ovulation is hastened by this mad courtship, and copulation is necessary to stimulate the ripening and descent of the ova through the oviduct, some days before fertilisation. In the stay-at-home monogamous rabbit, however, breeding more often and with larger litters, the doe, immediately on coming on heat, achieves a fertile mating with her buck the same day.

The doe accepts her uxorious mate for a few hours only, but during the pregnancy of four weeks the rabbit pair maintain the sexual bond between them by mating at approximately seven-day intervals, including shortly after parturition, when the doe ovulates fully again, and is ready to conceive the next litter. One might compare them with a staid, sexually satisfied and comfortably housed, human couple.

In the breeding cycle of the homeless hare we see admirable adaptation to the wandering life: living solitary for most of the year, the female accepts the male for only a brief period of oestrus and stores the sperm after copulation, in advance of the ovum's ripeness to be fertilised. In effect this is nature's insurance against the absence of a potent male at the critical moment when the egg descends the oviduct and is ready to be penetrated by the sperm.

There is still some mystery about conception and gestation in the hare. It has lately been discovered that some jills will conceive a second litter, which begins to develop before the first litter is born (a phenomenon which also occurs in some marsupials). In these instances, known as superfoetation, a jill hare might litter more frequently than the female rabbit does (at monthly intervals). The mystery deepens if it is true that the jacks only seek the jills in those mad spring junketings, and do not co-habit again. More research is necessary to find out how long the jill can store viable sperm, or delay implantation of the blastocyst (as in seals and some mustelids).

The adaptation of the hare to a life of lone wandering begins early. Already, born at the end of six weeks' pregnancy, the leveret, in comparison with the baby rabbit (which at birth is blind, naked and helpless, in an underground nursery), is twice as large, eyes open and fully furred. It is able to run within a few hours and graze immediately. After two weeks at most it is independent of the jill, whose milk quickly dries up as her metabolism is geared once more to the demands of the next batch of embryos already developing in her womb.

While the rabbit conceives up to twelve in one litter, the hare seldom exceeds four or five, usually four, at one birth. But the period between conception, and weaning of the resultant young, is about the same in both. The shorter gestation period of one month in the doe is balanced by longer suckling of her kittens, to make a total maternity period of seven weeks in both.

Both animals exercise the same form of birth control. During pregnancy, if external conditions are harsh, such as in cold weather or drought affecting the quality of the food supply, the jill and the doe will reabsorb some, or all, of the embryos, without abortion.

This reabsorption is quite rapid: the foetus dies and dissolves totally, carried away into the blood stream of the mother within a few days, and usually before half term of the pregnancy has expired. A fresh mating takes place immediately the last embryo is reabsorbed, when the jill or doe ovulates again. But if food and living space are abundant full litters are born – to thrive upon the plentiful grazing and browsing. Thus by a conveniently neat internal process the number of young born is regulated to the capacity of their environment to feed them.

In May I searched Sink Fence Meadow for the leverets which had been born of the March madness. Usually the jill deposits each (sometimes two together) in a separate form in the grass, many yards apart; thus reducing the risk of losing the whole litter to a predator. Baby hares are not easy to find: they lie still all day in a form, half-hidden by the long summer grasses. Normally our Jill Hare herself was invisible, likewise crouched all day in her form. But when cattle or sheep were grazing in the field she would sometimes boldly stand up and feed close to them, as if aware that her small outline would be overlooked in the presence of larger animals. However long I watched her through the binoculars, she would not visit her leverets during the day. But I flushed them out by dragging the field with a rope stretched between two observers walking some fifty yards apart.

When handled the mature female has a strong, not unpleasant, musky smell; but according to my gipsy friends both the jill and the leveret are able to suppress their body scent when danger threatens, as they crouch immobile in the grass. 'Jill an' lev'rets, they shuts their fur down tight,' declared old Elijah, 'so even a fox, or a whippet, can't smell 'em. But a jack hare 'e'll run away, 'is smell is allus strong, an' 'e knows nothin' can't never catch 'im once 'e gets goin'. Unless 'e be old an' sick; or unless 'e's been put in bag an' set free in front o' batch of grey 'ounds or whippets; that's coursin' – I don't 'old wi'ut – its wicked cruel. Th' 'are ain't got chance, taken from th' bag all dazey an' tremblin', an' chased all directions by dogs rested an' mad fresh fr' exercise. Terrible cruel, is that.'

How long may a hare or a rabbit live? Not long; a high reproductive capacity in any animal must be matched by a correspondingly high mortality rate, if numbers are to remain relatively constant, as they do in nature. Our ear-tagged Jill Hare vanished after one successful summer helping to repopulate the estate with her kind. She was two years old when last recorded by us.

But individuals have lived much longer, under sheltered, unnatural conditions. 'Puss,' wrote William Cowper, 'is still living, and has just completed his tenth year, discovering no sign of decay, nor even of age, except that he has grown more discreet and less frolicsome.' On the death of Tiney earlier, Cowper had written his well-known *Epitaph to a Hare*. 'Old Tiney, surliest of his kind' had lived 'eight years and five rolling moons . . .'

> But now beneath his walnut shade
> He finds his long last home,
> And waits, in snug concealment laid,
> Till gentler Puss shall come.

Puss lingered on, but at last, on 9 March 1786, Cowper wrote: 'This day died Puss, aged eleven years eleven months. He died between twelve and one at noon, of mere old age, and apparently without pain.' And he added a commemorative postscript in Latin, entitled *Epitaphium Alterum*, to his funeral oration on the death of Tiney.

* * *

In succeeding seasons of planting and harvesting early potatoes, which became a regular and normally profitable part of our farming routine, fitting in well with Jersey milk production, I came to know Elijah and his wife better, and to admire them. At first his lean seamy-faced woman had been taciturn in my presence. But there were some days in the field when her rheumatism troubled Eliza sorely, and she would retreat to the warmth of the cab of my farm van. I would find her there sucking her black pipe and knitting some small garment for her youngest grandchild. She would apologise for occupying the passenger seat, and offer to leave.

Gradually she became relaxed and talkative in her broad dialect, expounding her considerable gipsy lore of the countryside.

She would politely refuse the refreshments of hot tea or cold lemonade and scones when these were brought to the field, as was customary on any cold February day of planting, or warm May or June afternoon of harvesting. She preferred to drink 'mookeri-mungeri', as she called it. She would swiftly and skilfully whip up a hot fire with 'keeks and crannocks' (twigs and sticks), on which she would put her black gallon kettle. When the water boiled she would throw in a concoction of tea and sugar with some wild herb for flavour (herb robert usually). She and Elijah and most of her tribe drank this black brew strong and without milk and seldom ate anything during the day. She had a passion for eggs, however, and would ask for new-laid ones, which she would boil in the kettle along with the tea.

One morning when I told her that a fine fat hedgehog had been drowned by falling into the ornamental pool in front of the manor overnight and failing to climb out over the smooth concrete sill, she offered to 'trolly' (cook) it for me; or if I did not want it, she'd be glad of it herself.

'Tidden often us gets urchin these days. Too many killed off on they roads by them cars. Us'll want some clay – see'd some in next field, been old brick pit there?'

Her sharp eyes had noted the rough ground, with red clay exposed, from which many years ago the bricks which lined the inside of the wall around Alf Hitchcox's four-acre market garden had been made; clay I had used to stop up leaks in the Lily Pond dam, itself built of the same Orielton clay.

I brought her the limp corpse and half a bucket of wet clay. She tested the hedgehog's weight in her naked hands, careless of prickles and, satisfied it was worth cooking, rolled it into a ball and plastered it with clay.

'When I were young gal, us ate urchins reg'lar. Nowsaday them prickly ones be scarce. Us be terrible fond o' urchin meat, it be sweet smellin' an' 'ealthy – must be fresh-baked an' 'ot when yer eats urchin. Real delicacy, is urchin.'

She began building a wood-fire in a depression in the ground.

'Old brock (badger) 'ull tear open urchins with's terrible powerful claws. But old toddy (fox), 'is paws be too tender. So, what does toddy do? 'E stands over an' pees on th'urchin, so's ut'll open pretty smart wi' that big stink troublin' ut. Then toddy, 'e darts in an' rips th'urchin belly open. Aye, I seen old toddy with me own eyes doin' ut; but yer cudden' eat hedgepig once fox's made water on't. Nor no other beast 'll touch it so. Stinkin' crittur, male toddy be, but our liddle vixen, she be sweet. I baths 'er every day, an' she loves th' water.'

Eliza plastered more wet clay on the dumpling which contained the hedgehog and presently inserted it beneath the red-hot ashes of the fire, heaping more wood above it.

'Them hedgepigs, as yer calls 'em, they'll suck cows o' dark nights. As a gal me and me brother, us'd look for urchins by goin' thru' 'erd of cows lyin' down 'o nights. 'Tis said th'urchins be lookin' for wormses an' beetles comin' to surface wi' th'weight o' th' cows lyin' heavy. O' course urchins eats wormses and beetles, but I seen 'em wi' my own eyes suppin' milk spurtin' from cow's udder, like ut do when she'm sore heavy wi' milk – an' she pleased ter let th'urchin drink then.'

She had often eaten badger. A fat badger ham was delicious. As a girl she had once eaten roast rat, done up in clay by her brother as a joke and presented to her as tender young urchin meat. 'Ut were different, ut were very tasty, but I were sick after when th' liddle devil told me what ut were! I paid 'im for ut, though! I slipped rat's tail in 'is stew next day! "Let 'im 'ave taste for 'isself!" I says to meself. I never said nothin' ter 'im, nor did 'e dare t'admit enjoyin' rats-tail stew! It cured 'im of 'is dirty tricks.'

Eliza raked the urchin dumpling out of the hot ashes in the noonday break from work, three hours later. She broke it open. The prickles, dead fleas and fur came away neatly with the clay, revealing the perfectly cooked carcase, which gave out an appetising aroma. She split it lengthwise with her sheath-knife and offered me half. When I politely declined, Elijah ate it with relish.

The sight of the diminutive roast body banished all curiosity I had to taste its flesh. I had kept too many hedgehogs as pets ever to enjoy eating one.

'Did yer ever see th'urchin kill pois'n snake, boss?' asked Elijah, smacking and wiping his lips appreciatively as the last tender morsel vanished down his throat. 'Us thort ut good sport when us was foolish cruts (boys) if us caught viper – they be common enough on th'moors in summertime – to save ut to try out on th'edgepig.'

Two snakes are common in Wales. I had kept both as pets when I was a boy. The adder or viper, whose bite is fatal to small creatures, haunts open country and sunny slopes. So far I had never found one within the walls of the lush tree-embowered Orielton estate, but the larger grass-snake, harmless to man, was frequently to be seen – a lover of shelter and the proximity of water, where it swam and hunted small fish, shrews and frogs – and one fine female regularly deposited her eggs in Alf Hitchcox's large compost heap. You could find her sunning herself on a summer day close by, if you trod softly. Snakes have poor or no hearing, but are highly sensitive to the vibration of a footfall; they hunt by sight, and above all by their keen sense of smell (the darting forked tongue 'tastes' molecules of scent in the air) which enables them to track down their prey, or warns them to flee from their enemies. A few snakes have developed a sense of temperature in a pair of pit-like organs located between the eyes and the mouth; radiant waves or infra-red warmth from a short distance, given out by a live mouse, lizard or other creature, are received by a drum-like membrane in each pit, enabling the snake to locate prey accurately even in darkness.

Having explained to me how to catch a snake, by holding it down first with a forked stick and then picking it up by the neck – as I had often done in the past – Elijah continued: 'In me young days me dad was fond o' cockfightin', many tussles to death 'tween gamecocks 'ave I watched wi' 'im. When us'd caught a viper us'd 'ood make bit o' cockpit, smaller o' course, but so's snake couldn' escape. 'Twood be mortal 'fraid o' th'urchin soon as us'd drop 'er in pit. Us'd 'ave to keep viper lively an' battlesome with stick. Soon as th'urchin spotted snake movin' she'd go sniffin' cautious-like towards 'em. 'O course 'er'd be mighty 'ungry – us allus starved th' 'edgepig for a day afore snake fight. Soon as she knew she 'ad snake in front o' 'er, 'er 'ead'd go down an' 'er prickles shoot up like cock's 'ackles. Put up guard, us called ut. Then she'd creep up very slow, and make sudden lightnin' grab at snake – no matter what part o' 'is coils. Never 'is 'ead, for 'e'd draw 'is 'ead back ready ter strike. An' strike 'e did, but she'd never let go, she'd crunch an' munch while 'e was slammin' 'is jaws an' pois'n fangs 'gainst 'er spines, an' they stickin' straight out. But 'e couldn' never get 'is fangs into 'er flesh. Th'urchin jest goes on chewin' an' eatin' hadder or viper alive. I seen 'er eat two-foot snake, pois'n fangs an' all, in less than 'alf a day.'

'Aye, but I mind th' day,' said Eliza, 'when me wicked young brother put 'alf-grown urchin in viper pit. Poor liddle 'edgepig, 'er didn't know 'ow ter tackle big viper. So 'er got stung on snout proper, and 'er died in n'our or two. Me old dad were wicked cross; 'e lamblasted wicked liddle crut proper . . .'

'An' Eliza's dad 'e were gentle soul, I'll say that, not like me cockfightin', 'are-coursin' dad. Mind you, th'urchin don't allus win. Now an' then viper'll get 'er fangs into 'er face, what's 'er only vulnurr'ble spot. But if 'tis big strong urchin, 'er'll sicken for few days, then'll gradual get over pois'n. Very 'ard to kill is th'urchin. 'Er'll eat all sorts o' pois'n berries: f 'rinstance – harum (arum) an' nightshade an' the like! 'Er'll eat young frogs and toads, but I never seed 'er tackle a full grown toad – nasty pois'ns slime on old toad's skin. One evenin' when I were rabbutin' in North Wales I seed strange sight, goin' round traps: big fat hadder were wrigglin' away from urchin, 'er were 'bout yard behind snake, trottin' 'ard ter keep up with 'im. Them snakes can travel mighty fast when them is scared! That snake streaked 'long rabbut run, an' snap! 'E were caught in one of me gins. I just stood, watchin' what would 'appen. The clap o' trap made th'urchin jump in th'air, but 'er kept comin', cautious-like now, watchin' th'adder wrigglin' in gin. 'E were caught tight by middle, an' pres'nly th'urchin made 'er usual dart an' grab, an' begun eatin' 'im tail first. Me, I didn't 'ave all that time to spare watchin' any longer. I killed 'em both. 'E weren't hadder after all. 'Er were viper, 'er belly full o' live young.'

So much for some of the many tales my old tinker couple told me about the small animals of the woods and fields. They preferred to call the male the adder and his mate the viper. They believed that the viper opened her mouth wide and took her new-born young back into her belly if danger threatened the family; a fable arising from the fact that this snake is ovi-viviparous, that is, hatches its eggs within its body, whereas the grass snake deposits its eggs in a natural incubator such as a compost heap. Both guard their young only for a limited period after they are born.

The strange habit which hedgehogs indulge in, of licking and covering their spines with saliva (produced copiously during the chewing of food), which I had seen in my tame hedgehogs, was explained by Eliza as the urchin's attempt to smother to death the great numbers of blood-sucking fleas which live under the forest of prickles. It must be irritating not to be able to get at the fleas with tooth or claw. But, of course, the saliva has no visible lethal effect on the parasites, although Eliza considered it was antiseptic (many country people believe that animal saliva, sweat and urine have healing properties when applied to wounds). It is possible that the habit of smearing saliva over as much of the coat of spines as the tongue can reach procures for the hedgehog an agreeable cooling sensation as the liquid evaporates on a warm day.

In our mild corner of Wales hedgehogs are not numerous. Eliza thought that this was because there were too many brocks tearing them open (I had never seen any evidence of this habit, by the way). Perhaps their comparative scarcity at Orielton may have been due also to their inability to hibernate during most, if not all, of our mild winter. On any temperate midwinter night, and sometimes by day, you might encounter a hedgehog hungrily seeking worms and insects which are in short supply at that season, so that it had to seek for sustenance for a longer period than in the summer, if it was not to starve to death. Sleeping (but not hibernating) in cold spells, then foraging in mild weather with meagre results, must be far more exhausting than the complete deep sleep of hibernation which hedgehogs undergo in countries with severe winter cold – as in northern and continental Europe.

When the ground temperature drops below 10°C the hedgehog becomes sluggish and remains in the snug nest of leaves and dead vegetation it has built or burrowed into, usually in a dry spot above ground. Here it maintains its normal body temperature of approximately 36°C (slightly higher in summer). Despite the absence of warm fur beneath its covering of spines it is generally insulated from cold by a layer of subcutaneous fat built up in heavy feeding in late summer. The young hedgehogs born late in summer are the first to die; they have failed to put on enough fat in the autumn to last them over the privations of winter.

True hibernation only occurs where the ground temperature remains below 10°C for several months. The hedgehog rolls up into a tight ball, and as the outside temperature drops, that of the hedgehog's body also falls, until it reaches a critical point at about 7°C. Some internal switch now operates (no one knows what this is) to prevent the body from freezing; no matter how low the ground temperature falls below zero, the temperature of the hibernating hedgehog remains static at between 1.30°C and 6°C (Konrad Herter).

The hedgehogs which from time to time my sons and I kept would sleep through the day. They would wake up hungry for their evening feed of milk and house-scraps. It amused us to watch one find food out of doors on a fine evening. Waddling along with a rolling gait, its hind legs lifting it well up in the rear, tilting its nose down to ground level, it snuffled noisily from side to side, hunting almost entirely by scent. It would detect the smell of a bacon rind thrown a couple of feet to one side. Although its hearing is said to be acute, it took little notice of the crackling of dead twigs as we followed it over the grass and through the shrubbery. Its sight is relatively weak, and hardly much adapted to seeing far in the twilight. Having located a worm, beetle or other food it would pounce and eat greedily, with smacking noises, holding the food down with its forepaws. It would devour carrion we put in its path, such as a small dead fish, rabbit guts, or half a rat.

Tested with eggs, it pushed around those of hen, pheasant and duck, but failing to get an edge to bite upon, it soon gave up; but there is no doubt that the hedgehog will eat the eggs and young of small ground-nesting birds which it may scent out. On encountering a half-dried cowpat our tame individual would work with nose and paws to dig out and devour any beetles or larvae it could uncover.

Hedgehogs quickly become tame and will show little real fear of house cat or dog, soon sharing the same drinking bowl, only shrinking and erecting its spines if the dog barks. Sudden loud noises of any kind cause this brief reaction. A half-grown hedgehog I kept as a boy would respond to its name Prickles when I called, knowing that I never called it unless I had some food to give. It slept by day in a nest of dry grass in a box in the garden, where it did good work devouring snails, slugs, woodlice, beetles, earwigs, millipedes, nests of young voles, and other animals undesirable to the gardener. Despite a popular belief that the hedgehog dislikes deep water, Prickles regularly swam and waded across a small brook.

The mating of hedgehogs has seldom been witnessed. H. Stieve has disproved a popular belief that the female lies on her back in order not to inconvenience the male with her dorsal coat of sharp spines. She lays these flat as she elevates her hindquarters to present her genital region, which is free of spines; the male organ is located well forward (as in pigs, cattle and sheep) and disproportionately long; copulation takes place in the usual quadruped position, and lasts about two minutes. After ejaculation the sperm is sealed within the vagina by a plug of hardened mucus secreted by the glands of the male reproductive system – as in some bats. Yet another safety device, ensuring conception in a normally solitary animal; after mating, the boar takes no further interest in family affairs.

Up to ten, usually seven, young are born about thirty-eight days later; they are blind, deaf and pink-naked, with tiny soft spines which are invaginated (and so cannot scratch the mother) during parturition. These natal spines are shed at about one month and replaced with the sharp, pigmented adult spines. The sow is an excellent guardian, remaining in the nest with the new-born for a day or so, keeping them warm and cleaning them. If disturbed, she will remove them one by one to a fresh hiding place. The youngster is not able to roll up into a ball until it is about one month old, at which age it starts walking out with mother.

The hedgehog is comically porcine in behaviour: the piglets squabble for the teats at milking time, and at all times are noisy, competing gustily for any insects, worms, slugs and grubs found by mother, or siblings. The sow fossicks ahead of her brood, snuffling as she finds and devours or shares food. If a youngster, earnestly foraging on its own, strays too far, it utters a squeal of alarm at finding itself alone; the sow at once rushes to the rescue and leads it back to the family crocodile, and on they trundle. As long as her milk flows – for a period of about forty days, at the end of which she may be pregnant again – the sow guards her brood zealously.

The young urchins gradually disperse, and wander alone farther than they ever will later in life, perhaps for several miles. Many young hedgehogs are killed on the roads during this autumn exploration; those which survive settle down to winter quarters, and remain thereafter sedentary within a feeding zone of about half a mile around their established nest.

Eliza's animal lore included the ancient belief that the hedgehog gathers fruit as well as nesting material on its spines. It is easy to understand how this legend arose, for I have seen a hedgehog emerge from its nest of dead vegetation with some leaves accidentally impaled on the dorsal spines. But all nesting material or food is gathered in the mouth. No food is ever stored for the winter – except in the form of body fat.

IO

In her first summer, once the dew had evaporated, That Rabbit would be put out to graze in her wire-netted pen, moved daily to a fresh plot of grass on the lawn, as already related. I had long explained to her, in those intimate private talks we enjoyed, that I could not entirely trust her not to nibble the petunias, zinnias or dahlias, or other exotic flowers in the beds against the house-walls, which the outdoor-loving Jesus and my secretary (when I had one – she was usually a temporary help) tended with care, more ashamed of the shabbiness of the garden than I was. TR had accepted this routine amicably, and would graze hungrily for an hour.

When I placed her in this solitary confinement for the first time, I pitched the pen upon this ancient sward of red and white clover, yellow corniculatus, eyebright, centaury and green grasses. The bumblebees were annoyed, but TR sniffed appreciatively at this bouquet of many colours. She explored the wooden wall of her new prison briefly and, finding no way to escape, began grazing voraciously.

I accepted this action as her gesture of dismissal. At tea time I found her stretched out, breathing heavily, her snowy belly bloated with clover. She had overeaten and was suffering the consequences.

Subsequently she grazed more frugally; in fact her appetite for green food was small, once I had added the corrective of a dish of cereals – porridge oats, cornflakes, poultry wheat – to her diet. But one day she would have to return to the wild, and in preparation I must gradually reduce this artificial feeding. In nature the wild rabbit living free is able to nibble a variety of herbs as medicine, to balance its diet.

TR was mostly a delight, but at times she could be a worry, as when I had to go away for a few days to some conference or on other business; and with my sons in school, I feared that she would be both upset and not looked after properly by those left at home. I had given up an earlier plan to dispose of her by placing her in the study enclosures with the confined populations of rabbits. Not only would she be a disturbing new factor, resented and harried by the established inmates, but my sons had once more forbidden me 'to be so cruel', after we had watched her behaviour there one afternoon. Experimentally released into the Intensive Enclosure, TR had made a rapid circuit of this heavily grazed pasture (which she had gazed at so often with apparent longing during our walks outside) sniffing at dunghills momentarily; then suddenly, as if in panic at this considerably olfactory evidence of a vast, hidden (all the inmates had retired into their burrows on our arrival, as usual), overcrowded and perhaps sinister city of her species, she had fled to our feet, and leaped through the door to freedom.

'All right, TR, all right!' I took her in my arms to comfort her. No need ever to identify her with a numbered ear-tag. The two pellet holes from the cartridge which had killed Madame Goateyes were still plain in her left ear, though the wound had healed long ago.

There was a daily ritual of releasing her to enjoy tea with us on the lawn – if fine. She still liked her tea weak, with sugar and a little of the rich Jersey milk. She would caper around for a moment, happy to have space in which to frisk her limbs. When she wandered up to the edge of the flowerbeds I would call out a sharp NO. She understood, and obeyed, with drooping ears.

Twice a strange cat was found crouched upon the netted top

of TR's grazing pen, glaring at the alarmed rabbit huddled under the wooden lid which made one corner rainproof. She was breathing heavily, stamping her hind feet to warn us of her peril. Visitors with dogs were not infrequent; our friends knew they must keep them under control, nor was TR much afraid of those canines she had met before. Like Cowper's hare, when approached in our presence (which seemed to give her added courage), by a dog (or cat) which she knew, she would strike at it with her forepaws if it came too close, causing it to beat an unceremonious retreat. But a strange cat sitting on top of her cage was a different matter, although now that she was full-grown I felt sure she would have faced it courageously, had it tackled her in the open, and boxed it away. In the enclosures I had seen a mother rabbit boldly attack and put to flight a cat attempting to stalk one of her weanlings outside her nursery burrow.

Most fine afternoons after tea when I was free to do so, I would stroll along the outside of the rabbit enclosures and down to the Lily Pond, or wander up to the American Garden, and TR would follow eagerly, or lead ahead like a dog. I enjoyed these peaceful perambulations in her company, prepared to identify and record a fresh bird, wild flower, butterfly or other phenological event.

One evening TR kept unusually close to my heels, and was almost embarrassingly affectionate, thrice demanding that I take her into my arms on some slight alarm of a bird's shadow, the squawk of a heron or the crack of a dead twig. This she did by attracting my attention, by mewing her feeble 'Please!' or by a loud thump with her feet – and a leap towards my arms.

After lunch next day, which was wet, when I called her to leave the cat basket where she normally slept all morning, crouched under the blanket, she was missing. When at last I found her, hiding in a corner of the study, she resisted my attempts to pick her up. At first I thought it was just playful behaviour, but in fact she was distraught. She kicked and struggled when I cornered her. When I dropped her into her grazing pen and fastened the wooden lid, she immediately clawed at the wire roof and double-stamped as I walked away.

This new behaviour was a little puzzling but not unnatural, I thought: evidently she was growing more wilful with maturity. She was taking advantage of my fondness for her, to get her own way. Soon I would have to set her free altogether. I looked forward to that day with some misgiving – I should miss her sorely – and a certain amount of scientific curiosity.

'Calm down, TR,' I called out. 'What's bitten you? You've never been afraid of a drop of rain and anyway, it's stopped, and looks as if the sun is coming out. See you later. Just now I've a lot of work to do. We'll have a stroll together after tea.'

But again she clawed at the netting and thumped her emphatic warning with her hind feet, that she was angry and upset.

In the following days when I placed TR in her grazing pen after lunch she continued to object by kicking and grunting when I picked her up, and by clawing at the roof and stamping. During these afternoons she even made attempts to burrow under the wall of the pen, but as the pen was moved each day she failed in this enterprise.

As I walked away she would stare at me through the meshes of her prison roof with those expressive shining eyes, making me feel a cad for abandoning her. I would wag a finger at her and tell her:

'Stop it, TR! You're utterly spoiled! You're a big bouncing rabbit now – so be your age. Alright, alright, I'm going to set you free sometime soon, when we get a spell of really fine weather. St Martin's little summer is coming.'

*   *   *

Then it happened.

One drowsy afternoon I was roused from a day-dream at my desk by the high quavering scream of a rabbit *in extremis*. Something was attacking – was killing – That Rabbit! Rushing headlong from the house I leaped the steps of the portico in one bound, crashing ignominiously on the gravel, twisting one ankle, nearly breaking both legs. I stumbled weakly to the lawn, a terrible fear in my heart.

A long brown snaky creature was fastened to TR's throat – had cornered her there, within her pen!

I heaved the netting frame aside and saw that TR's eyes were glazed in a helpless coma of fear. Her continuous scream faded to a last heartrending wail. She made no attempt to escape, although no longer imprisoned. In that moment I remembered that I had read somewhere of the complete paralysis of the limbs and brain which made a rabbit or rat incapable of escape when attacked by a mustelid (polecat, stoat or weasel), sometimes before the predator has touched it. TR was already quite unconscious of me – the opaque nictating membrane was drawn over her eyes, instinctively shielding them, as a man will close his eyes when a blow threatens them.

I grabbed the stoat by its hind legs below its short black-tipped tail and tore it away. It doubled back lithely upon my hand and dug its fangs deep into my thumb. With a yell of pain I released it. It fell to the grass, but undaunted, and guided by TR's last whimper, loped back to its victim.

It had plenty of courage! I landed a tremendous kick with my sound foot, which sent it flying into the branches of the Japanese maple. Even so it scrambled back, but more cautiously, sniffing around the spot from which I had lifted TR into my arms.

The fang bites on That Rabbit's neck were not mortal; in fact not deep at all. Her long dewlap fur had protected her throat, even as the stoat had tried to work its jaws around to her jugular vein. TR, although paralysed with fright, was scarcely bleeding; the copious blood on my hands was flowing from my bitten thumb.

TR did not recover from her paralysis for over an hour. As I nursed her in my arms in the shelter of the house, I talked to her soothingly, trying to reassure her – and myself – that all would be well. Victoria, who had heard the commotion and rushed to the lawn soon after me, seemed to think that this talking to a mere rabbit was perfectly natural and necessary. She, too, mumbled words of comfort in broad Andalusian, as she dabbed the rabbit's neck with iodised cotton-wool. Then, discovering my bleeding state, she insisted on washing my hands and bandaging my thumb.

'Fury's bite bad, damn bad poison! Makes tetanus – what you call lockjaw? Victoria wash away terrible bad stink, Don Ronald. Fury's stink make little rabbit frightened when she wake up!'

This was sense. The stoat had emitted a frightful stench from its anal glands when I had grabbed it. I was glad to let Victoria wash the smell away in warm water.

'That's better. You alright, Don Ronald? You rest. Victoria make coffee for make you OK!'

Victoria had interesting notions about wild animals, from her childhood living with superstitious peasantry. She shared a prevalent folk belief that most long, lean, sharp-snouted animals, such as ferret, stoat and weasel – the 'furies' – are highly dangerous because their bite is held to be poisonous. As long ago as 1188 Giraldus wrote, in his description of this corner of Wales:

> In our time, a person residing at the castle of Pembroke, found a brood of young weasels concealed within a fleece in his dwelling, which he carefully removed and hid. The mother, irritated at the loss of her young, which she had searched for in vain, went to a vessel of milk that had been set aside for the use of the master's son, and raising herself up, polluted it with her deadly poison; thus revenging, as it were, the loss of her young by the destruction of the child. The man, observing what passed, carried the fleece back to its former place; when the weasel, agitated by maternal solicitude, between hope and fear, on finding her young again, began to testify her joy by her cries and actions, and returning quickly to the vessel, overthrew it; thus, in gratitude for the recovery of her own offspring, saving that of her host from danger.
>
> In another place, an animal of the same species had brought out her young into a plain for the enjoyment of the sun and air; when an insidious kite carried off one of them. Concealing herself with the remainder behind some shrubs, grief suggested to her a stratagem of exquisite revenge: she extended herself on a heap of earth, as if dead, within sight of the plunderer, and (as success always increases avidity) the bird immediately seized her and flew away, but soon fell dead by the bite of the poisonous animal.

Beautifully written, and both events could have happened; but Giraldus loved to adorn a tale and anthropomorphise natural events.

Reclining on the couch as she administered to me and talked, I had an irresistible desire to tease Victoria. I began to tell her that her fears went back to her primitive ancestors – I had been reading about the stone-age artists of Les Eyzies in the Dordogne – living in dark caves, where bats and creeping small animals would enter for shelter and to hide by day, terrifying the women waiting at home for their men to return from hunting. A few snakes and scorpions might be poisonous, but otherwise any blood-poisoning from the bites of small mammals would certainly be the result of secondary infection by virus or bacteria.

I soon realised that my dissertation, uttered in basic English with the odd Spanish word thrown in, was quite beyond the comprehension of Victoria in her present fussing mood. I decided that it would be ungracious, if not improper, even if she could follow my argument (and most women will deny the suggestion) to tell Victoria that some ethologists and students of the human animal, such as Konrad Lorenz and Desmond Morris, believe women are frightened at the sight of the lean thrusting faces and bodies of these lowly animals because these probably represent in the subconscious female mind the active threat of the thrusting male organ, a sword to destroy virginity – or a sower of seed. In contrast the round baby face of TR, or of her beloved Mr X, was suggestive of the fecund roundness of female attributes: the breasts (which Victoria presented so prominently before my eyes, though decorously hidden by her high-necked blouse) she would dearly have loved to offer to a child, if only she might conceive; the warmth of the womb; and the round vaginal entrance through which man is expelled into a harsh cold world, and to which haven he longs subconsciously to return . . .

Nevertheless several folk fears about poisonous bites of some animals are now found to be based on fact. When the coffee arrived I pleased Victoria by telling her that it had recently been established that the saliva of certain small creatures such as moles and water-shrews does contain a toxic substance, not necessarily causing death, but paralysis, in their prey which they first bite and then store as live food in their subterranean larders. (The mole, to make doubly sure it doesn't wander away, bites the head off the worm.) I forbore to tell Victoria that I had originally gleaned this last tidbit of natural history from the gipsy woman Eliza, (for she distrusted her) whose brother had been a mole-catcher. Eliza had said that a mole-bite was poisonous to man. I had been suspicious of Eliza's story, but it has since been confirmed.

Coffee was Victoria's panacea for all upsets. Afterwards I stretched out with TR in my arms, my sprained ankle propped on cushions. We needed time to recover from shock and heal our wounds. I had forced a shot of brandy and glucose down TR's throat and now I could feel her heart, overworked at the moment of crisis, beating abnormally slowly. Perhaps she was about to die? I prayed hard that she would not.

'That damned stoat was smart enough to scratch a hole under

the edge of your prison, or perhaps he used the one you tried to escape through?' I whispered in her ear. 'No wonder you've been so upset every time I put you out to grass! That beast has been trying for days to get at you, and all the while scaring you sick, and I didn't realise you were trying to warn me. Forgive me, TR. Bravely you tried to escape by digging your way out, and every day I stopped you by moving your pen to a fresh plot. Idiot that I am not to have realised that all your clawing and stamping meant you were in dire danger!'

Gradually TR regained full consciousness. I watched the little nictating shutter which protects the huge eye in danger slide slowly aside. She raised her head presently; then, recognising where she was, she gave me (I will swear it) a grateful stare. Soon she relaxed, burrowing deep into the cradle of my arms and breast, and fell into a normal recuperative sleep, lulled by my quiet monologue.

'Just sleep your cares away. Don't worry, my dear TR. I'll never put you under hatches again. You'll be as free as you like from now on. Of course, when at last you live wild and alone you'll have to take your natural chance with stoats and weasels, foxes, badgers and hawks. But at least you can run a mile from them, or dodge in and out of cover, like your wild brothers and sisters do. You shall go where and when you like. If you want to sleep in the house, we'd be pleased to have you. If you want to sleep outside, you can do just that. There'll always be a bowl of food ready for you in case you feel hungry. I'm going to put a little door in the side entrance. I'll teach you how to use it. But mind, this means you are placed on your honour not to nibble the garden flowers; although I suppose at this season, it won't matter very much.'

Winter was not so far away. The flowers and weeds of summer were seeding and their leaves dying. Human visitors were fewer.

I got to work next day, pleased that in twenty-four hours TR seemed to have recovered almost completely, although for a few more days she would not go outdoors alone.

She watched with great interest my amateur carpentry in the side entrance door, her big ears twitching at every sound. As usual she seemed to listen with pleasing attention to my monologue, which I kept up for that reason. As I sawed and banged away she popped in and out of the hole I had cut to her size in the lowest panel of the door.

She even had the effrontery (or was it pure coincidence?) to hand me the little rectangular piece of wood I had cut out, and which she had playfully seized in her chisel teeth. As soon as this flap door was hung on brass hinges she began to play jack-in-the-box, butting the flap open with her nose, faintly grunting with joy as she saw me, then withdrawing from sight behind the door.

'Very clever, TR,' I said admiringly, 'but the hardest part is still to come. I don't trust that stoat – those sly beasts have long memories.'

I did not tell her I had seen it again, questing around the empty grazing pen that morning.

'Supposing it tries to follow you – or your scent more likely – when you come back to the house after your stroll outdoors, what then? Why, it will certainly follow you and push its way through this little flap-door. So you'll have to learn to operate some sort of safety catch or latch on the door. Simple it'll have to be, yet it must fool anyone that doesn't know how to work it. Ah, here's Victoria with the tea. We'll have it here, indoors, please.'

Victoria placed the tea-tray on the side table where the postman dumped the letters. (What a sensible postman he was! In winter, when correspondence was light, he often wouldn't cycle the long half mile up our dank wooded drive. We had an understanding that if there were only bills, newspapers, or unimportant post-cards – I asked him to read them and judge for himself – he need not trouble to make a morning delivery. But of course he must come and collect our letters for post on his afternoon delivery, otherwise he would miss the bait of tea and home-made scones in the kitchen.)

Victoria regarded me, I believe, as some half-mad but interesting phenomenon. She liked to study me, as I liked to study (and admire) her, on these occasions when I was alone and she could bring coffee or tea, and she might have a chance to gossip and flirt mildly for a moment. She could not understand what I was doing with the splendid mahogany door and its walnut panels, and did not approve the mutilation she could see taking place. It was her custom to place the old kitchen saucer on the ground for TR and pour out some weak tea, diluted with milk and flavoured with the right amount of sugar; then she would make clucking-hen noises with her tongue and offer TR a wholemeal biscuit. Meanwhile I would stir the pot, and let the tea-leaves subside before pouring the adult brew into a genuine porcelain cup (which grandfather had brought from China – it may be pure fancy, but I believe that tea tastes best when drunk from thin translucent china).

Presently Victoria would sigh, shake her head, smile affectionately, politely, at me, and depart, to get the postman's tea. TR would lap hers and nibble a biscuit tentatively, in her desultory fashion. She was never hungry at four in the afternoon; her stomach was usually filled with greenstuff by that hour.

The prowling stoat bothered me. Older inhabitant of Britain than the Norman-introduced rabbit, it was an acceptable and in some ways desirable part of the natural heritage. It had been greatly reduced in numbers during fifty years of intensive rabbit-trapping. Gamekeepers justifiably feared their attacks on pheasants and partridges in rearing pens, and shot and trapped them. But stoats are not entirely noxious to man. I well remember how, as a young farmer, I had watched a stoat hunting some quarter-grown chickens in my poultry-rearing enclosures. The stoat dragged its easy victims to a hole under a chicken house. When I heaved this house over on one side I discovered a 'larder' containing three large brown rats (vicious predators of young chickens) and three young chickens, all freshly killed and handy to a warm feather-and fur-lined nest, in which lay – I quote from my diary of that date, 28 May

'six half-grown, crawling stoats. Out of curiosity I carried the baby stoats up to show Molly, my pet white ferret. She sniffed them keenly, then started in to slay them. I was not in time to save the first victim, but rescued the others – only, regretfully, to be compelled to kill them all later. They were charming little creatures with dark brown coats, fat faces and pure white bellies. Their scent was most objectionable, clinging, musky. It made my sister flee in haste! Next day the mother stoat was busy having her revenge on me. In the rearing paddock at noon I saw her chase and catch a two-month-old chicken. I intervened in time to save the chick's life, though it was bitten in the neck. Two more were killed by the stoat later. I have had to move all the chickens from the rearing paddock to a house nearer home, and scythe down summer growth of wild plants, to reduce cover for "vermin", as the local gamekeepers call them.'

Persistent and courageous, the stoat is a lithe, beautiful animal, well adapted to survive with every man's hand against it. This it does, like the otter, by leading a nomadic existence, except when suckling young at the nest. Where snow lies long in winter it changes its coat to become the pure white, much-prized, ermine; only the tip of the tail remains black. In temperate Wales this rarely happens; here its upper-parts are a handsome tawny or russet throughout the year. The male is one third as large again as the bitch.

In the spring the dog stoat tracks the bitch down by her scent, which is even more pungent during her oestrus. He takes no real interest in his progeny, but only in mating; but because this takes place soon after, and often before, the young are weaned, he remains near the nest, neither molesting nor helping the family, but simply waiting for the bitch to become oestrous. He drives away rivals fiercely – and here we see the importance of size, for a young male may not be strong enough to win a mature female until he is at least two or more years old. However there is little to stop him mating with a virgin bitch – so long as a stronger male is not on her trail – during her first oestrus, which takes place very early, in the late summer while she is still not full-grown.

After mating, each fertilised ovum remains free in the uterus, in the form of a pin-head blastocyst. At the turn of the year the blastocyst implants in the wall of the womb, and the true pregnancy begins. In case the blastocyst has meanwhile been lost or died, the bitch will come on heat again about March or April. The true gestation period is not much above one month.

The tawny-coated weasel, recognisable by its smaller size and lack of black in its tail, was often seen at Orielton, peeping in and out of mouse-runs and vole dens too narrow for a stoat to enter. I doubt if the weasel is strong enough to kill a full-grown healthy rabbit, although it will hunt down a weanling; it lives on smaller rodents, shrews and moles. It would enter the small Longworth live-traps in which I caught these, and in spite of the warm nest of hay provided, this restless mustelid usually died – probably of sheer frustration or chagrin, a form of claustrophobic terror. I believe that these wandering hunters cannot tolerate close captivity for more than a brief spell. To be shut in suddenly, hardly with room to turn around, is to experience 'psycho-physiological insult', often causing so great a metabolic shock or overstimulus of the endocrine organs that the heart fails – the animal breaks out into a sweat, gets chilled and dies of pneumonia in a few hours. An Assistant Keeper of tame and wild rats used for research at a government laboratory which I visited told me how, when perfectly healthy stranger rats were introduced into a small enclosure occupied by an established colony whose inhabitants lived peacefully with each other (having long sorted out the peck-order or hierarchy), the strangers would make no attempt to fight or fraternise but, smelling and hearing the residents without necessarily seeing or being attacked by them, they would crouch down in the open and die rapidly – from shock.

TR had nearly died from the terror of the stoat's visit, but it had not even drawn blood, except superficially. It has been suggested that the stench given out by its scent glands is a further weapon of a hunting mustelid, causing its small prey to become semi-paralysed with (what must be largely instinctive or inherited) fear. One day while eating lunch in the car outside the National Trust house of Upton, Warwickshire, I watched a quarter-grown rabbit hop across the lawn and graze tranquilly at random, as rabbits do. Presently it moved from sight under some bushes of a large shrubbery. A stoat now appeared, following the wandering scent path of the rabbit, its nose to the ground. It entered the shrubbery where the rabbit had disappeared. Half a minute later the rabbit re-appeared from another part of the shrubbery and, evidently greatly agitated, ran hither and thither on the lawn as if uncertain where to flee, but at last it retreated around the back of the same shrubbery and was lost to view. The stoat once more appeared, accurately following the rabbit's new line of scent. When the little rabbit next came into view its movements had slowed down considerably; it seemed almost to be dragging its hind legs. Without looking backwards at all, it tottered towards the car, finally halting in the middle of the lawn. I believe it had not yet seen the stoat, but could hear and smell it, having by now crossed and recrossed its own and the stoat's scent lines. When the stoat re-appeared for the last time it still had its head down, tracking the rabbit by scent. A magpie flew over and chattered angrily at the stoat which, sniffing forwards, now raised its head and stared at its quarry, seeing it possibly for the first time. The unfortunate rabbit began to scream heartrendingly, but did not move. The stoat loped up in a leisurely manner, seized it by the neck and dragged it into the shrubbery. The magpie, alighting in the top of the shrubbery, cursed the stoat for several moments after.

Hunting stoats, foxes, owls and hawks are often mobbed by birds – at a safe distance. Large birds like magpies, jays and crows, are probably alert to the possibility of snatching up a portion of the predator's prey. But small birds seem to mob their enemies out of sheer curiosity (just as ducks in a decoy will swim inshore close to the bank on which fox or dog is moving). The various alarm calls of the birds attract other birds to join in. Both fox and stoat will cunningly distract their avian spectators during mobbing sessions, by rolling on the ground and dancing about in one spot, so arousing their curiosity that they draw closer. At the right moment the fox or stoat leaps upon the nearest. The dying squawk of the foolish bird does not necessarily warn off the others; they may flutter at a safe distance, and continue to mob the predator until it has carried its victim into cover.

*   *   *

It was time That Rabbit had full liberty. But was she clever enough to manipulate a latch to her escape door?

I experimented with two parallel buttons, one each side of the door but actuated by a common bolt or pin. Although she quickly learned to push this device up with her nose and pass through the swinging flap, she could not be persuaded to lock the door afterwards, but each time allowed it to swing in the draught.

'Stupid TR!' I remonstrated, after several attempts to get her to push the button down, into the locked position, holding first her nose to it, then her forepaws. She did so once, almost casually, at my repeated urgings, but then immediately unbuttoned the door (as I had taught her to do), pushed her way through, then came and sat beside me, complacently refusing to try again.

'See, I have done it!' she seemed to say, as she glanced up at me. 'And now can we stop this tomfoolery, please?'

After several such trials on successive afternoons I hit upon the solution. She had swiftly learned to press the button which released the flap for her to pass through, but could not seem to understand the necessity for locking it afterwards. And why should she? There are no doors to the labyrinthine underground home of the rabbit. I was worried about the cleverness of stoats – natural investigators of the holes and tunnels of small mammals. But of what was TR thinking when she passed so blithely in and out of the swinging door? Not of her enemies – she seemed perfectly happy now. Perhaps some rabbit thoughts about food, about food and companionship, about her 'imprinted' love for me. All through her young life so far, when she was not eating or sleeping, she seemed to have only one other clear-cut objective or fixation – to keep me within sight, or smell, to be close to me!

Very flattering, but I would make use of it. Trading on her knowledge of how to open – but not to shut – a door, I reset the flap with the hinges on one side and fixed a small wooden latch to the other. In a few lessons I taught her to press down the trigger with her front paws (a cat or dog can be taught to do this). The released door at once flew open under this pressure, and TR hopped outside. A small spring drew the door back against its frame, so clicking shut the latch after she had passed through; and no amount of pushing would open the door against the latch. I next cut, at the same level, a replica, one foot apart from the first, but opening inwards. This second door made it possible for her to push her way into the house, as before using her forepaws to press open its latch; it too had a spring to draw it shut and lock it afterwards.

I thought that my carpentry had been reasonably competent, but Jesus remarked in his forthright way that I had made it simple for a burglar to insert a long arm inside and unbolt this side entrance to the house. I thought it best not to deny this; although Victoria or Jesus bolted the back door every night, the front and side entrances were my responsibility, and I never locked them. In this corner of Wales it is – or was – the custom of country neighbours to keep open house twenty-four hours of the day.

The little In and Out doors seemed to delight TR, and for a while I deliberately played hide and seek with her, as a form of training. I would leave her in the porch, open the door quickly and shut myself outside. There would be a click as she pressed open the latch of her little OUT door, her beautiful head and shoulders would emerge, her eyes and nose twinkling at me, then a little leap over the door sill, and she would be at my feet. The door automatically clicked shut after her.

'Clever girl!' I congratulated her. Then, running in a small circle below the approach steps, I retreated indoors, shutting her outside. She immediately followed – operating her IN door with accuracy, guided by the fact that the spoon-shaped trigger of its latch was the only visible projection in the lower panel of the door. I was satisfied that even the clever stoats and other 'furies' would never learn to operate TR's private exit and entrance.

TR accompanied me for longer bird-watching crawls through field and wood. She was thoroughly enjoying her freedom, and would trundle away for a while on her own, on a fine evening. On our walks her natural alertness would make her crouch down at the sudden appearance of a large creature such as a fox, buzzard, or crow. If the threat continued she might run between my legs, and I would reassure her:

'Only a fox, TR. See, it has fled from us, hates the sight of a man; it could never catch you if it tried, not the way you can dodge when we play hide-and-seek.' Or: 'Only a silly buzzard, TR, couldn't harm a full-grown rabbit like you – too feeble to carry you off the ground. Remember – I've taught you how to face your enemies. Stand up and fight! Box 'em with your dagger claws – and bite with those terrible chisel teeth of yours!'

In reality I was reassuring myself, for I was still worried about stoats. But none appeared again, and TR seemed to be exercising her inborn wisdom to survive wild and free. More and more she made little excursions of her own, disappearing down the faint woodland paths made by small creatures, sniffing their tracks, eagerly following some which pleased her, shrinking back from other scents – such as that of the fox, which even my poor nose could identify. Badger signs did not seem to trouble her; old brock is far too slow to catch a healthy rabbit.

Sometimes, when she was preoccupied thus, or in eating a clump of juicy sow-thistle or birdsfoot, I would walk quietly on, then step sideways from the path and hide. I was amused to watch her catch up, over-shoot the scent left in my footprints, stop, and work around with her nose until she had traced my steps to my hiding place.

'Clever TR! I wish you'd tell me what your nose is saying to you. I wonder if you've met another free rabbit yet? Where are your parents? Do you ever meet them when you go out at night now?'

Probably her parents were dead. The average life of the adult wild rabbit is under two years, although the protected individual in captivity can live up to a dozen years. Nevertheless lately I had noticed the odd rabbit pellet here and there in the woods, smaller and less spherical than that of the hare, and TR had sniffed at these, too. One or two survivors of the myxomatosis epidemic (and TR herself had been a survivor) must be living scattered about the estate.

An outpost badger colony was occupying the site of TR's mother's nursery burrow, and TR showed no interest in her birthplace. But in the late autumn she was more and more inclined to run ahead of me when I entered the central part of the American Garden. I liked to wander here and had trimmed a path free of tangling bramble, old-man's-beard, bryony and sycamore seedlings, tracing the former ride or vista, along which in September 1736 Sir Arthur Owen (see Chapter Two) may have conducted the distinguished politician William Pitt, to approve 'his designs and plantations'. A few moss-grown stones still edged this track, from the entrance in the ha-ha, past the fragmentary wall of a summerhouse and paved pool, and up to the quarry and the broken stone staircase leading to the old rampart walk. I would remain for a few moments, admiring the vast view from the walls: the Severn Sea and, nearer, the life of the fields, the soaring ravens, rooks, buzzards, perhaps a cloud of gulls following the plough; and, overhead, the autumnal song of larks softened by the wind soughing in the crowns of ancient beeches standing sentinel inside the quarry wall.

One afternoon, looking down from the rampart walk, I witnessed TR establishing communication with a wild rabbit for the first time (but perhaps she had been meeting him previously, by night?) She had not followed me up the stone stairs, but had paused to sniff, and graze in her desultory fashion the thin woodland grass, opposite a clump of seeded nettles. Then, raising her head, she remained still for a moment, staring at something. Suddenly she ran back a few paces as another rabbit emerged from the nettles, sat up and stared at her. Training my binoculars upon its head, I recognised, from the broad skull, that it was a buck. (Could it be her own brother? I remembered there had been two weanlings together when I first saw TR.) After they had stared at each other for several more seconds, TR lowered her head and rubbed her chin on the grass. She had left her visiting card. The buck hopped forward cautiously to sniff at the same spot. Then he too pressed his chin there.

The introduction had been effected, without the embarrassment and dangers of close contact. On meeting for the first time – or after a long interval – most animals of the same species go through certain formalities; it takes time to break down the distance barrier by which the individual guards against surprise attack. Signals of appeasement are made through various actions; and in the rabbit sex-recognition is by scent.

I was amused to watch TR hop a few feet away from where the buck was still sniffing her invisible scent molecules on the grass; and with an air of complete indifference, without another glance at the buck, she nibbled the ripe nodding heads of the woodland grass. When the buck suddenly leaped in the air and did an about-turn, alighting with his white bobtail presented towards TR, she bolted and raced up the steps to my feet.

Her violent departure seemed to alarm him, and he disappeared whence he had come. I walked quietly to the nettles; these usually grow luxuriantly around the entrances to rabbit homes. They are not eaten by the inmates and thrive on the nitrogen from animal droppings. Sure enough, I found that the buck had a well-established burrow, opening amid the nettles. At my feet TR gave me what I could swear was a sly glance, or was it a nod of approval . . . ?

'TR, you're a flirt! Showing off like that!'

*　　　*　　　*

It was the beginning of the end of our close intimacy. TR spent more and more nights outside and would not come back before dawn – to sleep soundly in the house each morning. But November is the natural time of pairing in wild rabbits in this corner of Wales, and I was both pleased and sad that by the end of the month TR ceased to sleep in the house.

She still allowed me to see her. I would walk up to the American Garden to look for her each fine afternoon when I was at home. But after a period of many days when I was away, I had to accept that her allegiance to her artificial life with us was over. She acquired the wariness of her wild mate, whose alarm thump was often the first sound I heard, approach as soft-footed as I might. I could call her to come back into the open, however, if I sat quietly near the clump of nettles; for she had taken up residence with the buck living there.

'TR, TR, where are you? Tea-time!'

It was no longer practical to carry her tea and biscuits. But she would hop into view, a little nervously now, when I rattled some grain into the familiar saucer. I might sometimes allow her only a spoonful of grain, in order that she should plead for more, which at first she did by her old trick of scratching my ankles. I would talk quietly to her, which she still seemed to enjoy. But presently I noticed a new tendency: she would move away when I offered to stroke her back. I wondered if she had learned from her mate that human scent represented danger to the rabbit nose and brain?

I had been too fond of TR. But I was happy for her that she had found a mate at the right time, and was living within a short walk of my home. My chief anxiety was that she might not survive the dangers of predators – especially stoat and fox. But so far she seemed to be coping successfully with every situation she was meeting in the wild; perhaps learning from the example of her mate, who was also her bodyguard and sentinel of the burrow.

The buck was as suspicious as any wild rabbit and would seldom appear, even when I climbed into a tree close by and waited for an hour. On the rare occasions when he did come into view, I was delighted with his courtly behaviour towards TR. I need not go into details of their mating; but afterwards they would relax and stretch out in the mild winter sunshine filtering through the leafless boughs.

Then a strange event occurred. One winter evening, when as usual we were gathered round the fire in the drawing-room, with Mr X comfortably asleep on the hearth, there was a scratch at the door. Young Stephen went to open it – and in hopped TR. Without a glance at anyone she loped quietly up to the cat basket, picked up the little doll's blanket and retreated with it into the hall. But the blanket jammed as she passed through her OUT door. She abandoned it and vanished into the night.

I was astounded, but Stephen said, casual as ever:

'Oh, by the way, Pa, I forgot to tell you. She's making a nest. I saw her digging a burrow, this afternoon, up in Bluebell Wood. By the size of her tummy she's going to have a family soon.'

Evidently not liking her mate's burrow as a nursery, TR dug her own secret quarters in the woodland much nearer the manor, where Stephen had surprised her at work. Here her first litter appeared just after Christmas; four babies emerged from this nest which, as is customary in the doe, she had covered smoothly with earth after each suckling, once or twice a night, while they were helpless.

Before the first litter was weaned, a second was well on the way; and thus the original nursery 'stop' developed in the usual fashion into a new warren of several entrances and exits in the red sandstone earth. Her buck moved in, lord and master of his children. And now TR no longer tolerated my visits. As soon as I crept into view, alarm stamps were given and all ran below ground.

In the next few months TR and her mate proceeded to repopulate some of the places where rabbits had formerly dwelled at Orielton. In this first breeding season she produced four litters. At least one daughter of her first litter moved to a site at the far end of the American Garden, and was breeding in that same summer, making That Rabbit a grandmother within one year, indisputably matriarch of a flourishing dynasty – which has survived to this day.

Alas, I wish I could add that TR lived for many years after that successful first season of motherhood. But in those hot July nights when I would take my sleeping-bag to Bluebell Wood, hoping I might find her in the quiet hours of the dawn, I could not see her pierced ears among those of the several rabbits watched from my couch. Breeding had ceased, the 'neutral' season of peace and the annual moult had begun, when rabbits are no longer fiercely territorial and even go visiting other burrows. The young of the year disperse and find new homes, although an established queen like TR seldom sleeps away from home – she is too house-proud, that is to say, she will not risk having her burrow and position usurped by a young home-seeking female taking possession in her absence.

All nature seemed to be on the move in late July. Parties of chattering newly-fledged birds crossed the canopy of green leaves over my head – willow-warblers, whitethroats, blackcaps, titmice, nuthatches. A yellowhammer promenaded over my sleeping-bag one dawn, picking up gossamer spiders which the dew had brought down from their parachuting adventures in yesterday's thermals of rising air. A young robin, in patchy spotted plumage, came out of its midsummer hiding place, hopping after insects and worms which the weight of my body had encouraged to come to the surface around me. In the sky high above, the first swifts, flying there all night, were enjoying the warmth of the rising sun, its light shining in their deep brown eyes, while I lay yet in shadow. The bumblebees were already at work in the pink bells of the foxgloves.

Orielton was a riot of wild flowers at midsummer. And amidst this beautiful display of dog rose, tufted and yellow vetch, ragged robin, guelder rose, meadowsweet, stitchwort, yarrow, moon daisy, agrimony, and a hundred others, That Rabbit, my beautiful TR, had vanished for ever.

II

The immense colony of honey bees still flourished in the south-eastern corner of the roof. Fortunately these bees had made their entrance under the outer eaves; they did not annoy those who slept or sunbathed on the leaden flats enclosed by the protective rampart of the slate roof. They were quite inaccessible behind the water tanks and forest of rafters. An industrious hum could be heard each summer day; as this became subdued at dusk, the chittering of the bats began.

'Of course,' said Walter Francis Grimes, who had come on be-half of the Historic Buildings Council to advise on the possibility of my obtaining a grant towards the repair of the Manor, 'you would have to fumigate and destroy all insect pests. This old-fashioned roof has been beautifully built and lasted a long time, but more than likely it will have to be stripped bare and rebuilt if it is to be saved; and will you need all those chimneys today?'

'But if I fumigate I would destroy the bats! There's a splendid roost of long-eared bats in one quarter of the roof. And what about the white owls nesting in that corner where the down-spout is – the lead box engraved with the arms of the Owens?'

'I am an archaeologist and historian, not a naturalist. But I'm specially interested in Orielton, for I was brought up in this neigh-bourhood – just a few miles away, at Pembroke Dock. I would like to see this lovely, historic house preserved for as long as humanly possible.'

We talked of how it might be done. I was unwilling to use poisons of any kind. After all, the bats were useful guests: they killed a great many of the moths, beetles and other woodwork- and fabric-devouring insects at the imago or flying stage when they were potentially most dangerous, that is, when these pests emerged from months or years of burrowing under cover and flew forth to mate and lay their eggs and infest more of the fabric. And the owls were totally beneficial, feeding on rats, mice, voles, etc.

As for the bees, if only I could get at their vast stores of honey . . . but all we saw of this harvest was a yellow stain and a sweet smell when, in the late summer, honey dripped from inaccessible combs built in the dense web of rafters hidden above the plaster ceiling in the top floor loo of the former nursery quarters. Martin had poked a hole there, too small for a bee to pass, and hung a jam-jar below to catch the drips which oozed on hot days; a mixture of honey and propolis. But he had read that the people of the Caucasus, subsisting largely on this sweet-tasting compound, held the world longevity record, some men remaining alive and virile up to 150 years of age.

Professor Grimes was fresh from the excitement and glory of excavating the Roman Temple of Mithras in the City of London. He had also lately surveyed the considerable evidence of human occupation of Skomer in the Iron Age.

It was Skomer (just visible on the western horizon from the roof of the old manor) which we were endeavouring to secure as a permanent nature reserve. It contained many stone remains of houses, gardens, and field boundaries, suggesting a very large population for such a small island (722 acres). This had puzzled him; but I too had studied these and similar enclosures on certain other Atlantic islands. As a naturalist, I believed that it was because of the enormous colonies of sea-birds breeding on these remote windswept sites that they had been occupied by flourishing human communities – at least for periods of many years of exploitation of this rich supply of protein. As on some Icelandic and Faeroese small islands within the present century, the sea-birds would be harvested carefully and enough cured to last the winter. Curing was by smoking or wind-drying in small turf-roofed stone huts (known as *cleits* on St Kilda), the remains of several of which exist on Skomer; and these too had puzzled Grimes, for they are too small for human habitation, until I had suggested this explanation.

'Yes, it all fits in! You naturalists have your uses at times,' exclaimed Grimes. 'I agree that as you suggest human settlement, from time to time over the centuries, would result in over-exploitation of the resources of a small island, and with diminishing returns of birds, seals and fish, the inhabitants might at intervals decide to abandon Skomer. Doubtless, too, they were forced to flee by invaders. In the distant past the Scandinavians harried this coast, and gave their present names to islands and many places along this shore. Skomer has a typical cliff-top fort into which the inhabitants would retire in time of danger.'

I could not bring myself to agree to fumigate the manor roof and destroy the bats, birds and bees – not yet, I told Grimes. I heard nothing more from the Historic Buildings Council and supposed Grimes' report had been unsatisfactory; no doubt the Council had far more urgent calls on its limited funds. I repaired the leaks in the roof myself.

Grimes continued to visit his native county, deeply interested in the numerous remains of neolithic peoples, of Bronze and Iron Age, and later populations, along our coast, the result of waves of invasion by Iberian, Celtic, Saxon, Norse and Norman peoples. I attended some of his field excavations of the homes and tombs of these bygone people. Was I not living in a house of Norman provenance, and were not the burial mounds of the late stone-age tribes within sight of our windows?

Other distinguished and some less well-known students of the past also called at Orielton: geologists, archaeologists, historians and genealogists. My new friend, the ex-miner Ifor ap Rhys, came again; he was looking less healthy, coughing more, but determined to unravel the tangled pedigree of his connection with the famed, and legendary, princes of Wales of true Celtic stock, from before the visitations of the Vikings down to the lordly Rhys ap Thomas (hero of my young son Stephen), who gave his daughter in marriage to the Wiriet squire. Our file of published and unpublished notes on the history of Orielton was gradually filling a wide shelf in my library.

But who were the first people to build a dwelling in this pleasant well-watered vale within the long peninsula of southern Pembrokeshire?

After the sea retreated from this corner of Wales, the Old Red Sandstone bedrock of Orielton, laid down under a primeval ocean, was exposed to the Atlantic climate. Neanderthal man roamed the land of what is now the Severn Sea. He hunted woolly mammoth and rhinoceros, cave bear, giant deer and other animals now extinct but whose bones are preserved in the limestone

238

caverns along the coast. He vanished with the advance of the last glacial period about 70,000 BP (Before Present).

With the melting of the last ice, New (Neolithic) Stone Age man moved gradually north into the pristine land of Britain, not yet separate from Europe. He lived on into the centuries when the first pyramids were built in Egypt. From this south-eastern Mediterranean civilisation, colonists sailed westwards to Spain and, passing through the Pillars of Hercules, explored north to the new island of Britain, bringing with them the religious custom of burial of chieftains, priests and other men of rank in sepulchres of stone. Along the coasts of the Irish Sea these tombs are numerous and known in Pembrokeshire as *cromlechau* (sing., *cromlech*). Each consists of a passage and a vault walled with unhewn stones; a rectangular capstone weighing many tons rests upon three supporting unhewn blocks. After the ceremonial placing of the corpse within, with suitable grave offerings of weapons and food to enable the occupant to survive the transition to the afterlife, the entrance was sealed with a door consisting usually of one gigantic stone placed between the two portal uprights, and the whole was mounded over with smaller stones and earth several metres thick.

In due course most of these splendid sepulchres were plundered by alien peoples who knew not of or no longer feared the solemn *tapu* placed upon such tombs; and almost down to the present farmers have continued to remove the earth and stone coverings for use on the land. The mighty capstone and uprights were too heavy to carry away; fortunately these skeletons are now protected from further spoliation by local bye-laws.

The neolithic builders of *cromlechau* tilled the soil, grew wheat, barley and rye, but possessed no means of fusing metals. They herded cattle, sheep, goats and pigs by day, shutting them into enclosures at night to protect them from wild beasts and thieves. They fished in river and sea, and in this part of Wales hunted deer, wild boar, bear, wolf, beaver and other animals. With stone, bone and wooden tools, they fashioned coracle boats, clothes and other household chattels from the hides, bone and horn of animals, and from native woods; and weaved garments from the wool and hair of sheep and goats. As tribal warfare grew, strongholds were built by throwing up ramparts, often double or triple, of earth and stone. They commanded a wide view of an approaching enemy and were used for many centuries by successive waves of settlers.

They crown almost every cliff headland within a few miles of Orielton.

The *cromlechau* were contemporary with Stonehenge, built some 4,000 years BP. And strangely, as the geologists have proved, the stones forming the inner ring of some thirty huge dolerite and rhyolite blocks at Stonehenge must have been dragged and rafted (150 miles as the raven flies) to Salisbury Plain from an outcrop on Presceli Mountain. This suggests that this county, lying but fifty miles from Ireland and rich in stone tombs and monuments, was of special significance to the high priests of the prevailing neolithic religion. As priests have always followed trade and wealth (and there was gold in the nearest hills of both Ireland and Wales) evidently Pembrokeshire was the scene of much sea-traffic between the two, then and for centuries to follow.

In some fields west of Orielton, south of the crossroads where stands *The Speculation* inn, there are several swelling mounds, marked *Tumuli* on the Ordnance Survey maps, which the farmer finds inconvenient; generations of cultivators have hacked at them and ploughed them down, some almost to the level of the surrounding land. More than once I rented some of these fields when short of grazing for the Jersey cattle. The grassy tops of these burial mounds of the Bronze Age people who succeeded the Neoliths became wind-dried in summer; the fawn-eyed cows liked to stand together in the sea-breeze there, each flicking its neighbour's face with the switch of its tail to reduce the mutual annoyance of biting flies. Their restless hooves kicked the dust of deserted rabbit-burrows, scattering many bones, broken and bleached, exposed by the digging of rabbits – but all these bones were those of domestic animals.

The long-headed Neolithic men placed their dead chieftains in vaults, but the Bronze Age round-headed invaders, originating in the steppes of Russia, cremated their men of rank and placed the ashes in beakers or urns, raising above them a round barrow of earth. Edward Laws, who opened several tumuli near Orielton, describes how they were built, in his fascinating *History of Little England beyond Wales* published in 1888:

> I conclude the method of construction was as follows: First a circle of large stones seems to have been formed; then the enclosure was filled up with soil to the level of the stones; on

this raised platform the pyre was built, not generally in the centre, but on one side; on this the body was burnt. Then a kistvaen (stone coffin) was erected on the other side to that on which the pyre had been made, in which were placed the funeral urns, one, two or three. These in Pembrokeshire are usually of such a poor description that they rather resemble baked mud than burned clay; still they are generally more or less decorated with a pattern made by running a piece of string or twisted hide round the vessel at intervals, and filling up the interstices with lines and dots made with a sharp instrument. The urns vary in size, the largest I have examined being two feet in height, with a diameter of twelve inches. They are usually found with the mouth downwards. In order to introduce the remains of a human being into one, very complete calcination must have taken place.

Either before the pyre was lit, or after it was put out, the friends of the deceased held a funeral feast on the earthen platform. They ate horse-flesh, oxen, sheep or goats, pig, dog, red deer and shellfish. When the funeral feast was over the mourners completed the tumulus and departed; but either on anniversaries, or some other holy days, it seems to have been their custom to return and hold feasts on the summit of the tump. When these were over they repaired the outside, adding a few baskets of soil which buried the fragments. This theory would account for the bones, shells, etc., which we find stratified in the higher levels of the tumps.

*   *   *

Ifor ap Rhys would start up from his chair in the small drawing-room which now served as a library to make some dramatic declaration, inspired by his intensive research in his determined effort to perfect the genealogy of his forbears:

'Listen, Ronald! I am an original Celt. I feel it in my bones that I was spawned in a skin tent on the far eastern steppes of Russia! It was more than 3,000 years ago, yet it seems like yesterday that I left my native Samarkand, astride a beautiful Kazakh steed and roamed by the waters of the Caspian. I hunted the huge herds of the fat-nosed deer of the Volga marshes. I galloped westwards along the Danube to its source in Helvetia. I fished from my *crannog* [lake-dwelling] in the waters of Lake Tène, using the new iron weapons snatched from the furnaces of Hallstat ... and I came to Britain down the Rhine, from the source to the sea!'

'So, you are a Druid yet? Can you claim descent then from Hu Gadarn, whose praises are still sung at your Welsh bardic assemblies? Have you read George Borrow's romantic description of your ancestors?'

> Many will exclaim who was Hu Gadarn? Hu Gadarn in the Gwlad yr Haf or summer country, a certain region of the East, perhaps the Crimea, which seems to be a modification of Cumria, taught the Cumry (the Welsh) the arts of civilised life, to build comfortable houses, to sow grain and reap, to tame the buffalo and the bison, and turn their mighty strength to profitable account, to construct boats with wicker and the skins of animals, cultivate the vine and encourage bees, make wine and mead, frame lutes and fifes and play upon them, compose rhymes and verses, fuse minerals and form them into various instruments and weapons, and to move in masses against their enemies, and finally when the summer country became overpopulated led an immense multitude of his countrymen across many lands to Britain, a country of forests in which bears, wolves and bison wandered, and of morasses and pools full of dreadful *efync* or crocodiles, a country inhabited only by a few savage Gauls, but which shortly after the arrival of Hu and his people became a smiling region, forests being thinned, bears and wolves hunted down, *efync* annihilated, bulls and bisons tamed, corn planted and pleasant cottages erected. (*Wild Wales*)

'What on earth were *efync*?' queried Ifor.

'Imaginary water monsters – like the Loch Ness monster. But in fact, I believe, they were simply colonies of innocent beavers who built dams across rivers and created morasses.'

The Celts brought the Druidic religion to Britain, which lasted until Christianity reached south-eastern Ireland – probably because of its gold trade in the first place – about the third century AD. From Ireland the earliest Celts, the Gaels, re-invaded Britain, and their monkish evangelists established cells in western Wales. Both St Patrick and St David are said to have been born in Pembrokeshire about this time. The Romans tolerated the religious practices of the conquered Celtic peoples, so long as their priests did not interfere with military rule and civil prosperity – the Pax Romana. This peace was utterly destroyed, however, along with the splendid but feudal Romano–British towns and farms, as the Roman garrisons withdrew in the fifth century AD, and succeeding hordes of Angles, Saxons, Vikings and other invaders arrived from Europe.

'We Welsh Celts and Irish Gaels are the only true survivors of the original British people,' said Ifor proudly. 'We have retained the ancient British language. We have never yet been dislodged from our mountains and deep valleys, though we were driven from England and often attacked by Roman, Saxon, Norse and Norman adventurers. These freebooters brought none of their own women with them to breed replacements. If they took a Welsh wife, they soon became Welsh, like our old Norman friend – or was he Saxon? – Gerald de Windsor, who married my illustrious ancestor, the lovely Nesta, Rhys ap Twdwr's daughter. And then they turned against the Norman king. For well de Windsor knew that, expert and trained as they were in formal warfare, the Norman soldiery had no idea how to cope with the hit-and-run tactics of the Welsh. Read what Nesta's grandson Giraldus Cambrensis has written about the Welsh character – the first ever description of guerilla warfare – "Bold in the first onset, they are swift and rapid in their advances and frequent throwing of darts. Their mode of fighting consists in chasing the enemy or retreating. Although they do not display great fortitude in open engagements and regular conflicts, yet they harass the enemy by ambuscades and nightly sallies. Neither oppressed by hunger or cold, or fatigued by martial labours, nor despondent in adversity, but ready, after a defeat, to return immediately to action."'

'Yes, but Giraldus also wrote that because of their love of feuds among themselves they lost, first of all under Mailgon, King of the Britons, Troy in their former empire of Asia Minor (for the Galatians, to whom St Paul wrote an epistle, were Celts); and secondly Britain. He wrote that brothers show more affection to one another when dead, than when living: "for they persecute the living even unto death, but revenge the deceased with all their power". He admires as well as execrates the Welsh character and habits in his *Description of Wales*: "These people are no less light in mind than in body, and are by no means to be relied upon – a people quick in action, but more stubborn in a bad than a good cause, and constant only in acts of inconstancy. They pay no respect to oaths, faith, or truth . . . preferring base lucre to the solemn obligations of oath and good faith." Giraldus also writes that the crime of incest has much prevailed, "even in the third degree of consanguinity. They do not engage in marriage until they have tried, by previous cohabitation, the disposition, and particularly the fecundity, of the person with whom they are engaged . . ." '

'Aha!' exclaimed Ifor, with ripples of joy. 'You're in trouble there! Have you seen the local paper today? You're accused of – where is it? Ah, here – big headlines! "Author accuses Welsh of Trial Marriages." It's a review of your latest book (*Pembrokeshire*, one of Robert Hale's Regional Books). It seems you've quoted dear old Giraldus on that very subject, and you go on to say – page 17 of your book: "The custom is still recognised in some of the more remote Welsh homes, even in Pembrokeshire. The young farmer or farm hand may have access to his sweetheart of a Saturday or Sunday night, the parents of the young woman retiring to bed and leaving the warm kitchen, with its perpetual fire, and the stairs clear for courtship of an approved suitor, who may stay until milking time in the morning. The week-end is chosen for the good reason that on Saturday the young man has had his weekly shave . . ." You don't spare the Welsh character, Ronald, do you?' Ifor added, scratching his chin, not yet shaven that day.

'I am not decrying the Welsh character – don't forget that I had a Welsh priest as great-grandfather. I wrote in all innocence of thought of offending the reader, from the pleasant experience of employing young Welsh countrymen when I was farming in the hills of north Pembrokeshire. I can tell you they were the finest workers I have ever had, the most skilled in the difficult conditions of that rainy, mountainy land . . .'

'Don't interrupt, my dear Boyo, let me finish. ". . . his weekly shave and, like the young woman, will be wearing his best clothes and be free from farm duties. The young man realises he must marry the girl if she becomes pregnant; and he does so joyfully in expectation of setting up home with the mother of his unborn children upon whom he will depend for cheap labour on his farm when his need is greatest. As they grow strong enough his children will work, often without wages, to build up the farm. Their reward comes later, when they wish to marry: they will each be given money or goods then."' Ifor finished with another roar of laughter as he put down the newspaper.

'Well?' I said, slightly nettled. 'There's nothing very amusing about that is there? It is – or was until very recently – a sound custom in the hill districts of Wales. One of my farm hands at that time – I could give you his name – was the son of a poor road-man, but aspired to be a farmer on his own account. He courted an attractive mountain farmer's daughter in the district. They were married four months before their first child was born, and he is now a happy and proud occupant of his own hill farm.'

'Duw, man, I wasn't laughing at you! Your description is pure poetry – almost as lovely as dear old Gerald's! And how practical it is: a barren woman is useless as a farmer's wife. It's never been a disgrace in Wales to have children out of wedlock – many of my illustrious ancestors were bastards – love-children. No, Boyo, I was amused at the way the local journalists try to raise a scandal whenever they can. Best of all there's a laugh for you in a letter here from a woman living in the Welsh mountains – in the correspondence columns. She says it's not true that these trial marriages (What a stupid word – why not say outright fecundity tests, as Giraldus more or less does?) take place, and she ought to know, having lived all her life in the hills! I bet she's still a spinster – never been lucky enough to be sought out, courted and mated in the romantic style you and Giraldus have described, poor girl, and it's soured her!'

Ifor was busily constructing an enormous genealogy on a strip of plain wallpaper ten feet long which, for convenience sake, was laid out on the billiard table in the basement and held in place with snooker balls (while he was at work here he would try to dissuade anyone from playing billiards). He was much preoccupied in proving his descent from Cunedda, the Christian king of the Brythons, who conquered North Wales about AD 500, for thereby he was related to almost every king of England, Scotland and France, as well as a great number of Welshmen of noble pedigree. A task of deep interest, but I was more immediately concerned to trace the story of the occupation of Orielton: which – at the risk of boring the reader – I shall endeavour to summarise in the rest of this chapter.

*   *   *

The name Wiriet (variously spelt Wiryot, Wyrot, Wyrriot, Wirriot) first appears in the writings of Giraldus Cambrensis. In his *Memoirs of the Ancient Family of Owen of Orielton*, seven centuries later, J. R. Phillips writes: 'It is manifest that Stephen Wiriet must have been a considerable person, or the priests would not have taken the trouble they did in the matter, nor would Giraldus have otherwise transmitted to us this curious picture (of the poltergeist which resisted exorcism). Moreover the priory of Monkton was close enough (two miles) to Orielton to enable the priests to assail the spirits without much inconvenience . . . I am inclined to the opinion that the name Orielton is no other than an euphonious transmutation of Wiriet-town . . . others have ascribed the founding of this house to a Norman follower of Arnulph de Montgomery of the name of Oriel.'

Evidently the first man to build a substantial fortified house on the site was one such follower of Arnulph, who was the son of Roger de Montgomery, Norman baron created Earl of Shrewsbury. Arnulph and his men began building the great castle of Pembroke upon its tide-surrounded limestone peninsula in 1090. He placed Gerald, son of the castellan of Windsor, in charge of this new fortress. It was several times attacked by the Welsh, but never capitulated. It was a turbulent period when, as Giraldus wrote, the Welsh princes allowed their lands to be invaded and filched from them through failure to unite against the common invader. Instead, each invited an alliance of Dane, Saxon or Norman, to overcome a brother prince in the bloody struggle to conquer all Wales for himself. The *Brut y Tgwysogion* (Chronicle of the Welsh Princes) reveals that this fratricide procured the premature deaths of some fifty Welsh rulers in twice as many years: they were slain in battle, murdered, tortured (four were deliberately blinded), enslaved, and some died of misery in dungeons.

Perhaps the first Wiriet to appear in Wales was defending the new castle at Pembroke when the Welsh first lay siege to it in 1092. The garrison was down to its last provender – four pigs – when Gerald de Windsor arranged that a letter to his master Arnulph, informing him that the castle needed neither food nor reinforcements for four months, should fall into the hands of the investing troops. He then cut up the pigs and threw the joints over the walls as a further trick to deceive the ever impatient Welsh, who forthwith gave up the siege.

The power of the Norman barons occupying the splendid castles erected during the reigns of William the Conqueror (the Bastard, as he was called by his enemies) and of his son William Rufus, had greatly increased by the time Henry I came to the throne; and the new king demanded fresh oaths of fealty. The Montgomery sons resisting, Henry raised a large army and attacked the new stronghold of Shrewsbury. While he was holding out, Arnulph ordered his castellan at Pembroke to seek reinforcements from Welsh and Irish sources. The Welsh princes Cadwgan and Gruffydd gladly joined their Norman enemies – they were more than ready for a good fight and prospects of plunder – and were delighted when Gerald sought in marriage Nesta, daughter of Prince Rhys ap Twdwr of South Wales, and sister of Gruffydd. She was reputed to be the most beautiful woman in Wales.

Her noble father Rhys had been beheaded in 1092 after a skirmish with a force of Norman soldiers invited to attack him by the Welsh turncoat and adventurer Einon ap Colwyn, aspirant to the princedom of South Wales, who intended to marry Nesta to consolidate his claim and as his reward for defeating Rhys. But he never caught up with this remarkable lady.

Henry I, seeing clearly how the Welsh mind worked, himself

now engaged in an intrigue with the Welsh princes, promising them much in the way of property and rights. They – of course – accepted the bribes and abandoned the Montgomery faction. The Montgomery sons were banished, and Gerald de Windsor called to account. However Henry, falling in love with Nesta, pardoned her castellan husband during a period when Nesta was the King's mistress and, restoring Gerald to favour later, granted him authority to endow Nesta with 'fair lands and to build a castle at Carew', a few miles east of Pembroke.

'Oh, for a picture of this beautiful Welsh princess, this Helen of Wales!' sighed Ifor ap Rhys, my fellow historian, who claimed descent from her with deep pride. 'She must have been ravishing, to be so often ravished!'

Her next adventure is described by Laws:

> During the Christmas holidays of 1108 Cadwgan ap Blethyn, Prince of Powys, held an eisteddfod at Cardigan. To this entertainment every man of position throughout Wales was invited. Bards sang their songs, the mead passed round, the revelry was fast and furious; then one of these wandering minstrels told of Nesta, the fairest of the fair, old Rhys's daughter, royal Grufudd's sister; told how she had enslaved the English king, and now was wife to the robber chief Gerald de Windsor, he who had seized on the Kymro's land and had perched like a foulbird on Penvro Crag [Pembroke]. Fired by this song Owain, Blethyn's son, determined to wrest the Kymric Helen from her foreign lord. When the feast was over Owain collected a number of his friends together and sallied forth to Pembrokeshire. Claiming kinship with Nesta, he was well received by her husband Gerald, and left the castle lust mad. That night he returned with a considerable following, and having in some way obtained an entrance, laid siege to the room in which Nesta and her husband lay. The latter, finding resistance hopeless, was persuaded by his wife to escape through a garderobe, she letting him down with a rope and thus saving his life. Meanwhile the ruffian Owain burst in the door, seized Nesta, her two boys, and two other children [the illegitimate offspring of her husband], fired the castle, and carried off his prisoners into Powys.

'There's grand romance for you,' declared Ifor as we sat talking one day in the library. 'I've explored every one of the chambers still existing in Pembroke Castle, trying to locate the lofty bedroom where the lion-hearted Owain snatched up the glorious Nesta, while her craven husband made his escape through the draughty, stinking garderobe! I daresay Nesta was ready for yet another romantic adventure, for it must have been very boring and tedious for a woman of her beauty – and experience, as mistress of a king – to spend her days rearing children, both her own and the bastards of her husband! No doubt she would have been imperious enough to command her doting spouse Windsor to provide her with entertainments – tournaments and all that. As Rhys' daughter, she must have been a first-class horsewoman, eh, Boyo?'

'As for me,' I replied, 'I like to picture her riding out on a fine day in early autumn to go a-hawking with her husband – for the Normans were passionately attached to falconry. Very likely she would be attended by a Wiriet squire when she rode west upon the plain of Orielton, ideal for hawking, with its meandering streams and bosky dells, and plenty of herons, favourite quarry for the noble peregrine. These falcons were nesting in the cliffs a few miles away. Not so many years later in 1172 Henry II tested the falcons of this county on his way to Ireland to investigate the banditry there of Nesta's son Fitzstephen. Laws says "One day as the king was out hawking near the cliffs he chanced to see a peregrine falcon sitting, as they often do, on a crag. The king was carrying on his wrist a valuable Norwegian gerfalcon, which he forthwith flew at the wild bird. But the native hawk managed to rise above the gigantic foreigner, and, swooping, struck it dead at Henry's feet. Henceforth Pembrokeshire had the honour of supplying the royal mews with falcons."'

Wild boars and wolves had become scarce in the peninsula by then, but wolfhounds would be used to hunt foxes, and there were badgers to be baited and hares to be coursed. And at Orielton the squire had established his *coneygarth*, which was the name given to a warren constructed for breeding the wild rabbits the Normans had introduced into Britain. To this day one of the fields within the estate walls is known locally as 'the Cunnigar', consisting of a meadow surrounded by belts of trees, ideal shelter for game of all kinds.

Prince Cadwgan made his impetuous son Owain return the children, and Nesta was duly reunited with her lawful husband. However, when Gerald died she returned to Cardigan, marrying its castellan Stephen. Thus she was foundress of three noble families by her liaison with king and castellan. Of her sons, Maurice Fitzgerald and Robert Fitzstephen, and all her grandsons (save Odo) took part in the conquest of Ireland in 1170 and, but for the intervention of the outraged Henry II two years later, might have annexed much of Ireland for themselves.

One of her grandsons, our invaluable historian Giraldus Cambrensis, was commissioned to accompany the eighteen-year-old Prince John (created Lord of Ireland) to Dublin in 1185. As a result Giraldus wrote one of the earliest if partisan, descriptions of that island's topography; a work which, he tells us, was much criticised by contemporary scholars for its free and unconventional style, but a delight to read today, with its mixture of truth and superstition.

Giraldus was born about 1145 at Manorbier, in the castle of the de Barri family, his Norman father Gerald having married Angharad, daughter of Nesta and Gerald de Windsor. He gives an endearing account of his boyhood at home with his brothers Robert and Philip. Playing together on the sands under the castle he would build a cathedral – his ambition was to become Bishop of St David's, even Archbishop of Wales. But his brothers built castles, as befitted the warriors they were to become. Giraldus must have visited Orielton, the haunted house which he describes as belonging to Stephen Wiriet, a few miles on horseback along the open coastal lanes.

He loved the land where he was born, and quaintly says that its air is twice purified, firstly because it blows from Ireland where there were no poisonous snakes (banished by St Patrick), and secondly because the great ocean to the west sweetens it. Above all he loved Manorbier, with its rich-yielding orchards, vineyards, nutgroves, fishponds, mill, columbarium and deer park. A little off the beaten track, neither Manorbier nor Orielton seem to have been besieged in their long history. Giraldus regarded his birthplace as the fairest part of all Wales and 'as Pembroke is the fairest part of Demetia, and this spot the fairest of Pembroke, it follows that Manorbier is the sweetest spot in Wales'.

*   *   *

The pedigree which Ifor was compiling had some question marks here and there, chiefly attached to names of the British chieftains of the Dark Age. There was an annoying gap between Cunedda (c. AD 500) and Rhodri Mawr, King of all Wales, who in 877 had been slain in that Viking stronghold, the Isle of Man.

With a swan quill as pen, Ifor inscribed in copper-plate each ratified ancestor – the doubtful ones remained in pencil. Incurably romantic, he preferred to use a long wing-feather from a mute swan which had 'died of a broken heart' – so the decoyman Greenslade had informed him – in the Lily Pond. It happened in the year of the death of Arthur Gaddum and, like Alice, the cob swan had moped on the demise of its mate, refused to leave their home and, as swans mate for life, had quite possibly died of a broken heart. The wings of this pair had long been hung in the old harness room, from which Ifor plucked a fresh quill each time he needed to replace the previous one, blunted in the service of his genealogical enthusiasm.

Through the descendants of Rhodri, and his scholarly grandson Hywel Dda (Howel the Good) who with wise laws ruled the whole kingdom of Wales, Ifor traced his pedigree and his link with Orielton to the last Prince of South Wales, Rhys ap Thomas, the hero of my son Stephen's bed-time serial. Taking advantage of the struggle between the Yorkist and Lancastrian factions for the English throne, Rhys had become so powerful that his bards could sing:

> All the kingdom is the king's
> Save where Rhys doth spread his wings.

But Rhys was careful to acknowledge his duty to the reigning monarch, of which there had been a rapid succession – by death or murder – of Yorkists to the throne, while yet young Henry Tudor lived in voluntary exile in France. When the unpopular hunchback Richard III became King he feared the growing strength of the Welsh prince Rhys. He demanded that Rhys make a fresh oath of fealty and hand over his four-year-old son as hostage. Rhys took the oath, but declared his son was too young to be taken from his mother. In a letter to Richard dated 1484, Rhys promises:

> I hold myself obliged without further looking into the cause, faithfully to observe your Majestie's commandes to which I

deem it not unreasonable to annexe this voluntary protestion; that whoever ill-affected to the State, shall dare to land in those parts of the Wales where I have any emploiment under your Majestie, must resolve with himself to make his entrance and inception over my bellie.

Richard was satisfied: he intended to strengthen his weak claim to the throne by marrying his niece Elizabeth, elder daughter and heir of Edward IV of the White Rose. But the heir to the Lancastrian succession was also a woman, Margaret Beaufort, widow of Edmund Tudor and mother of the exiled Henry. In writing to Richard, Rhys must have been aware of a new plot, talked of freely in Wales, to marry Henry to Elizabeth and so unite the Red with the White Rose against the hunchback King.

Rhys seemed to hold aloof from this plot at first, bound by his oath of fealty. But Henry's supporters included many of Rhys's dearest friends. Margaret Beaufort herself was a not infrequent visitor to Pembrokeshire. And was not her son descended, through Owen Tudor, from the noblest of Welsh ancestors, as was Rhys himself? At last the Bishop of St David's, as his 'spirituall and ghostlie father', promised Rhys absolution from his bond of fealty, and wrote that if Rhys still had further scruples 'I shall never hold it as any disparagement to your humilitie to lay yourself prostrate on the ground for the true and indubitable lord of us all to make an easy entrance over you'.

In June 1484 Richard issued a warning proclamation declaring that 'Henry Tidder, son of Edmund Tidder, son of Owen Tidder, in double advoutrow goten' was a bastard born of bastards with no title to be king.

On 1 August 1485 Rhys ap Thomas, riding his battlehorse Fetterlocks, with colours flying and drums beating, met Henry and his uncle Jasper when they landed with 2,000 French soldiers at Dale, fourteen miles as the raven flies from Carew. Rhys lay prone on the shore, so complying with his oath. Henry, a young man of twenty-nine, stepped over the belly of the thirty-three-year-old Rhys, and there was much rejoicing, and planning, that night in the comfortable, modernised castle at Carew.

Richard lay at Leicester, to block the advance on London. The two armies clashed on the field of Bosworth, watched by the vacillating Lord Stanley who was in command of 3,000 disciplined men of his own, held in reserve for the king. For three hours the battle ensued, in the midst of which Stanley deserted the king and joined Jasper. Laws wrote of the last desperate courage of Richard: 'The white boar now was indeed at bay; he (Richard) left his bodyguard and charged full at Henry, hoping thus to end the strife in Homeric fashion. Sir William Brandon, who bore Henry's standard, fell before him; one Sir Richard Cheney, a doughty champion, was slain; Henry at last was reached, and met the shock of battle like a soldier, yet the desperate king seemed to be the stronger man.'

'At this juncture,' said Ifor proudly, 'my noble ancestor Rhys ap Thomas cut down the last of the Plantagenets! The new king knighted Rhys on the field immediately after his impromptu coronation by Stanley who, according to the well-known tale, found the golden coronet which had rolled from Richard's helmet lying under a thorn bush! Great honours were heaped on Rhys. He was made Knight of the Garter, and Governor of all Wales. . . .'

Sir Rhys and his army took part in further adventures to help Henry VII, and later his son Henry VIII by Elizabeth of York, against the King's enemies both at home and abroad. In 1513 'Henry Wirriott of Orielton' brought a force of 74 men to join Sir Rhys and Henry VIII against France. The noble knight Rhys was then over sixty, still riding his veteran battlehorse, Fetterlocks.

Although Rhys ap Thomas had only one legitimate son, Griffith, by Eva his first wife, and his second wife died childless, he had fourteen illegitimate children whom he brought up with loving care and suitable endowments. He had ten children by Gwenllian, sister of his secretary, the Abbot of Talley, which was a religious house more than fifty miles away in the Welsh mountains. (Evidently Gwenllian lived for these years in concubinage at Rhys's house.) He had four more children by four other ladies: of these bastards Margaret was his favourite. Before he died in 1527 he gave her in marriage to Henry Wirriott.

According to a story of this period told and retold in Pembrokeshire, Thomas, probably the father of Henry Wirriott and a sheriff of Pembroke, came to the rescue of the young and wanton beauty Tanglost, who had been seized for her ill-fame as an adulterous witch by the Bishop of St David's, and imprisoned in his fortified palace of Llawhaden Castle, some twenty miles north of Orielton. Whether because as sheriff Thomas Wiriett felt that the bishop had exceeded his powers in arresting the woman, or for more personal reasons, Thomas stormed the castle with his mounted troops and carried Tanglost away. What happened in the intervening nights before Tanglost appeared far away in Bristol is likewise not recorded, but in the safety of that city she made an effigy of the Bishop and stuck it full of pins, a piece of sorcery which seems to have been successful in causing his lordship dire physical and mental anguish. After much parleying by messages between them, and the refusal of the Mayor of Bristol to extradite Tanglost, she was pardoned by the Bishop on her promise to abandon her evil ways and live peaceably.

The scattered references in the public archives and other papers of the period to the Wiriets of Orielton show clearly that from their settlement there early in the twelfth century for the next five hundred years the male heirs of that name were men of importance, holders of land by military service, holders of local offices and sometimes knighted. They were staunch King's men, and remained strong to resist the raids of the Welsh upon the Norman stronghold of Pembroke Castle, retaining their private army for the purpose, as well as to defend and augment their property in quarrels with neighbours.

In 1384 one Richard Wyrriot was ordered by the King to seize the birthplace of Giraldus, evidently on some default of its occupants; but Manorbier does not ever seem to have become tenanted by a Wyrriot. The old castle became a ruin by 1540; its cellars and stables a smuggler's store. But Orielton flourished under the Wyrriot accession.

Richard was followed by his son, grandson and great-grandson, all named Thomas. Then comes Henry, who married Sir Rhys ap Thomas's daughter. Their son George, last of the Wyrriots, described as a Justice of the Peace in 1587, married Jane, the daughter of John Philipps of Picton Castle, some ten miles by water up Milford Haven from Orielton. Their only child Elizabeth was married in 1571 to Hugh Owen, a barrister practising on the local Great Sessions, a man who could claim descent from the fifteen noble tribes of North Wales and, as Ifor insisted, back to Cunedda. Settling at Orielton with the wealthy Elizabeth, Hugh had eight children by her; he engaged in a good deal of litigation – at which he was expert – over property, became High Sheriff of Pembroke-shire in 1583, and achieved a knighthood.

For nearly three hundred years, up to 1857, the Owens of Oriel-ton – squires, knights or baronets – were to continue to live in much the same style, born to privilege, marrying into the best families, improving and fiercely retentive of their estates, seeking and obtaining local offices (with all the perquisites thereof), and most of the time providing a succession of Members of Parliament representing their local town or county.

*   *   *

That autumn when Ifor rolled up his unfinished genealogy, and departed for home via Aberystwyth, where he intended to copy relevant material from the archives in the National Library of Wales, he declared: 'One day soon I'll be writing to ask you to put up with me again for a spell in this magic house of yours, Boyo.'

He was looking better for his stay in the sweet air of Orielton, but was still frail and coughing too often.

Not a word did I hear from Ifor. After several weeks I wrote reminding him of his promise to come again, hoping he was well, and addressed my letter to Ifor ap Rhys, Esquire, at his Rhondda home, where he lived with his sister. She replied:

> I meant to write to you before this. Ifor was always talking about the lovely time he had with you at Orielton. I am sorry to say he took the flu bad on getting home from Aber. His lungs were rotten with the silicosis. He died very sudden from pneumonia two weeks ago. He was calm and peaceful and passed away quietly in the end, poor boyo.

> Yours sincerely, Myfanwy Price.

> P.S. Our family name is really Price, though Ivor liked to use the old Welsh way. Our Dad was christened Rhys.

The name Price after all is but an Anglicised version of Ap (= son of) Rhys, sometimes written Rice or Rees. Sir Rhys ap Thomas's grandson and heir was Rice ap Griffith ap Rhys; and since then the name Rhys has been transmitted in the less attractive form Rice to his descendants, the present Rice family, Lords of the barony of Dynevor, where stands the old castle which was once a seat of Sir Rhys, in Carmarthenshire, some six miles south of Talley Abbey, and over forty from his beloved Carew Castle where wrote Laws, 'the old warrior spent the evening of his life'.

These are the things I prize
And hold of dearest worth:
Light of the sapphire skies,
Peace of the silent hills,
Shelter of forests, comfort of the grass,
Music of birds, murmur of little rills,
Shadow of clouds that swiftly pass,
And, after showers, the smell of flowers
And of the good brown earth,
And best of all, along the way,
Friendship and mirth.

HENRY VAN DYKE

A voice which Ludwig Koch had not succeeded in recording satis-factorily was that of the badger. He was excited when one day in a BBC studio I told him that we had a colony under the floor of the stables. He promptly invited himself to stay, although I warned him that badgers were comparatively silent. At rare in-tervals they grunted what was supposed to be their mating call, which is as unattractive as the groan of the camel which Ludwig had recorded for his splendid library of animal sounds.

On their first visit Ludwig and his elegant wife were enchanted with the peace of Orielton and the music of its birds, soothing to nerves jangled by the incessant noises of their home near one of London's airports. Like young lovers, the old couple wandered arm-in-arm in our woods and lanes, reporting back to us what they had seen and heard – chattering squirrel, mewing buzzard, singing woodlark and croaking raven. Ludwig carried what he called his sound sampler – the newest in portable tape-recorders slung from the other shoulder – in order to judge where he might set up his formidable apparatus with its cumbersome batteries and parabolic 'zound-gadger'. Tony Soper, a new recruit to the BBC, who frequently came to stay, borrowed a trailer and cheerfully helped him to lug around these 'monstrous old-fashioned paraphernalia' (as the up-to-date Tony dubbed them). Ludwig himself, more lovable than tiresome, was accustomed to get his own way by a combination of guile and charm.

We helped him to set up this heavy gear in the open window of the loosebox immediately above the drain the badgers used to enter and leave the sett under the cobbled floor. The resulting playback was a medley of noises of the night, shrieks of the white owl, hooting of brown owl, the song of a cricket, and the muffled thumping made by the badgers underground as they preened and scratched and prepared for their nightly excursion into the woods and fields. Ludwig, however, considered it to be a true sound story of badger life. He proceeded to dub into the record his inimitable commentary, optimistically identifying the more weird noises as he thought appropriate. The result was an interesting animal fairy tale in sound, and I told him so.

'You've got a poor ear for ze finer music of nature, Ronald, vrom living too long on your vindy Velsh island as a young man. Remember 'ow, about ten years ago, I regorderd ze zongs of ze zeals in ze nurzery caves on Zkomer?' retorted Ludwig in his broad German accent which I shall not attempt to reproduce further. 'You were very rude about that record I made for the BBC but the public loved it. It's still one of the best records in the BBC animal sound library.'

'Too well, I remember, Ludwig! You sat comfortably in a dry tent on the top of the cliffs, surrounded by your batteries and other impedimenta, wrapped in warm clothes and with a thermos of hot drink, while we gullible volunteers climbed down on ropes, carrying your microphones and leads into the watery darkness of deep caves, wading through surf, braving the snarls and charges of angry adult seals and the sharp bites of cornered pups! All the while you listened in perfect ease, deciding with your powerful imagination which noises were most appropriate to bull, cow or pup. You recorded the snarl of a cow which had gripped my trousers, and my yell of anguish when she ripped that garment right off my nether parts, as the love-cry of the bull Atlantic seal and his mate's passionate response! The wail of a new-born pup was for you the siren song of a virgin cow seeking a mate!'

'What does it matter? Only the few experts like you would know it was a bit off the mark and inaccurate. The great British listening public adored my interpretation!'

On a later visit to us Ludwig had retired, having sold most of his library of animal sounds to the BBC, which had subsidised so many of his expeditions in the field.

'And now,' he announced, 'I devote the rest of my life to my first loves – music and my darling wife! I mean Nellie first and then music . . .'

'You mean,' interrupted the darling Nellie, 'Ludwig first, then music, then me! But I'm not complaining; he's really a very good husband, but rather annoying at times. Did I tell you what he gave me for Christmas? I had always wanted a pet alligator; and so secretly Ludwig bought one and brought it in with the breakfast tray!'

'But that's not the full story!' cried Ludwig. 'I knew my darling Nellie wanted one. But I did not know she wanted one so badly that she too went and bought one, secretly, to give Ludwig as a surprise. On Christmas day suddenly we had two new guests to feed – two alligators, each so long as my arm!'

'By the way, Ludwig,' I told him, 'you may be interested to hear that there is an old organ in a church a few miles away, which – it is said – once belonged to a renowned lover of music like yourself.'

'And who was he – to be so famous?'

'I'll give you two clues. His Christian name was Felix, and he died young just over a century ago.'

'Not the great composer Felix Mendelssohn!' cried Ludwig in disbelief. 'The composer of *Elijah*, and the *Overture to A Midsummer Nights Dream*? Impossible – he never lived in Wales!'

'Well, I haven't seen the old organ myself, but if you wish I can take you to the church.'

'Now, now! Let's go right away!'

Ludwig Koch was a remarkable character. A German of Jewish origin who had been an opera singer as a young man, he had married a ballet dancer. Persecuted during the anti-Semitic purges of Germany when Hitler assumed power, Ludwig and Nellie narrowly escaped the gas chamber. From Switzerland they came to England, Ludwig bringing with him some records of bird song and animal voices he had made – on now outdated waxed cylinders. Befriended by English naturalists and especially by Julian and Juliette Huxley, then living in their flat at the London Zoo, of which Dr Huxley was Secretary, Ludwig built up a library of animal sounds which were in great demand, principally for lectures and for broadcasting programmes. He became famous as a commentator, whose halting, accented English was a further unusual attraction, combined with the beautiful, strange or downright uncouth, music of nature which he had recorded.

His appetite for new sounds was insatiable. When he was seventy-five Ludwig asked me if I thought he could scale the sheer rock stack of Ortac in the Channel Isles, on top of which Roderick Dobson and I had some years before discovered a new colony of gannets. I said 'No – much too dangerous for a man half your age!' He voyaged there nevertheless, and returned with a record of which he was intensely proud: gannets squawking vulgarly (as they do), the roar of the swell on the rocks, and Ludwig's vivid commentary on the saga of his ascent and descent of the cliffs. He was justly boastful of his successes; he loved to talk of famous people he had met, of his friendly relations with the royal families of Europe; and of his visits to Buckingham Palace to teach Princess Anne about birds. (V I P occasions which plentifully besprinkle the autobiography he was writing during his retirement, and now published.)

* * *

The badgers occupying the sett or den under the stables floor had provided amusement for our very first visitors. The animals had almost at once become accustomed to a red light we had fixed above their exit in the wall of the loose box where a window conveniently gave full view of their activities on a summer night. The occupants at this season comprised a very large boar, his wife and four children.

While it was delightful to watch this colony so conveniently, the badgers were a considerable hindrance at first to my rabbit study project. And, from their point of view, I was a great nuisance. For I had erected the containing fence of wire-netting across a well-worn badger trail between the stables and their foraging ground in the woods and fields. The badgers would brook no such obstruction. This fence was sunk a foot into the ground with an inverted, T-shaped baffle to discourage digging but the badgers simply tore a hole where it crossed their right of way. Each day I mended the gap with strong netting; each night they re-opened the gap.

Jesus, who had never seen a badger before, was an eager observer at the stable window under the red light. The little bear-like animals excited his hunting instinct and, aware of my problem, he planted a strong wire loop-snare across their walkway, unknown to me. But I soon discovered it, for the sow badger which blundered into the snare was strong enough to wrench its peg out of the ground, and she appeared under the red light with snare and peg hanging loosely around her neck. Fortunately, even as we watched, one of her cubs playfully tugged at the wire, and the snare slipped free over her narrow head.

Jesus suggested that we smoke the colony out with sulphur candles, or with exhaust fumes from a car. I accepted the advice of forester Arthur Cadman and built a swing door at ground level in the fence; but not where their long-established trail crossed it; for that would have given the badgers access to the new inner enclosures I was building to contain my marked rabbits. Johnny Johnson, local amateur naturalist, had had success in enticing badgers at night to his house by laying a line of dried raisins between the nearest badger track and his back door. At last, after many nights of experiment and more holes torn in the fence, we were successful in redirecting the badger family along a new path, bypassing the rabbit enclosures and leading to a heavy swing door, eighteen inches square, in the outer fence. But first it was necessary to mow down and clear away the grass along this diversion (badgers prefer to travel as dry underfoot as possible), then trick it out with a bait of raisins.

We made the old track unattractive to the keen nose and weak sight of the badger with a row of rags, soaked in paraffin, propped on short sticks and interspersed with half a dozen storm-lanterns, lighting these each evening until the new route was fully established in use. In addition, as badgers live largely by their sense of smell, I thought it advisable to smear the new route with this colony's own scent, by dragging along it a flattened stick which I had dipped in badger faeces.

Badgers are fastidious about personal hygiene. Unlike the fox which will foul its own nest or 'earth', the badger is as careful as the cat is to deposit its faeces in a shallow slot which it digs beforehand, but unlike the cat it does not scratch the soil back and bury its waste matter. It may continue to use the same slot until it is filled to the level of the surrounding ground. These lavatory

pits are usually discreetly dispersed in or near cover of bush or tall plants.

The happy play of the four piebald-faced cubs was a pure delight to watch, as on midsummer nights the family emerged soon after dusk. Usually the boar or the sow appeared first, with the cubs peeping close behind. While the old ones stretched, yawned and scratched their fur, the cubs at once began their games, such as follow-my-leader, leap-frog, somersaults and wrestling. They would try to involve their parents in this tumbling and chasing, and their mother would respond more freely than the boar. He tolerated his children, cuffing them gently when they persisted in climbing over him, but was principally occupied in a prodigious preening exercise. Scratch, scratch, scratch – using in turn the claws of each foot or the teeth and tongue to reach every part of the body. As scratching is infectious, soon the whole family would follow the example of father – a comical sight as they sat in various attitudes at this healthy exercise, which got rid of some of the dust and parasites which had accumulated in their fur during the long rest below ground.

Ursus, as we dubbed the boar, was enormous by comparison with his wife Goldilocks. He was undoubtedly much older, and walked with a ponderous rolling waddle. After the scratching session he would rise up on his hind legs and clean and sharpen the long claws of his forefeet against the trunk of the old elm – near the top of which the kestrels reared their family in an old crow's nest. His toilet completed, he was first to depart in search of his supper – or rather his breakfast – beginning no doubt with an hors-d'oeuvre of hermaphrodite worms, which at that hour would already be coming to the surface to mate in the dews of midsummer, slimy bodies linked across the turf, tails anchored in separate holes. The early badger catches the worm, but there were plenty of worms at this season; the young cubs would stuff themselves on this soft abundant manna, so easy to swallow and kind to tender, moulting milk teeth.

Although the badger has the powerful canine teeth of a carnivorous mammal, its diet is omnivorous, like that of the bear which it resembles in appearance more than it does the mustelids (in which family it has been placed). My tinker friend Elijah declared that once a badger had taken hold of a terrier (set to 'bait' it – yet another pastime of his sporting father), its jaws would lock together and could not be forced apart except with a steel chisel. If a badger did lock its jaws on to a dog in the arena, the badger was judged to have won and would be saved for another contest. (To separate them, Elijah declared it was necessary to throw them together into a tub of water.) It is a fact that the jaw-joint of the badger is so constructed that the lower jaw cannot be dislocated without breaking the bone; it remains firmly hinged, ball-and-socket fashion, even when the skull is cleaned and dried.

Our badgers ate worms, slugs, snails, beetles and other insects, and would dig out wasp and bumble-bee nests, careless of or immune to stings. There were virtually no rabbit nests available in that summer, but plenty of young mice and voles could be found helpless in the little nests made in thick grass or shallow burrows in the ground. Food is detected by scent, and taken in a leisurely fashion, for the badger is too slow-moving to catch a healthy adult mammal on the run; except the hedgehog, whose first reaction to an encounter is to roll into a prickly ball. Although I never saw the evidence of this, the badger is said to tear open the ball, skin the hedgehog and devour the flesh.

Our badgers rooted with claws and snout to find and eat bluebell bulbs and other underground fruits; they liked wild strawberries and in the autumn they fattened like pigs on acorns, beech and other tree mast, blackberries, mushrooms and windfall fruit. All food is seized with the front teeth, crushed with the broad molars and gulped down without chewing.

On some evenings Goldilocks would return home early. Presently she would emerge with a bundle of old, soiled bedding – dead grass, crushed leaves and fine twigs – which she would discard around the mounds of hard-trodden earth and stones thrown out by generations of badgers which had excavated their labyrinthine sett beneath the stables floor. Later she would push together a new heap of bedding of fresh materials and, tucking the mass under her long chin, she would carry it below; in order not to get stuck in the entrance with this load, she would enter rump first.

At first the young cubs remained timidly near home after their parents had wandered away. But by July they were more independent; the whole family would disperse, as soon as hygiene had been attended to, along the scent-marked badger paths radiating from the hole in the wall. The cubs found plenty of food within the enclosure of parkland and wood around the Lily Pond, and did not at first find their way through the swing door in the outer fence which their parents used regularly to gain access to the open fields and forest. On moonlit nights it was possible to watch the half-grown cubs sniffing in search of their wormy supper close to the exotic geese and ducks which I had lately introduced from Peter Scott's collection. But not too close, for the geese would challenge, hiss or honk at and even attack a badger; ducks would usually retreat.

It was not until the mating time of the badger in late August that Goldilocks' four cubs, now three-quarters grown, at last passed through the swing door in the outer fence – a difficult and frightening experience for them. Knowing the strength of a badger's claws and jaws I had increased the weight of this door with a lead strip along the base and I had also inserted a button catch each side, which clicked it shut and prevented it swinging in the wind, but made it necessary for any animal attempting to pass to use greater force to push through the door. I knew the adult badgers from long habituation could easily do this; my main reason for making it harder to open was to reduce the risk of foxes entering this part of the enclosure, now that I had a mixed flock of pinioned and wing-clipped waterfowl. Although many of these birds slept afloat on the Lily Pond, others were vulnerable as they roved the land nocturnally or roosted on dry land.

Fortunately the foxes which nightly patrolled outside the fence never discovered how to enter through this heavy swing door during the year it was in operation. It was my custom to inspect this door each morning. One day the smaller pad and claw marks of the cub badgers were plain in the soft ground *outside* the door, alongside the big footprints of the adults. Within a week I could find no fresh spoor of the cubs within the enclosure, although the adults returned home regularly. Evidently the cubs had summoned up courage one by one, as each followed close behind the scented rump of a parent, to make their exit. These youngsters never returned; not only was it alarming to feel the weight of the door pressing on your back as you squeezed through, and to hear the sharp click of the door as it slammed shut behind you, but why return at all? You had been longing for many nights lately to explore beyond the fence the enticing country of tall trees, bosky dells, open pastures and ripening cornfields – a land you had never seen or heard of but somehow you knew it awaited your pleasure from the example of your parents (and the ticking of the biological clock of inherited wisdom you were born with, which informed you it was time to go wandering).

Late summer was the time to be completely free of parental control and, like so many adolescent creatures including man, to explore a new exciting world and encounter others of your age and species. Food was abundant, it was warm, there was no immediate need for shelter: and adolescents at this stage seem to be accepted as harmless guests when they visit other setts, probably their immaturity – identified by their sexless smell – arouses no jealousy. Badgers do not mate until they are about fifteen months old, in their second summer. Instead, feasting and fattening, the youngsters form friendships, which ripen into partnerships as winter approaches. Some young badgers will fill the gaps left by the death of the master or mistress of an established sett; others will den together as innocent sweethearts and, finding both the sett and the company congenial, will by the test of proximity become man and wife. The wandering urge and dispersal in young mammals ensures a minimum risk of inbreeding, a mingling of unrelated blood to maintain the vigour and uniformity of the species.

I had never studied the badger in captivity. But one day the RSPCA brought us a small cub in a terrible state. It had been dug out of a sett destroyed by a local farmer incensed on finding his young barley crop flattened – so he declared – by the romping of a family of badgers. It was bruised, and its wounds suppurating. Close to death, it was taken care of by Tony Soper. Tony had been recording the croaks of our ravens inhabiting the Gazebo, and the eerie nocturnal singing of a herd of some three hundred Atlantic seals in their hidden winter haul-out – the Red Wilderness – which I had discovered under an immense Welsh cliff, but which I feared to reveal save to a few reliable friends because of what might happen if the general public knew of it. Tony had helped catch and mark seals with numbered flipper rings, and had made films of this work. (Such, indeed, was Tony's enthusiasm for the wild life of Orielton and its unspoilt sea-coast that when he married and brought his bride for their honeymoon at Orielton, she was wearing an unusual wedding ring: a metal numbered band out of a series supplied to us by the London Zoo for the study of seal migration and life history. It had been cut down to fit her slender finger. I wonder what the keeper of seal-marking records at the Zoo thought of the entry in the copy of our seal marking register we sent him that year: '[Human] female, over 21 years' – with ring-number and date of marking.)

Orphaned or wounded wild animals were frequently brought by the RSPCA and others who supposed we had the leisure and knowledge to care for them – despite my protests that we did not keep an animal hospital. Tony was helpful and gave them loving care; a mutual love, for they became attached to their patient benefactor. In return they were useful, during convalescence and tame enough on recovery, to feature as stars in Tony's broadcast programmes. As such Plapp the cormorant, Diana the common seal, and Brock the badger – to name just three – achieved some fame on television.

It is hard to kill a badger. Young Brock recovered from his cruel wounds rapidly, and became playful and affectionate. He slept most of the day, but was extremely lively in the evenings when he fed greedily on bread, chopped fruit and scraps of meat we mixed in a bowl with a little milk. Taken for a stroll on the lawn when worms, snails and slugs were crawling in the dew, he sniffed eagerly after them, smacking his jaws with gusto as he gulped them down.

He demonstrated early the importance of the sense of smell in the badger. Every new place he visited he marked with scent droplets from the gland at the base of his stubby tail. He adored his keeper and would amble back to Tony's large feet periodically to sniff the shoe-leather, and now and then squat upon it and renew the scent which assured Brock that this treasured human possession of his, this living source of food and affection, was there as part of the security he needed to enjoy his young life to the full. It was a sad hour for us when Tony took the cub away to his Devon home.

The Duke of Beaufort relates the story of a captured sow badger which was placed in his stables, where she became tame and lived alone, quite isolated from any opportunity of meeting other badgers. Nearly a year later however she gave birth to two cubs. In the wild the sow usually mates in late summer when she is beginning to lay up fat for the winter. As in some others of the mustelid family her egg or eggs remain dormant in the form of a pinhead-sized blastocyst – usually until the rest period of winter. In the instance of the female in solitary confinement at Badminton the psychological shock of capture must have caused a longer delay than usual in the implantation of the blastocysts in the wall of the womb. Normally, after implantation the (true) gestation period is only two months.

Our badgers did not hibernate in our mild climate, but like the hedgehogs remained snug in their dens during cold and frost. They had laid up enough fat not to need to dissipate this reserve by foraging when food was scarce in such weather. But on mild evenings in winter when worms and insects were active on or near the surface of the ground, they would be abroad, and we would try to remember to scatter some raisins and other food around the entrances to their setts at Orielton.

One day early in the winter the decoyman Greenslade told me he had found a 'girt big dog badger dead in Limebridge 'oods. 'E be masterly size. 'Tis my belief 'e'd got too fat to live. Prob'ly 'e 'ad an 'eart hattack, an' died very sudden in a coma o' fat.'

Few wild animals die directly from old age. Many badgers are run over and killed or mortally wounded by road traffic at night;

we had found one now and then which had obviously been hit by a vehicle and crawled away, to die in the open, without reaching home. But there was no sign of external injury on the large carcase of this old boar, which lay in one of the entrances of the sett in Limebridge (Eastern) Wood.

Pointing to fresh claw marks in the disturbed earth around the cold stiff body, Greenslade declared that the other badgers inhabiting this sett were in the process of burying their master – and boss of this colony.

'Any gamekeeper 'll tell thee badgers allus buries their dead. Most particular they be, very clean an' tidy animals – thee might say almost reelijus. Never eats their own carrion, like a fox 'ull. Allus buries their dead proper.'

Greenslade asked if he could remove the skin from the carcase of the old boar, as he intended to soften it and pluck the long bristly hair, which could be sold at a good price for the manufacture of shaving brushes.

This individual was indistinguishable from the giant boar Ursus we had watched so often in the red light above the stables sett; so that later – as he never appeared there again – I became convinced it was Ursus who had died, possibly of sudden heart failure 'in a coma of fat', as Greenslade had declared. I like to think that Ursus had been on a visit to the Limebridge family, perhaps a patriarchal or avuncular call. In his long life he must have fathered a goodly number of badgers which had gone forth to dwell in setts within or near the Orielton estate. From his worn down teeth and claws, thick coarse hams and somewhat ragged fur, he must have been an advanced age for a badger, possibly twenty or thirty years.

Little is known about the underground life of the badger. It is believed that a mated couple, having established a home, share it as long as they both live. It is not known whether the boar is excluded from the nest chamber when his wife gives birth to the cubs – but this is likely for a short period while the young are very small and helpless. But later, as we have seen, he lives in amicable contact with the growing cubs. I resolved to study the domestic intimacy of the stables family during their quiet sleeping period over the winter, when I would have more leisure to open up the floor carefully and insert a plate glass roof above their chamber where, about February, Goldilocks would deposit her next batch of naked blind babies. I was already beginning to study the burrow life of the wild rabbit in a similar manner.

With the death of Ursus the stables sett became so quiet that I was uneasy that Goldilocks too might have left home, or died. Her cubs, as already mentioned, had long passed through the swing door to freedom and had never returned – at least I saw no traces in the enclosure. Now, when in that winter I examined the spoil heaps at the entrance to the stables den, there was no sign of activity, even on mild days when badgers normally emerge for a while, and attend to personal hygiene. No recent footprint, no old bedding thrown out; and the lavatories under the rhododendron bushes were unused.

Badgers are said – on little evidence – to abandon a sett when it becomes too verminous; but as they are forever cleaning out their homes (and in the case of a death below ground there is this hearsay evidence that they will bury a carcase while it is fresh), I doubt this. Many badger setts have been in continuous occupation for as long as old men can remember; one large sett which lies on the edge of the moat around Cole Park, my sister's home in Wiltshire, and in view from the windows of the house, has been in use every year, by one and sometimes two pairs of badgers, for at least forty years.

Pursuing my intention to insert a window above the stables sett, I began by prising up some cobbles. The air in the cavity was chill. Thrusting down a hay-testing needle three feet long I brought up in its eye only cold musty bedding. Goldilocks was not at home. Evidently, deprived of her husband and children, and unable to secure a mate or companion because no badger accustomed to live in the open woods would dare (or know how) to push its way through the swing door, she had decided to seek a new home. It was too lonely for her to endure a winter without a mate to share the warmth of the bedchamber and discuss in the dark whatever it is that a mated badger couple say to each other in the grunts and squeaks they utter below ground. The badger seems essentially a sociable animal. The boar is uxorious. For this nocturnal creature love is chiefly a warm presence, a familiar smell, a voice in the darkness. Its nose is keener than its eyes; but if the sight is weak no doubt the conspicuous white facial stripe has some significance – for recognition in the dusk of night?

I was sad about this voluntary departure; but as she seemed to be a young-looking widow I like to think that Goldilocks joined her children in another wintering place. She may indeed – if it is true that badgers mourn for and bury their dead – have been hiding that day in the sett outside which Greenslade had found the body of her husband. If so the decoyman saved her (as he believed) the trouble of completing the funeral rites – a considerable task, burying her husband's great corpse – for I had told Greenslade to inter the boar elsewhere in the wood after he had skinned it.

Goldilocks and her progeny, including the litter born of her last mating with Ursus (for at the time of his death she would be carrying the blastocysts resulting from their early autumn mating), may yet be living in our woods, as I write this. I like to think so. But neither she nor any other badger returned to the stables sett, which still lies empty under the loosebox floor, save for the occasional rat and toad.

In one respect I was relieved by the departure of the badgers: in the following spring, when the foxes were restlessly trotting along the outside of the enclosure in search of food for their growing cubs, I was able to nail the little swing door permanently shut against these potential marauders of our rabbits and waterfowl.

*   *   *

A shadow had fallen upon this beautiful coast and its wild headlands, islands, and quiet ports, and upon the tranquil life which we local residents and many appreciative visitors had worked so hard to preserve for posterity. As far back as 1948 I had shared with Julian Huxley, Clough William-Ellis, Leonard Elmhirst, and Lord Merthyr and others in the early planning of the Pembrokeshire Coast National Park which would secure the land in its ancient occupations of agriculture and fishing, supplemented by catering for summer visitors. The Hobhouse Committee on National Parks had met in the long kitchen of my home at that time, a former grange but now a farmhouse standing alone on the majestic peninsula of Dinas Island in north Pembrokeshire – that noble headland which is now included in the national park. On this seal and sea-bird haunted coast, at intervals during the War, many friends on leave had wandered with us in search of wild birds and flowers, to say nothing of wild foods so welcome under rationing: mushrooms and other edible fungi; delicious wild Welsh strawberries, blackberries, bilberries and nuts; and cockles, lobsters and seafood from the shore. In this seclusion Huxley had come to write his first report as director-general of UNESCO, and with typical enthusiasm had put the whole world right in a splendid essay. Afterwards, thanking us for our hospitality, he wrote ruefully that the Commission were delighted with his exposition of the ideal world state, and now awaited the strictly factual report on his year's work for UNESCO . . .

Enthusiastically we had included, in the plans for the new coastal park, areas of great beauty not strictly coastal: the whole of the low massif of the Presceli Mountains – that windswept and archaeologically interesting region inhabited only by shepherds, their sheep and mountain ponies; as well as the peaceful wooded upper reaches of Milford Haven. Subsequently the new National Parks Commission had invited me to walk the outer coast and map out a suitable footpath which future generations of ramblers and visitors would use. A pleasant task which had occupied several weeks exploring and scrambling – for much of the wilder northern shore had no path – to fix an accessible route along the hundred miles of winding shoreline. My report advocated that the pristine wilderness of many of the bays and headlands be left as inviolate sanctuaries for the rich wildlife I had found there.

Cyril Hurcomb, ardent amateur naturalist, at that time Chairman of the British Transport Commission, came to Dinas Island to discuss the disposal of some twenty miles of a branch line of the former Great Western Railway, which wandered delightfully along the southern foothills of the Presceli Mountains between Clunderwyn and Fishguard. He had procured a single observation railcar, in which we trundled slowly along this overgrown track, passing abandoned hamlets and unmanned level crossings and halts. We quickly became absorbed in making a list of spring birds and flowers, from time to time asking the driver to stop so that we could get down and identify merlin, ring-ouzel, peacock butterfly and early purple orchid.

Since the railways had been nationalised they were deeper than ever in debt. Was it possible that this delightful no-man's-land of embankment and ravine could be saved as some sort of linear nature reserve (which it had already become), making the inland boundary of the new Pembrokeshire National Park?

'Why don't you make a bid for it – buy or lease?' suggested Hurcomb. 'British Railways can't afford to maintain it any longer. The slate quarries it once served at Rosebush are closed, and the few mountain hamlets have a dwindling population, so it's highly unprofitable. But you and your local naturalists could let it run wild as a nature reserve with very little expense of upkeep. It would be a great summer attraction to the national park, with an explanatory leaflet listing the fauna and flora. As Chairman of the Transport Commission I would help all I could; no doubt we could arrange a short-term lease while you naturalists were making a public appeal and raising funds for acquisition.'

Alas, neither our local naturalists nor the National Parks Commission at that moment had sufficient funds for such a splendid enterprise; and soon the hard-headed and impecunious Treasury advised the Transport Commission to discard Hurcomb's 'fancy plan'. The branch line was sold piecemeal to local landowners and residents. But Cyril Hurcomb, knighted and soon to be made a peer for his war services, came often to Pembrokeshire, to help us when the first shadows blighted the national park.

On a sunlit April day Hugh Dalton, Minister of Town and Country Planning, escorted by supporting MPs and local officials, assembled at Ceibwr Bay for the official opening of the Pembrokeshire National Park coast footpath. As much of it was no more than a coastguard track, I led the way until the ebullient Hugh Dalton masterfully took the lead, his long legs striding the crooked badger and fox trails.

Suddenly there was a metallic crunch, followed by loud curses, as the ministerial heels, one after the other, were caught in steel-jawed traps hidden under earth, illegally set by local rabbit-trappers. I was glad of this diversion – which raised discreet laughter from Dalton's escort – because his indignation might well help our efforts to outlaw this horribly cruel trap. Then, it could be legally used only if set in the entrance to rabbit burrows; it was not banned altogether until the Pests Act was made law in 1954.

Moving more cautiously along the cliff edge we reached a sheer headland facing Dinas Island. The rare wild centaury, the single-flowered species *portensis* which Julian Huxley's keen eyes had rediscovered here only last summer, was not yet in flower. I thought I would not interrupt to reveal its presence to such a cosmopolitan

272

party just then; for although Dalton was limping somewhat still, he was back in great form, wise-cracking about politics with his renowned wit. But for me that day his most important statement was that this beautiful coast was now 'secured forever from industrial or building development under the provisions of the new National Parks Act'.

Seven years later, with the Park fully established by law, and drawing many visitors to our beautiful coast, the shadow of destruction darkened. We had begun to gather funds for the purchase of Skomer as a national nature reserve when it was announced that British Petroleum proposed to acquire land within the Park boundary and open up an ocean terminal for their new supertankers to discharge oil cargoes. The company had in fact already privately bought for this purpose an old Victorian fortress on Milford Haven's south shore, only four miles as the raven flies from Orielton. Of course there would be a public enquiry, but it would be useless to appeal against this violation of the National Parks Act because already an enabling Bill was drawn up and would be approved by Parliament. It was in 'the National Interest' that BP should be allowed to build piers and an oil depot here because – it was declared – nowhere else in Britain was there such deep safe water than in the sunken fiord of Milford Haven.

Our objections and those of the National Parks Commission were overruled. It was explained at the enquiry that BP had agreed with the County Planning Department to disguise as much as possible the holding tanks within the massive walls of Popton Fort, and in the valley below; and the sixty miles of pipeline which would convey the crude oil from the tankers to the refinery at Swansea would be buried and leave no scar on our landscape.

When I interviewed the Chairman of BP, the newly-knighted Sir Neville Gass, in his palatial London office, he offered the same reassurances and was very sympathetic. The interview ended with his offer, on behalf of BP, to make a substantial contribution to the fund we had just opened for the purchase of Skomer.

For a few months the countryside around Orielton was disturbed by excavating and pipe-laying machinery, and gangs of Irish labourers who were not inexpert at poaching in our woods – for the pipeline passed within fifty yards of our boundary walls. Then, as predicted, the scar healed over.

But the threat remained, and presently increased. It was next announced that a large oil refinery was to be built, with an ocean terminal quay extending halfway across Milford Haven from the opposite, northern, shore, capable of berthing the largest tankers ever built, well above 100,000 tons.

Once again the public enquiry was a mere formality. The argument we put forward that the land was sacrosanct under the National Parks Act was swept aside by another enabling Act of Parliament, to be passed 'in the national interest'. The fact that the site selected for the refinery was also rich double-cropping farm land counted as nothing; the Esso Company had already bought it at ten times its agricultural value. The danger we naturalists pointed out, of oil pollution of the tidal waters, was quite remote (learned counsel for Esso stated at the enquiry): a modern ocean terminal had safeguards against every risk of accidental leakage; even if there were a malfunction in unloading or loading, the berthed tanker would be surrounded with an air-filled rubber boom which would automatically contain any spilt oil, and as this would naturally float on the surface it could easily be pumped back into receiving tanks ashore.

'What about the prevailing gales and the seven-knot tide-races for which Milford Haven is notorious?' we challenged at the enquiry. The question was regarded as unworthy of reply.

Cyril Hurcomb had retired and was serenely occupied in watching birds and helping wildlife and conservation projects. He was soon to be elected President of both the Royal Society for the Protection of Birds, and the new Field Studies Council, as well as Chairman of the Nature Conservancy. He counselled acceptance of the inevitable . . .

'Unfortunately we cannot do without oil, but we must certainly fight oil pollution; and when it occurs we must make these companies pay very large fines – they are rich enough! And by the way, why not ask them to contribute towards your Skomer purchase fund? I may be able to drop a hint in the right quarter.'

'At the moment, unless you can raise more from them, Esso has already offered £500, to match a cheque we have lately received from BP for the same amount. I am not sure that our Trust should accept – too much like hush-money . . .'

'Don't be ridiculous! If they really wanted to, either company could afford to buy Skomer outright and present it to the nation as a permanent nature reserve.'

'One oil company, not BP or Esso, has already approached me, through an agent who won't divulge the name of his company, to buy Orielton.'

'Really – most interesting! Have you named your price? I hope you made it a substantial one? But of course, you wouldn't ever think of selling Orielton.'

'My reply to this gentleman in the pin-striped suit was that I would sell for a reasonable price only if his company agreed to keep the whole estate as a nature reserve and place for field studies – as I keep it at present. Of course that scared him away! His company wants it as prestige offices and as a country club with a golf course for their employees.'

'No, no, that would be horrid, for this lovely old place,' agreed Hurcomb, who had his binoculars trained upon a flight of large birds circling and soaring upon a thermal above the Lily Pond. 'Six buzzards and five ravens in the air together! Ah, yes, and a sparrowhawk! They would probably employ gamekeepers . . .'

'The pin-striped gentleman,' I continued, rather bitterly, 'hinted that I was foolish not to consider what would be an advantageous sale for me. He said that other oil companies were now buying land along the shore of Milford Haven, and it could well be that the government would soon consider erecting an oil-fed power station near Orielton, close to the site for the latest new refinery. I had to admit that I wouldn't want to live close to the industrial complex he envisaged, with smoke and flame stacks dotting my view! He said he would call again, but I had better make up my mind as there were other large houses locally which might fit the requirements of his company; but Orielton had a more pleasing prospect . . .'

In haste to exploit the new facilities of the first refinery in Milford Haven the Esso Company extended their wharf half a mile into the tideway, and their separating and distilling plant was rapidly completed. The new complex stood starkly upon the skyline of the hill above, where formerly Pembrokeshire cattle and sheep had peacefully grazed behind the ancient hedges of stone and gorse which divided the rich red soil into little fields, south-facing, yielding the earliest crops of this frost-free shore. By agreement with the planning authorities the company were planting trees which, however, soon died in that windswept position; and even the hardier conifers could never grow tall enough adequately to screen the huge storage tanks, the towering chimneys and flare-stacks. They stand in full view there today, as grim as ever.

For the opening ceremony splendid marquees had been erected to accommodate over a thousand guests, many brought by special trains (for the new refinery was quickly linked by a private line to the railhead at Milford), who would enjoy the great feast, wines, speeches and tour of the works – an entertainment said to have cost Esso at least £100,000 which, I reflected sadly, was ten times the sum we needed to buy Skomer.

As if this violation of a beautiful coast which man had but lately declared inviolate against all industry, had put 'all Heaven in a rage', a savage gale completely wrecked the marquees on the day before the great picnic was to take place. The opening ceremony had to take place in the brand-new, commodious, machine-repair shop. As a leading reactionary I had nevertheless been invited and – somewhat grudgingly – decided to attend.

One other unwilling guest enlivened the smooth proceedings for me. The chairman of the parent Standard Oil Company (Esso) had come specially across the Atlantic to open the proceedings, to explain, in his rich voice, the importance of Milford Haven; and even to express a mild regret for the necessity of invading our beautiful national park, 'but my friends, it is ness'ry: Milford Haven provides what our newest super-tankers must have – deep wa'rer!'

In the middle of this speech, a bewildered sparrow, accidentally imprisoned in the building and despairing of the glare of the arc lights in the roof, suddenly flew down to perch on the rostrum in front of Prince Philip, Duke of Edinburgh. His Royal Highness – a keen bird-watcher – smiled upon the impudent bird, which circled for a moment around the princely head when he rose to read a speech and press the button which would officially put the refinery 'on stream'.

* * *

Despite the reiterated declaration that safety precautions at a modern refinery made it virtually impossible for crude oil to escape and pollute the sea, the first tanker to berth at the Esso wharf suffered a tragic accident. During discharge the metal coupling to a flexible pipe fell and struck the steel deck of the ship. The resulting spark ignited the highly inflammable vapour from the hold. There was a series of tremendous explosions, which sounded at Orielton like heavy thunder. Men were killed and wounded, the tanker burned fiercely, the flames spreading over the sea around the wharf. The rubber containing-boom was burned and perished – it was a complete failure in that strong tide-rip which makes the berthing of large ships in this haven a tricky operation, needing the highest skilled pilot. The boom was never replaced.

But this was only the first of many accidents, large and small, which have ever since continued to pollute the tideway of Milford Haven. The fines for these spillages have been increased, but are still a trivial item in the budget of the wealthy oil companies, which severally operate half a dozen large installations there today.

'Don't despair yet, Boyo,' were almost the last words of Ifor ap Rhys, who lived just long enough to see the flarestack of the first refinery lighted. 'One day oil won't be wanted any more, or there won't be any left. But our Rhondda coal will outlast all the oil in Arabia – or elsewhere. Then the cormorants and gulls will be nesting on the derelict crumbling ocean terminals, and the jackdaws in the tumbling smokeless chimneys. And there'll be greater need than ever for Orielton. You must hold on to the dear old place . . .'

Ifor, with his hacking cough, going back to the rain shadows of the Rhondda Valley, made me feel ashamed of my present gloom and foreboding while yet I lived in the sunlight of this still (almost) peaceful peninsula.

Another winter passed and, 'Don't despair, we'll find a way to save Orielton,' said Peter Scott one warm June day, as we sailed around the islands I knew so well. Peter had never landed on Grassholm, and thither we sailed for a picnic and survey of its vast colony of gannets. We called at my old home of Skokholm, then on for the night with the shearwaters at Skomer. It was not a time to despair, only to enjoy the glorious midsummer weather in perfect human and avian company. Yet next day, gliding on thermals high above the coast, we could see all too plainly the long scar of the developing oil port smeared across the sunken fiord of red cliff which is Milford Haven, and the iridescent whirls of escaping oil.

(Typically, Peter, shortly to win the gliding championship of the British Isles, had towed behind his car for 150 miles his new sailplane *Mallard*, simply because of a letter he had received from some local enthusiasts who, getting wind of his visit to Orielton, had written to ask him to help boost interest in the new gliding club being set up at the old aerodrome at Haverfordwest. He had allowed the more expert among them to fly his *Mallard* solo.)

Cyril Hurcomb, too, had come to Orielton again. He was encouraging, even optimistic of its future, despite my groans of despair when I motored him to the hill from which we could look down on the new refinery. 'Don't give up yet. Somehow we must work out a plan to keep Orielton the way you have made it.'

Lord Hurcomb had come for another, but very different, opening ceremony.

13

For him the woods were a home and gave him the key
Of knowledge, thirst for their treasures in herbs and flowers.
The secrets held by the creatures nearer than we
To earth he sought, and the link of their life with ours:
And where alike we are, unlike where, and the vein'd
Division, vein'd parallel, of a blood that flows
In them, in us, from the source by man unattain'd
Save marks he well what the mystical woods disclose.

GEORGE MEREDITH
Melampus

The crippled collarless dog had been picked up by Ellen, grand-daughter of Elijah and Eliza, on the day of her wedding and her seventeenth birthday. Everyone loved Ellen as well for her lively graceful manner as for her rose-bloom beauty. I had good cause to admire her dexterity in the field, where her flying fingers would earn the maximum piece-work wage of the day. Eliza had told me that Ellen was saving up for her marriage to her cousin, the mechanic David; and would I like to attend the reception? Ellen wished me to come, but was too shy to ask me herself, perhaps afraid I would refuse. I was amused and honoured by the invitation.

Some days earlier I had been involved with the intending bridegroom, who had offered to buy my rather worn-out farm van. With a typical tinker nose for a bargain David had asked to be allowed to try the van out for a few days, although he must have known, from driving it occasionally during work-days in the field at Orielton, that it was reliable, despite its battered appearance.

A fair price had been agreed, subject to David taking the van on those 'few days on trial' – which turned out to be for the whole of the honeymoon, to be spent in Ireland. I was a little surprised, but made no demur, and joined heartily in the farewell cheers when the happy couple drove away from the reception in the van, with the usual tin cans dangling from the rear, packed with tent, cooking pot and other gipsy chattels.

The party resumed the festive country talk, merry with the

279

occasion and Eliza's potent home-made herb beer. A little sad for me in one way, for the clan had yet again been ordered by the local authority to leave Redstone Quarry – this time on the excuse that the site was to be incorporated in a new housing development in connection with the developing oil refinery industry.

'Aye, us'll 'ave t' clear right out this time,' said Elijah cheerfully. 'But us'll be back some day, never fear. Just drop us line, boss, when thee needs 'elp wi' th' spuds . . .'

His gipsy soul was perfectly happy at the prospect of roaming once more, and I knew that he had added that promise solely to please me and avoid hurting my feelings. A natural gentleman, Elijah had imbibed the art of polite prevarication and procrastination with his mother's milk, it was part of a gipsy's survival mechanism in an abrasive modern world.

'Thanks, I will. But how'll I know where to write? Going far?'

'Up north, I 'spect. Ellen an' Dave, they'll know where us'll be. They'm stayin' 'ere for spell. That Irish overseer 'oo give Ellen 'is 'ome haddress to call in County Cork, 'e's promised Dave job on th' 'finery site. Top mechanic is Dave . . .'

At that moment there was a familar mechanical noise of loose bearings as my old van rattled back into the quarry. The tin cans had vanished from the rear door, which David flung open to reveal a young sheepdog of nondescript colour and doubtful ancestry. It snarled at Ellen when she tried to lift it gently.

'Poor Jack!'

Ellen had given a name at random to this pitiable bloody object which, squeezed into a narrow space behind the camping gear, was half-dragged and half-fell to the ground, whimpering in agony. It lay there, three good legs in the air, the fourth, broken at the hip, trailing in the grass.

'Poor devil! 'E's done for. Better knock 'im on th' 'ead,' said David. 'Ellen, she made me stop when car in front 'us run o'er stupid dog when 'e rushed out barkin' from side o' road! I were goin' ter chase bugger for not stoppin', but 'e were drivin' too fast, and Ellen, yer know 'er, she's proper soft 'earted. I told 'er 'twere no use, but Ellen, she wanted ter bring 'im back.' His next words were mumbled: 'Couldn' leave 'im dyin' like that. Bad luck on 'er weddin'day.'

David, uncomfortably overheated, strange-looking in a borrowed suit, collar and spangled tie, shut the van door and caught

Ellen's hand. 'Come on, littul wife, us'll be late. Mussen' miss the Rosslare ferry.'

Ellen, prettier than ever with her veil thrown back from her rosy face, her dark eyes brimming with tears, gave the company a swift look of appeal, momentarily pausing as her eyes caught mine (perhaps I imagined this – but in that glance I read her demand to save the dog). She returned to the passenger seat where she sobbed with the excess of her mixed emotions over wedding, birthday, honeymoon and dying dog, as the vehicle rattled out of the quarry and disappeared.

Jack lay where he had collapsed while Elijah's lurchers inspected and sniffed the whining helpless animal. This attitude, prone and submissive, was correct canine etiquette for a stranger entering another dog's territory, and inhibited attack.

Eliza, splendid in her traditional coloured dress, adorned with necklaces, beads, bangles, rings and other finery for this special occasion, hurried into her caravan. Elijah, searching the heap of wood near the open fire, found a long flat stick. He picked up a hatchet. When I touched his arm, meaning to restrain him, he said, mildly as ever:

'I were only goin' to cut splints for Jack's leg. Eliza's makin' drench o' poppyseed ter deaden 'is pain.'

'Surely, Elijah, such a bad break ought to be set in plaster? May I take him to the vet – at once?'

So Jack crept into my life inadvertently, but perhaps at the right moment. Most of my farming life I had had a sheepdog, except at Orielton, where one might have been a nuisance during the wildlife studies. But the rabbit life-history observation was about to be wound up. This study had lingered on (although the grant from the Nature Conservancy had long ago run its course) only because I had been reluctant to break up the enclosures.

No one claimed Jack, no one wanted a sheepdog with a broken leg, or a lame one when the leg healed. Yet through his accident Jack was to claim my affection by his near-human response to my care and companionship, beginning with the moment he awoke from the anaesthetic, free from the agony of broken bones grinding together.

During a convalescence of several weeks he lay in my study, unable to walk. I persuaded myself that here was a splendid opportunity to study the canine mind – about which many books had been written, explaining and not explaining why alone of all mammals the dog attaches itself so irrevocably to man, and often to one man or woman only. Of course, in any such study I would resist the tendency I had noticed in myself to anthropomorphism and sloppy sentimentality in communicating with a dumb animal.

Thus I tried to harden my heart and adopt a scientific approach when I saw him watching my every moment with eyes that shone with approval, while his tail, somewhat restricted by the plaster cast on his thigh, quietly thumped. But he would avert his head and roll his eyes to one side if he detected by my voice and manner that I was in a bad mood. With nothing else to do but watch me, he seemed instantly to interpret the state of my mind and emotions, happy when I was happy, angry if I was angry – with another human being (I had no anger for him). He would growl a warning at the approach of anyone, even my wife, sons and Victoria; for although I feel sure he knew they were harmless and kind, his love for me rapidly became possessive and protective. He barked aloud and snapped at Jesus.

I was puzzled but could only guess why, once the plaster had been removed and he could hobble around (but never run again), he continued to exhibit an active hatred for the human race. The accident of course had been a serious upset and he had been ready to bite his rescuers, but his sudden deep devotion to one man seemed odd. In spite of extensive further enquiries in the neighbourhood of his accident I had been unable to find anyone who would admit to owning Jack as a pup, and could only surmise that his previous master must have been a cruel person. Sometimes when I looked into his grey eyes, he seemed to be mutely thanking me for my sympathy for his lameness, his lost youth and for his mysterious origin and, if only he could, he would explain that he was bad-tempered because he had been beaten by the inhuman being who had owned him as a pup; and that, in his rage against all men, he had been attempting to attack the brute – possibly it *was* his master – in that car which had run down and abandoned him.

Because Jesus had claimed to be – and indeed was, Andalusian style – an expert in the management of sheep, I had not thought to buy a sheepdog to tend our stolid Dorset Horn ewes which, highly profitable with their ability to lamb thrice in two years, suited the rotation of grassland and crops which we practised.

Jesus would catch a ewe by one leg now and then, and take off surplus milk to make a tasty cheese to a Spanish recipe. He tended the flock somewhat irregularly, however, because of his duties as houseman; and I was glad, and he was upset, when Jack took a deep and active interest in the flock at first sight. For Jack hated Jesus and would not work the sheep in his presence, but would skulk beside me, growling his disgust and distrust at this interference in a sheepdog's lawful business.

Alone with me and the flock Jack (he may have had some training as a pup but I doubt this) responded instinctively, with rapidly developing skill, to the slight signals I would give – a pointing finger, a soft word or whistle. His lameness and quiet manner were acceptable to this heavy breed of sheep, which tolerated with dignity his gentle manoeuvres and barked orders; and his delight in the work was a joy to watch. He earned his keep, and my pleasure in his companionship increased.

This swift, intelligent response in a young dog evidently springs from an inherited and powerful instinct which matures as soon as the modern sheepdog, selectively bred over generations of training in shepherding, is introduced to a flock of sheep. It can be seen early in the untrained pup when it first follows a chicken around the farmyard with amusing, yet dogged, persistence. The inborn skill is an adaptation of the ancient hunting technique of those ancestors of the domesticated dog, the wolf and jackal, which pursue and encircle their prey.

Jack would follow me like a shadow everywhere, unless I forbade him, which I seldom had the heart to do. For his look of reproach when I said NO was heartrending. He would have spent the rest of his life at my feet; but I was obliged to agree with visitors to my study that, despite the occasional bath I gave him (a sponging down which he endured only for my sake, with stoic misery), the room reeked of hairy dog, a smell to which I myself was somewhat allergic. Therefore, as soon as he was quite as well as he would ever be, I told him:

'No, never again, Jack! Except perhaps for birthdays, or Christmas. You stink – and most people dislike your growling manner. Mr X hates you. Jesus is threatening to leave. Anyway, a sheepdog's place is outside.'

When he disobeyed this order the first time, my sharp reproof was sufficient to prevent him entering the house again. In future when we reached the door he would stop, lift up his head for the customary pat of approval, then avert his eyes until the whites showed; telling me plainer than words: 'What have I done to deserve this cruel banishment?' As soon as the door closed he would circle the spot twice and, inserting his nose under his long bushy tail, curl up on the doorstep, ignoring the warm kennel under the evergreen oak, watchful and distrustful of any visitor that dared approach the old manor.

'Ah, Jack! You flatter my ego too much. You cater too profoundly for the need of my vain and lonely heart – for every man, and every dog, is ultimately alone – by your extravagant devotion and excessive compliance, by the love shining in your beautiful grey eyes! Admissable as your watchdog guardianship of the master and the old manor may be, you are too much of a one-man dog; visitors complain of your surliness, children run away from your frightening growls. Away with you, unsociable beast! I have done my best to help and understand and unravel your twisted mentality, but at times I think I hate your stupid subservience to me, and that horrible temper you show to others . . . mostly, alas, I love you dearly!'

*   *   *

One sunlit morning a migrating grey phalarope alighted on the Lily Pond and pirouetted in typical fashion, paddling with its palmated feet, stirring the calm water, and snatching at amphibious insects and small specks of food swirling around the dainty wader. The onshore winds had brought these oceanic birds closer to land; we had seen many during recent seal-marking expeditions, feeding inshore amid floating seaweed torn from the outer rocks by the surf.

It seemed marvellous that this feeble-looking bird, nesting in the Arctic, normally spent its winter far at sea in the southern hemisphere, involving a migration of thousands of miles twice a year. But at least it thereby escaped winter altogether, and lived, except during its equinoctial migrations, in perpetual summer. While I watched its curious feeding technique of rapidly spinning (two-thirds of these phalaropes spin to the right), accompanied by side-to-side dabbing of the bill, and now and then a swift zigzag forward to seize a larger insect upwelling to the surface, my eye noticed a movement on the edge of the opposite shore.

It was the first water-vole *Arvicola terrestris* I had seen by the Lily Pond. There it sat, complacently observing me – and the phalarope – but was not to be put off eating some kind of small fruit which it held in its mobile 'hands'. Presently it dipped its paws into the water as if washing them, then squatted down and stared towards the restless phalarope.

I had often watched these amusing, chubby voles on the banks of slow-moving English rivers, where they are comparatively tame. From time to time we had seen a few in the Decoy Pond, shy and hunted by otters and other predators. And once a pair had spent a winter beside the freshwater spring at Martinshaven while I was building a lodge as a mainland base for my island home of Skokholm thirty years ago. But this creature is far from common in Wales.

The phalarope presently shot up into the sky like a snipe, to resume its astonishing migration. The stay-at-home water vole gave a nervous shiver, and seemed relieved. It began a meticulous preening of its handsome chestnut coat. The fur is dense and made waterproof by constant grooming with the oily saliva of its tongue, and by the fatty secretion from sweat glands situated on its flanks and transferred by the paws to those parts of the body the tongue cannot reach. Thus oiled the feet leave a scent trail which obviously has significance in marking out territory and indicating its presence to other voles: a useful but also dangerous advertisement in a semi-wandering animal. However it can escape strictly terrestrial predators by diving under the water. At this it is expert; its hind feet are broad and fringed with stiff hairs to assist swimming.

Live-trapping quickly established that a pair of water-voles was living by the Lily Pond that autumn. I marked each by snipping the edge of the short round ear (female in the left, male in the right), much as shepherds mark their sheep. When taken from the trap each squealed like a guinea-pig, biting a little at first, but they soon became tame and did not attempt to leap from my hands later. As a pet, I thought, the water rat (as it is often erroneously called) might be most attractive. Unlike the repellant smell of the brown or black rats, that of the water-vole has a faintly sweet musky odour.

The brown rat *Rattus norvegicus* will try to squeeze into the narrow burrows of the water-vole despite the latter's smaller size

(two-thirds as long as the rat at 17cm, and the tail much shorter at 10cm), in search of a feed of young voles. The vole is said to be driven into a frenzy of fear and screaming by the stench of the brown rat; although it is also recorded that a mother water-vole will attack a marauding rat with courage and slashing teeth, and will afterwards remove her young one by one to a safer place.

To my surprise, during the regular periods of trapping small mammals in the next few months, I caught four more (unmarked) water-voles along the edge of the ponds. Evidently the previous summer had been one of explosion of population for *Arvicola*, a sort of 'lemming year' enabling them to recolonise watersides long unoccupied. They were easy and amusing to watch, since if you wore neutrally-coloured clothes and kept perfectly still, they would ignore you, being largely diurnal in their activities in the quiet sanctuary of the Lily and Japanese Ponds.

Here they established a system of tunnels in the low banks, with entrances both above and below water-level; and grazed down the surrounding vegetation until it became a lawn around their doorways. Habitually a vole would appear, perhaps clutching a juicy plant, which it would devour, holding it in its forepaws, squatting at the entrance to a tunnel, gazing watchfully this way and that, like a country cottager enjoying a ray of sunshine and hoping for a little neighbourly small talk. This carrying of food, to be eaten close to the home burrow, was a precautionary habit, enabling a swift disappearance when the sight or smell of a predator disturbed the peace. The vole's beady black eyes observed all that was in view, but no action was taken when harmless water-shrew, duck or fish swam near.

The diet is not entirely vegetarian. Water-voles will eat small fish and young frogs, fragments of which I found near their burrow entrances, and probably caught when they are browsing in the dense aquatic vegetation inshore. The main food seemed to be swamp and littoral greenstuff which the vole reaped with its chisel teeth, ingesting each long blade from base to flowering tip with a rolling motion of the jaw, and an air of great satisfaction that was amusing to watch.

Necessarily these voles are meticulous about sanitation, depositing their stools in small heaps in the open within their feeding territory, a habit which must also be a clear indication of possession.

On sunlit days in April and May courtship pursuits and mating activity were easily observed. Engrossed in love affairs, the colony allowed a yet closer approach, provided you remained down wind. The male is larger and darker than his mate, and like the buck rabbit appeared to be uxorious, and a tolerant father. He would sit beside his wife – obvious by his broader skull – and allow his children to play and feed around him. A charming picture.

The babies are born naked, blind and toothless in a warm nest hidden below ground, after a gestation period of three weeks. They quickly grow a dense coat of red-gold hair; and at two weeks old emerge to nibble the lawn and play. But they are timid at first and seem afraid of the water, which they approach cautiously – to sniff and sip. Meanwhile the mother has already mated in a post-parturition oestrus; she is almost continuously pregnant during the spring and early summer flush of green vegetation which supplies her with the protein she needs to support this condition. Her mate, too, needs this rich food to stimulate a vigorous spermatogenesis; it is believed that male, rather than female, sterility determines the beginning and end of the breeding season. As long as this lasts he is as aggressive as the king rabbit is towards other mature males, and drives them fiercely away when he finds them too near his property of wife, burrow and grazing ground.

The half-grown youngsters became expert divers, frequently using the under-water entrance to their home. As soon as one emerged from the water it would shake itself like a dog, and its fur was instantly dry as the silvery drops rolled from the oily pelage.

By midsummer the multiplying colony had riddled the banks of both the Lily and Japanese Ponds with a labyrinth of tunnels. Some of these opened several yards away from water, giving access to more distant feeding grounds in the cover of damp vegetation and woodland. During one heavy thunderstorm in June the resulting flood water spurted through some fresh vole burrows excavated in the containing bank during a recent low level caused by drought. I muttered curses on the water-voles; for unless I repaired the dam, its winter level would be reduced permanently to this low summer level. Now I understood why human owners of riparian property sought to exterminate the burrowing 'water-rats'. And why water-voles are semi-nomadic – at least when they colonise artifically constructed lakes and reservoirs – it's because they destroy their own habitat by unplugging the water!

For a moment, while I sought for some clay to repair the dam, I wondered if I should not signal Tony Soper, who had wanted to introduce beavers at Orielton – he was currently keeping some young beavers at his Devon home. Beavers are expert at building and keeping a dam in repair; they would plaster up water-vole tunnels. But they too moved on, once they had eaten out all the edible young trees around the shores of their home-made lake . . .

Testing the soil near the ponds in search of some clay, my spade uncovered a roomy underground chamber stored with new potatoes, acorns and seeds of wild plants (including bulbs of bluebell and bulbils of our rare Welsh wild onion). The water-voles were hoarding a cache of food for the winter. The potatoes could only have come from the nearest garden – that of Cortez, some seventy yards away–quite a feat of (presumably nocturnal) transport for these small animals. I noted the contents, and weighed them: three kilos (two of potatoes). I replaced the hoard and covered the chamber with a tea-chest lid, then heaped earth over it.

Water-voles seem to have so many enemies that it is surprising that they survive as they do. Along the sluggish rivers of lowland England where their colonies are more or less permanent, they may have fewer predators; they will move to a fresh site, up or down stream, when the old one has become too heavily plundered, and perhaps lethally infected with the ectoparasites, bacteria and viruses endemic in this species.

The man-made ornamental ponds at Orielton were not a typical habitat for these voles. They had numerous enemies here: owl, buzzard, kestrel, raven and heron; as well as stoat, otter, weasel and feral cat; the badger could dig down into their burrows; while outside the enclosure the fox hunted them along the shores of the Decoy Lake. Water-voles are also eaten by large fish such as pike. Their numbers rapidly dwindled with the cessation of breeding early in the autumn. By December I could count very few visible on a fine day of winter.

In captivity voles are old at three years; in the wild the mature female, after one full breeding season producing four litters averaging five or six young, is worn out. She will not survive her second winter. The daughters of her first litter may breed once in the same summer, and will be the first to breed again when a year old in the next spring. Nor will the mature male, worn out by excessive sexual and territorial activity, survive the further strain on his metabolism imposed by the need to grow a new waterproof fur coat for a second winter. In this enfeebled state, and spurned by their progeny, the old adults, although but eighteen months in this world, are soon mopped up by their natural predators.

It is the juvenile voles, fat with good feeding by the autumn, which become vigorous and territorially minded at that time, and take over the best burrows and the store rooms, which they will inhabit over the winter. This youthful aggression has an important function: where there has been a successful breeding summer, and a surplus of young voles, the older, more powerful, adolescents drive out the late born. These go forth to found new colonies by watersides in fresh feeding zones, making thereby fuller use of the available resources, and escaping the harassment, and the risks of disease, in the old burrows.

In this manner had colonists taken possession of the vacant water-vole niche in the Lily Pond. The little city of wet and dry tunnels, and its bustling summer population so amusing to watch, lasted but two summers. In the third winter it was vacated as suddenly and as mysteriously as it had been built. I missed these golden-coated water gipsies and their amusing *Wind in the Willows* existence; and hoped they would return in the years ahead.

*   *   *

I first saw a red squirrel at Orielton – from the drawing-room window – while Alice Gaddum was still alive. She told me they had been numerous when she and Arthur had first taken up residence. Now, as she could no longer see, I described for her the antics of this lively tawny-coated beast, with the enormous bushy tail tipped over its head. It was plucking ripe acorns from the evergreen oak a few yards from the window. The scaly black branches rattled to its claws as it ran nimbly through the outermost twigs. Holding an acorn in its mouth it scuttered agilely down the main trunk, head first, pausing for half a second now and then to jerk its head watchfully. Finding nothing to disturb it, it ran along the ground between the rhododendrons, scrabbled furiously with its forepaws in the grass, and thrust the oak fruit into a shallow hole. Immediately, impatiently, it pushed soil and grass together to cover the acorn; then ran back up the holm oak to pluck another. This and several more were buried, each in a separate shallow hole, dug swiftly yet deliberately, and apparently carefully selected.

Students of animal behaviour believe that this so-called 'scatter-hoarding' by squirrels and other animals which store food is a habit as purely instinctive as the considerable skill of a squirrel – or other nest-builder, such as a chaffinch – weaving the nest characteristic of its species. That is to say this skill is not learned by the example of its parents, who build their nursery before the family is born. The chaffinch will construct its exquisite cup-nest of dry grass, hair, feathers, moss and cobwebs perfectly without having seen another chaffinch doing so. The information is already coded in the genes and chromosomes inherited when male sperm and female ovum coalesce in the maternal reproductive system.

The squirrel burying an acorn or nut for the first time does not do so as an insurance (which the action nevertheless is) against an anticipated shortage of food in winter. Its intentions are nil, its actions instinctive; at best it will find only some of these hidden acorns, simply by 'doing what comes naturally': by following much the same sequence of movements (determined in the first place almost at random but to some extent guided by the configuration of the ground and of obstacles in its path) which it made on the first occasion, descending the tree and scrabbling with its claws in the ground in similar fashion. Yet there must be an element of remembering, of learning, in the form of a 'live' picture imprinted in the memory cells, and partly a kinaesthetic or muscle memory of having done it once before, as man remembers with brain and body a previous action in like manner, often vaguely, sometimes vividly if it concerns a vital matter. So that having found one buried acorn, it is likely that a hungry squirrel will search for and find some more in 'likely' places near by, within its familiar feeding range. But many are never recovered; apart from the random way these fruits are buried, the majority of squirrels do not survive the winter. The same can be said of the acorn- and nut-burying jay, which was fairly common in our woods; both hoarders must have been responsible for many a healthy oak and nut tree flourishing there today.

As early as 28 January of my first spring as owner of Orielton I watched a pair of red squirrels chasing and chattering in high spirits in the leafless beeches above the sheets of new-flowering snowdrops. Even when snow fell lightly a few days later, reflecting a brighter light upon the lowermost branches, the squirrels continued to indulge their courtship antics, bounding agilely through the cool forest maze, disturbing the acrobatic flocks of coal, marsh and blue tits which had arrived that winter from the frozen continent. Squirrels do not hibernate in Wales but are active all winter.

Except at mating time the red squirrel is solitary. From the January and February couplings, after a long gestation of six or seven weeks, two to seven young are born blind and helpless in the warmly lined nursery basket or drey built close to the trunk of a tree. The eyes do not open for a month, and not until they are two months old do the young squirrels push their way through the elastic sides of the drey and begin an independent, and soon solitary, life. The mature female accepts the male again at the end of two month's lactation, and a second litter is normally born soon after midsummer, when food in the form of wild fruits is abundant.

Little is known about the life of the truly wild squirrel. The red *Sciurus vulgaris* was shy at Orielton, and grew scarcer every year. On a first encounter it would race high up a tree, and hide behind the trunk until you passed by. But if you remained perfectly still long enough, it would come peeping into view, and presently resume normal activities, although watchful of the place where it last noticed you. All food, even if taken on the ground, is carried aloft to be eaten.

Long before the 'foreign American' or grey squirrel appeared at Orielton the native red squirrel gradually became rare. At intervals I would find one on the ground looking very sick, scarcely able to run away from me, and disinclined to climb into the trees. At this time a fatal illness seemed to be spreading through the red squirrels in the deciduous woods of Britain. It was said that the grey, contemptuously referred to as 'that ugly tree-rat', was driving out the 'beautiful red'. One popular local version was that the foreign squirrel attacked the hindquarters of the male red and emasculated it – a sensational explanation but not satisfactorily proved. At Orielton the red had virtually disappeared when one day in June I saw the first grey squirrel amble boldly up the hard gravelled centre of the driveway – no attempt at a cautious approach by way of the bordering trees – and enter a shrubbery. It had all the air, it seemed to me, of a scout or emissary taking possession of the estate on behalf of the new wave of colonists. (Almost history repeating itself; as when the bold Wiriets from Normandy took possession from the less well-armed native Welsh.)

Symbolically, perhaps, this invasion coincided with the year of building the first oil refinery; an invasion I likewise resisted for, apart from its alleged lethal effect on the red species, the grey squirrel has the reputation of damaging crops and gardens. It is hated by foresters for its habit of stripping the bark of young trees; and by bird-lovers for its appetite for the eggs and nestlings of small birds.

Fearing these bad habits I would have destroyed this uninvited guest – but at that moment the Hitchcox gun was dismembered and locked in my study, and could not be put together quickly, or even used safely again. (It had not been fired since the death of Madame Goateyes.)

More grey squirrels were soon to follow the lone scout. In the next two autumns there was a lemming-like dispersal and march of adolescent *Sciurus carolensis* from the eastern Welsh counties and England into west Wales. As recorded in *Nature in Wales* (a new journal the West Wales Naturalists Trust launched at Orielton in 1955), numbers of the tree-rats were seen in 1961 far from trees, most of them making their way westwards in broad daylight across open fields, even over bare mountains, taking refuge here and there in rabbit-burrows and rock crevices, in barns, roofs and attics. This was a very remarkable population explosion and emigration in a tree-nesting animal, and difficult to understand, since most of the reports indicated that the travellers were in fine condition. Those which were halted by the sea lived for a while in rabbit-burrows, but winter and predators sorted out and exterminated these. A large proportion settled down in the main deciduous woods of west Wales, which they continue to inhabit, in fluctuating numbers, to the exclusion of the red species.

That autumn the tenant of North Lodge complained that not only had a colony of honey-bees settled in the roof since I had last marked bats there, but somehow grey squirrels had got in and were making terrible noises at night and sometimes by day. Would I do something about it? When I opened the trap door to the lodge roof a horrible smell smote my nostrils; the light of my torch revealed numerous half-eaten and putrid corpses of bats. Possibly the squirrels had entered in search of honey in the first place – there was still a lively hum from broken combs in the apex, and one or two bees buzzed aggressively at me as I hastily closed the trap door. It looked as if the bees had won: I had glimpsed a grey squirrel, evidently stung to death during its assault on the bats and the honey, stiff in one corner. (Subsequently the bees multiplied to such an extent in this small confined space that it was not safe for squirrel, bat or man to enter the roof of North Lodge.)

Rather larger and heavier, the grey lacks the rich colour and long ear-tufts of the native squirrel. Its breeding cycle is like that of the red, with two litters a year in a tree-nest or drey. It eats much the same food and tree-fruits, which it will scatter-hoard in similar fashion. The evidence now suggests that there is little real competition, because their ecology differs: the red thrives best in a coniferous habitat, but it had colonised broad-leaved woods in the absence of any other squirrel in Britain. When the grey was introduced from America, where it is perfectly adapted to the broad-leaved forest (but feeds freely on the ground) it found itself in a suitably familiar environment. Today in Britain the red survives principally in coniferous forests, where it is sometimes numerous; the grey claims the deciduous country, where it continues to be persecuted by most landusers. A resilient species, it freely enters town parks and gardens, becomes very tame, and amuses citizens and children; as the Americans say – a cute little feller.

*   *   *

At last we had persuaded Leonard Lee, the industrialist, to part with Skomer which (almost on a whim, he told us) he had outbid us for when the island was up for sale some years earlier. He had intended it to be a surprise present for his wife. He loved islands himself, and had hoped to restore the ruined farmhouse and live there – one day. But he was still a young man and not ready to retire . . . Each time I called to see him in his London office he was less sure about living there; for one thing his wife had first visited it on a stormy day, and had told him it was too wild and lonely. After two years of persuasion he had reluctantly agreed to sell Skomer to our naturalists' trust 'in the national interest', and at a figure which he declared would barely recoup his outlay.

With Lord Hurcomb and Max Nicholson at the Nature Conservancy we had worked out a partnership whereby the West Wales Naturalists' Trust would raise £4,000 of the purchase price of £10,000, and on the same day sell it to the Nature Conservancy for £6,000 – the limit which the government valuer had fixed as its current worth (with a derelict farmhouse, and with no nonsense about the importance of its vast sea-bird population, worthless in monetary terms). In return for losing £4,000 on the deal, the Trust would be granted a lease at a peppercorn rent, and at the same time obtain a safe landlord in the Nature Conservancy which promised to build a house for our warden at a cost of at least £4,000.

It was a neat arrangement, and has worked perfectly. The Trust as lessee appoints a resident warden, whose salary is recouped from the landing fees paid by visitors, many of whom join the Trust as well. The Conservancy is landlord of one of the finest sea-bird sanctuaries in the world, with virtually no maintenance costs. At the same time my old home of Skokholm remains a nature reserve under the Trust, with a resident warden and accommodation for a limited number of visiting naturalists.

It was now midsummer. The sea-birds had returned in thousands to the islands, although already some oil pollution from Milford Haven had affected those species – puffins, guillemots and razorbills – which spend most of their lives swimming in search of food, rather than flying. There was an expedition to Skomer to declare it a National Nature Reserve. Our party from Orielton forgathered on the island in the sun and wind beside the broken-down farm buildings where, not so long before, Lordy had tested his hopes of becoming a nature warden – in vain.

Already there had been a number of applications for the post of Skomer's first warden. One had been from a man who wrote that he loved birds, and had hatched a sparrow's egg, not in his bosom but under his armpit (for better humidity and steady temperature), and had reared the little chick by mouth-feeding it with masticated bread and meat from his rations. He hoped that this would be sufficient recommendation for him to become warden of Skomer – in a year's time – just now he was unavoidably detained at Her Majesty's pleasure; the address on this letter was that of an HM Prison.

Another person, distressed for a somewhat different reason, turned up the same day as his application arrived at Orielton. Lorent de Bastayai was a middle-aged aristocrat of the old land-owning class no longer *persona grata* in Hungary, whence he had fled penniless. He appeared in the splendid clothes he had worn when a-hawking after bustards on the great plains around Lake Balaton of his native land. In corduroy plus-fours, velveteen jacket, gaiters and falconer's leather gloves, he was a magnificent figure, adorned with Velasquez beard and sideboards, and a hunting cap plumed with feathers. When I introduced him to my wife he bowed, with a sweep of his hat, and kissed her hand. He was obviously, I thought, quite unsuited to policing Skomer, where the warden would not only have to control boatloads of visitors every fine day, but be tough enough to deal with seal-shooters, egg-collectors and other marauders including Breton fishermen who, at that time before we occupied Skomer, commonly poached by night from their boats anchored in the island havens.

Cyril Hurcomb, smiling beside me during the interview with Bastayai, felt obliged to agree that we should give him the post, purely on a temporary basis until we could appoint from the long waiting list a younger tougher man; but meanwhile we felt sorry for Lorent, and thought that his courteous manner and pictur-esque appearance would enhance the proceedings of the opening ceremony.

It had been a choppy crossing, against a strong north wind, but now in the shelter of the old farm buildings, the sun was warm. A picnic had been brought by the ladies of the Trust and spread on driftwood planks. De Bastayai opened the champagne and wine with a flourish, in the highest good spirits. Arriving the day before, he had found the cliff-nest of the peregrine falcons, and had to tell everybody of the joy this had brought to his falconer's heart.

As Vice-President of our Trust Sir Julian Huxley was there, to speak glowingly of the beauty of the island he knew well, to point out the puffins lumbering on stumpy wings overhead, to congratulate the Trust on its enterprise and co-operative effort in securing one of the world's finest sea-bird sanctuaries ... His ringing voice was mocked by the sardonic wail of the great black-backed gulls annoyed that we did not move away from their nest and chicks on the knoll hard by. Our honorary secretary, scholar and amateur naturalist, Dillwyn Miles, sword-bearer and Bard of the National Eisteddfod, who had worked so hard behind the scenes to bring about our triumph, responded for the Trust, in two languages.

Lord Hurcomb raised his glass and declared Skomer a National Nature Reserve safe for all time from every sort of exploitation, save that of some quarter of a million sea-birds 'which the latest survey by the Trust estimates may be nesting here at this moment'.

The party moved downhill to the narrow Neck, near which the Conservancy were to build a house for our warden. Leonard Lee, upon whom the Trust had bestowed the 'Freedom of the island because of your willingness to sell in the national interest' (to quote the citation that day) laid the foundation stone. We inspected the lay-out of the new building, which commanded the two landing places, the North and South Havens; a plan in which I had designed the cellar under the sloping foundations to accommodate a dozen or so pairs of shearwaters and puffins, with entrance holes a metre apart along the foot of the walls. (These, convenient for marking and observation, have been occupied each summer by burrowing sea-birds.)

*   *   *

That week the old manor was alive with the activities of friends gathered to celebrate a double delight: the opening of the Skomer reserve, and Julian Huxley's seventy-second birthday. My diary of 22 June 1959 records:

The ever-restless Julian as usual proposed some communal activity. Last evening he had read aloud to us one of Edgar Allen Poe's short stories, slamming the book shut just before reaching the climax – his usual, tantalising ploy – with the promise 'to be continued next time'; but tonight he decided we should play the poetry game. Each person in turn to compose a line in the agreed metre, the last syllable to rhyme with the last syllable of the previous line but one – the only clue visible when you passed on the folded paper to your neighbour. Some nonsensical verse resulted, of which one survives in our visitors' book:

Subject: *Wherefore art thou featherbed?*

Few birds upon our curious planet
Have plumes enough for feather-beds,
The Gull, the Guillemot, the Gannet
Moult every day (except on Weds.).

This being so, we can't deny
That sea-birds have a place unique;
But why, oh why, do they have to die
To feather our beds for the coldest peak?

But let's not turn to eider down
When plastic feathers are cheap in town.

Afterwards there was just time before dinner for one bout of word-making-and-taking. [Julian had played this game all his life, and with ten thousand combinations stored in his powerful memory, he invariably won. He insisted on 'handi-capping' himself by not making words of less than six letters; really a sly advantage, for while lesser minds were busy making words of fewer letters, Julian had time to plot the conversion of these to longer words, and rake them across the table to his hoard.]

Julian was in great form this evening, spinning witty tales even as he snatched up most of the words. He won DEMAR-CATED from our humble RATE, TRACE, CRATER, MEERCAT (spelling challenged); and BADGERS from our RAGE, SAGER,

GRADES; but lost 'POSSUM (spelling again challenged) to a brilliant conversion – SYMPOSIUM.

With such words on the table, dreamed up from our zoologically-inclined minds, the conversation tended towards the animal world. . . .

'Meerkats – that reminds me,' I said, 'of that bushbaby you kept at the Zoo flat years ago, Juliette. For me it was an interesting occasion – do you remember? We lunched that day at the Zoo restaurant. John Skeaping was telling an amusing story, something about a man with an immense black beard who suddenly opened the caravan door one morning when Skeaping was cleaning his teeth and his mouth was so full of water and white powder that, when he tried to answer the ill-timed visitor the poor fellow (who only wanted to ask how to get somewhere) went off with his splendid beard more white than black. It was at that critical moment in Skeaping's yarn that one of the Zoo keepers came up and whispered in your ear, Julian. A healthy human baby had been abandoned, warmly wrapped in swaddling clothes, in one of the rubbish receptacles outside the restaurant.'

'I remember it well,' said Juliette, 'a beautiful child and if only Julian had been willing – but with that orphan bushbaby already on my hands. . . .'

'*Galago senegalis,*' Julian took over the conversation in his masterful manner. 'Yes, I refused to have another muling, puking, defaecating infant in our flat. Lovely as a bushbaby is, with its enormous night-vision eyes, woolly fur and bare negroid, human hands and feet, which Juliette loved to show to visitors as it slept in its box all day, it had an odd habit which we didn't discover until too late. It was normally very clean, doing its solid business in the pan of dry earth which Juliette provided in an appropriate corner. But during its nightly climbing adventures, it left behind little dark stains here and there on walls and soft furnishings. Then one evening we watched it deliberately urinate on the palms of its hands, and rub them afterwards on the soles of its feet! It was only doing what comes naturally to bushbabies: like so many animals it was leaving an olfactory trail with its smelly feet, hoping in its dim mind that some other desirable bushbaby might smell it and come along, as well as leaving a reminder to its nose of which way to get back. Ronald's rabbits do it: rub their chin glands on the ground, on vegetation, on their spouse; and it seems the buck will squirt his urine accurately upon his doe to mark her his property – in place of a wedding ring. Almost all mammals do it in various ways: deer and chamois have scent glands with which they mark the local vegetation; martens smear scent on boughs of trees; mongoose and skunk do it on the ground. Civilised women do it, but in a peculiar way. While primitive human tribes prefer the good strong sweat smell of the other sex, our sophisticated wives and daughters disguise their body odour with so-called deodorants, highly-scented oils derived from sweet-smelling herbs and – did they but know it – essentially fortified with a base of civet, skunk or other stinking animal secretions . . .'

At that moment I had to leave the room to answer the telephone in my study. It was a familiar guttural voice:

'Of course, it's Ludwig, can't you recognise my voice? You remember that organ belonging to Mendelssohn you showed us at Castlemartin old church some time ago? Well, I've got the BBC interested, and with your help we shall put it in working order and I'm going to record it for the BBC! What fun we shall have, eh, Ronald?'

'Where are you?'

'Nellie and I are in a hotel in Tenby. Just arrived and pretty tired. We'll come over in the morning – if you do us the honour of inviting us. What? Julian and Juliette Huxley with you – impossible! Now I'm wide awake!'

'It's Julian's birthday. Why not come over right away? I'll send a car to fetch you. But we'll keep it a secret, a birthday surprise, until you turn up. It'll be marvellous. Tony Soper and Geoffrey Boswell, Dillwyn and Joyce Miles, and Cyril Hurcomb – all your old friends. What a lovely surprise for them . . .'

Nellie was fast asleep when Geoffrey reached the hotel; he brought Ludwig back to Orielton just as the company sat down to the birthday supper under the Spanish glass chandelier in the long Regency dining-room, with its painted plaster-work ceiling and white Italian marble fireplace installed during the Owen restoration of the rooms over two hundred years ago. Jesus was in attendance.

It was one of the happiest occasions of the decade I lived in the old manor, with a hint of sadness behind the laughter; for so many of my distinguished guests were old, and must soon pass away

(Julian, Cyril and Ludwig have just gone, but in a ripe old age); and at that moment I could see no future in this lovely home. A brief melancholy soon forgotten in present joy, well lubricated with wine and good fellowship, which prompted Ludwig to offer to sing some airs from his youth as an opera singer sixty years ago. Remarkably, the high notes were reached with hardly a quiver . . .

'According to your sensitive ear, my dear Ludwig,' teased Julian, bringing forth a favourite anecdote, 'when you were so busy recording animals at the Zoo on those wonderful machines of yours, the calls of the camel family are very distinct. The male camel in love says *Cra-ank*. Is that right, Ludwig?'

'Yes.' By now Ludwig's head was nodding.

'And the cow camel's response is very different, she just says *Cra-ank* [the same vulgar noise]. That right, Ludwig?'

A weary grunt came from the bowed head of Ludwig.

'And the baby camel is *totally* different – it just says *Cra-ank* [the same vulgar noise again]!'

Julian roared with laughter. Ludwig, who had been feigning boredom, stood up suddenly and accused Julian of being tone deaf to the subtle noises of nature. Bowing to Juliette, he invited her to waltz to his humming of the Blue Danube.

'So, now you are retired from making all those horrid grunts and groans at the Zoo,' Juliette said in a loud whisper for all to hear, as for a few times she swayed around in Ludwig's arms, 'you will record only music – your first love. How much nicer that will be, my dear Ludwig!'

'Of course, Lady Juliette,' Ludwig answered gallantly, 'not forgetting the nice music of your French–Swiss accent!' Triumphantly producing a miniature tape-recorder from his breast pocket: 'You see I have recorded tonight you and Julian, and all who said anything interesting – even perhaps snatches of old Ludwig's cracked voice. I shall sort it all out, and after I have removed Julian's rude jokes, and kept your amusing conversation in, I shall sell the record to the BBC at a very high price. You dance like a feather, Juliette: divine and beautiful. Now Ludwig is tired . . .'

He bowed to Juliette and seated himself on the settle by the fire, next to the elegant Joyce Miles.

'Tomorrow Nellie will come here and Ronald will take us all to see the famous Felix Mendelssohn's organ in the wilds of this

Welsh coast ... Next week I go to Buckingham Palace to play records to my dear Princess Anne ... Did you know that Princess Anne told me young Ronald here once gave her mother, Her Majesty the Queen, a sea-bird called the razorbill?'

'Ronald is always doing the unexpected. Tell us, please ...'

'Ages ago it was,' I complied modestly, but wine-willing to talk. 'I received a mysterious royal command that the Princesses Elizabeth and Margaret desired to possess a razorbill for a pet, and I was to take it to the royal pet enclosure in St James' Park. Also Cyril Hurcomb had asked me to bring some green cormorants to be released in St James' Park Lake for the amusement of visitors. It was long, long ago, in 1939 I think, and when I got to St James', there was a message to ask would I first show these birds on television – then I think only just started – at the Alexandra Palace. I was young and shy, but I did my best, after they had made up my face hideously. But when I lifted the shags and the razorbill from the hamper in front of the cameras each of them bit me, so everyone was delighted, although the film of course was not in colour, so the commentator had to describe how bloody I had become ...'

* * *

The old organ lay three miles away, in the Norman church of Castlemartin, which lies alone with its vicarage in this farthest south-west hamlet of Wales. During his brief life Mendelssohn (1809-1847) often visited England – he was a favourite of the young Queen Victoria – and lived for a while in Suffolk, where he practised on this organ. After his death it was acquired by the person who eventually presented it to the parish church of Castle-martin.

While Ludwig tested its keyboard, the vicar pumped its leaky bellows, and strange discordant sounds drove the rest of us to climb the belfry in search of owls and horse-shoe bars.

Ten months later and appropriately – said Ludwig – on the day of Princess Margaret's wedding, Ludwig achieved his ambition to restore the organ to full use. He had persuaded the BBC to assist in the cost of a complete overhaul. On 6 May 1960 we joined a television crew gathered in the old church to record Ludwig telling the story of the organ and its adventures in his inimitable accents, and music-master Whitehall playing Mendelssohn's immortal *Elijah*.

14

And must I leave this place –
This place where I have spent so many hours
Of careless joy, and labour light with flowers,
Where I have watched the country's changing face,
From the first primrose to the harvest home;
Now in a world still white, I leave, to roam . . .

But I shall not forget
The new brown furrow bright with April rain,
When blackthorn made the hedges white again,
And yellow kingcups where the land is wet,
The setting sun across a field of corn;
September, and the first white frost at dawn.

And I shall miss those folk
Whose friendliness I loved and needed so,
That makes it now so hard for me to go,
To be forgotten, as the faint white smoke
Of hedgers' fires . . . though tearless I shall part
I'll leave behind a portion of my heart.

WINIFRED KNIGHT

An overcast winter day, with a touch of snow. I trudged around the fields and woods, gloomy and alone, save for the faithful Jack limping at my heels. My sons were both at boarding school. I felt miserable as I tried to plan the future. There was plenty to do on the estate, too much, but I had little heart for such work. Soon the young spruce would have to be thinned for the profitable Christmas-tree trade. The next field in rotation for the early potato crop should have been ploughed weeks ago. But who would plant and harvest it? I had heard nothing from Elijah and his clan since Ellen and David, returning from their honeymoon in Ireland, had called and handed me a bundle of banknotes – the agreed sum for the old van. It was still crammed with their possessions, and they wanted to keep it.

'She went like a bomb!' declared David enthusiastically, 'all the way to Killarney an' Tipperary, an' back!'

'And no doubt, in passing, you kissed the Blarney Stone?'

'Ellen did, not me. Ellen, she's superstitious, but me, I weren't going to break me neck bending ass over 'ead!'

''Sides, 'e's full o' blarney already, aintcher, Dave?' teased Ellen, looking beautiful as ever. All through the honeymoon, said David, Ellen had been worried about the fate of the dog Jack; she was overjoyed to see him alive and on the mend in his box in the corner of my study, still helpless in his plaster and bandage, but with bright eyes and a growl in his throat for visitors. It would have been a bad omen for their marriage had the dog died; and the credit for saving Jack was really Ellen's.

'So now Dave, you'll be earning big money on that refinery job?'

'What, me? Workin' wi' that townee gang – not likely!'

'But Elijah said you had a job waiting for you.'

'Ellen, she wants ter go back to road. She's right – it ain't no life in town shack. Us's goin' to join Old Elijah an' Gran'ma an' th' family. They've gorn off, this mornin' – up th' coast for Anglesey . . .'

The departure of my gipsy friends that autumn was yet another, nagging reason for my present gloom. In the stables yard I stood irresolute, irritated by the contented cackles of the stupid hens in the deep-litter house, and by the whimper of Dulcinea's baby from the flat under the clock tower. I had never put that clock back into working order as I had once vowed I would; its face was more cracked than ever, its works were still missing; I had freed the weather vane but it had stuck once more, at north this time, pointing to the quarter from which snow was drifting.

That summer there had been six house-martin nests under the stables eaves. I propped a ladder against the wall, and tipped a spoonful of insect killer in each nest, to destroy the dormant larvae of those blood-sucking hippoboscid flatflies which tormented these useful birds. Then fixed a strip of sticky bandage (marked in bold letters DO NOT TOUCH) across each entrance, to block out sparrows and to warn humans that the nests were under study. This would deter Cortez and other tidy-minded persons who had been known to knock down these cup nests so neatly made of mud, straw and saliva. Before the martins returned in the spring I would remove the strips.

But would I be here in the spring?

I felt less gloomy after completing that annual service. Back in the house before a log fire I tried to review the future less despondently. As in a bad dream I had observed the continuing phenomenon of man's greed for profit which was driving international companies to destroy yet more of the smiling productive coast line which had been declared by law an inviolate National Park. But in today's news was confirmation that the Government itself, through the central electricity board, was to build an immense power station adjacent to a new refinery. Both sites were within three miles of the old manor! But worse than that, it was confidently predicted that, although the burning of low-grade oil to produce electrical energy for the national grid would be incomplete and would result in an estimated daily residue of 700 tons of sulphur being ejected into the air in the form of yellow smoke, a chimney 1,000 feet tall would carry the pollution into the sky where it would be dissipated by the notoriously strong westerly winds!

It seemed incredible, yet there it was, in an imaginative sketch of the new power station, with soaring stack, and pipeline connecting with the refinery. The report enumerated the advantages to industry and local employment which would ensue; it failed to mention what was in fact already happening – a rush of hard-working young Irish immigrants via the Rosslare–Fishguard ferry to take over the labouring jobs during the construction. But when the site job was finished, with no other work immediately available they signed on for the dole. Almost as if it were a special advantage it did mention, however, that the use of a large volume of sea-water would be necessary for cooling purposes, and the continuous discharge of the heated water afterwards would raise the temperature of the Pembroke estuary, giving interesting prospects of farming semi-tropical fish and shellfish for food . . .

Sulphur: 700 tons of it belched out daily in the heavens above Orielton and the National Park! We were on the windward side of the Atlantic gales, but the official records compiled for Pembrokeshire over the last thirty years showed many days of winds from every quarter – and frequent calms. What happened in calms? But our protests against the whole filthy project were subsequently to be met with an inflexible determination to build the power station 'in the national interest'. And there came the complacent statement from the Ministry that 'in case of rare calm days, if a sulphur layer should descend upon agricultural or other land any contamination thereby would be carefully monitored and its long-term effect studied'.

No, I would not, could not, live under the continuous shadow and stink of that volcano of sulphur dust! Visions of beginning life afresh on some remote island in the Hebrides or Orkneys, or in the far south-west of Ireland totally away from industry, came to me in the firelight. Perhaps I could live on Cape Clear Island with its dwindling population where I had once enjoyed the simple hospitality of home-produced food by a peat fire in that thatched cottage where lived the Irish-speaking Himself and Herself, ever smiling and content . . . But first perhaps, a holiday in New Zealand, where my daughter, a child during those care-free island days at Skokholm, had a few years ago married a farmer? She seemed perfectly content (who would not be?) as a pioneer on their holding upcountry in a place of record sunshine and productivity, appropriately named by Captain Cook the Bay of Plenty. New Zealand, I recollected, had fewer human inhabitants than Wales, under three million, yet was as large as Great Britain and almost wholly pastoral . . .

Of course I was an escapist, perhaps even a defeatist. In my heart I had no wish to give up this beautiful walled enclave, this oasis for wildlife I had found and escaped to a decade ago, and the study of which had been my joy. True, the old manor house was run at a loss, but the farm and forest were paying well. Now perhaps was the moment to rescue Orielton as a nature reserve by a bold stroke of turning it into a popular wildlife park or even a subsidiary of Peter Scott's Wildfowl Trust. For new residents were moving into the district, occupying housing estates springing up near the refineries, and some of these workers were already offering to buy or rent the cottages on the estate. These people, and some judicious publicity, would soon bring a profitable return in rents and gate-money. Alternatively there was that wealthy catering company which, owning holiday camps elsewhere, was urging me to sell or lease so that it could set up an exclusive country club in the manor house, with dance floor and swimming pool, and chalets discreetly set out and screened within what the promoter would designate (in his company's advertisement) 'the Old Walled Forest of Orielton'.

Both schemes were totally unacceptable; for both would mean the destruction or exile of those rarer species which had found sanctuary during the peaceful occupation of the estate by its nature-loving owners over the present century. The otters, badgers, buzzards, ravens and sparrowhawks would disappear; and would not sulphur smoke stifle the throats of the woodlarks when they flew heavenwards to salute the dawn, often in full song before the night was done?

Surely I had good cause for my wintry despair . . . ?

*   *   *

A rare heavy snow was falling when the postman delivered the letter containing a new hope. Somehow, I know not how, certain friends who occupied their several corridors of temporal power at that moment – Grimes, Hurcomb, Huxley, Nicholson, Scott and others – seemed to have shared in a conspiracy to retain Orielton in its present state as a nature reserve and place for outdoor studies. I had taken no part in these discussions except when, much earlier, during negotiations with the Nature Conservancy to purchase Skomer, I had told Max Nicholson I felt I could not endure living close to a developing industrial complex, with its prospect of more oil tanks, factories and flarestacks on my horizon.

'You should hold on to Orielton yet,' Max had counselled, who knew the place well, 'all the more because it is a bastion of nature against the wave of industry invading the National Park. It is an outstanding example of what man has achieved in eight centuries of patrician occupation of the land, with its gracious house and parkland, woods and water, walled garden, gazebo and miles of protective stone walls. It's no longer a gamekeeper's paradise, but is a perfect reserve for wildlife, with widely diverse habitat. Your studies for the Conservancy, your editing there of *Nature in Wales* to its present status as a scientific journal, and visits from naturalists from all over the world, have shown its importance for field studies. It must be saved as such. Don't despair about the oil companies – make use of them, as you did to help us buy Skomer. They can well afford to contribute to Orielton as a centre for research, perhaps into ways of combating oil pollution. That splendid large house, those stables – did you say they once housed twenty-four horses and three coaches? They'd be ideal, adapted for study and research without spoiling their attractive exterior; much needed research into conservation and environmental problems. We have lately taken over a similar mansion as a base for research on the Island of Rhum in the Hebrides. Go and look at it . . .'

I was, however, unprepared for the offer in the letter which the postman brought. The Field Studies Council wished to discuss with me the acquisition of Orielton as yet another of the several centres they had lately set up in England and Wales. I was surprised because they already had a centre in Pembrokeshire, only eight miles from Orielton, at Dale Fort. This solid stone Victorian structure commanded a headland just inside the entrance to Milford Haven. It had been converted thirty years earlier to private occupation, and in 1946 had been bought on a mortgage – supplied by a member – by the West Wales Naturalists' Trust (then the West Wales Field Society) as a base for the Society's post-war activities, which in that year included the re-opening of the Bird Observatory at Skokholm, and a six-months' survey and occupation of Skomer Island by visiting members (published in the book *Island of Skomer*). When the owner of that island decided to re-possess it in 1947 we moved the hostel and scientific equipment to Dale Fort, and in that year accepted the offer of a newly-constituted national body, The Council for the Promotion of Field Studies (now the Field Studies Council) to take over and operate Dale Fort – where our Trust would also have a base.

Magnificently situated on a steep cliff, Dale Fort had since proved ideal for the study and teaching of marine biology. Now the Field Studies Council wished to acquire Orielton because of its opportunities for very different ecological studies, with its warm sheltered woodland, farmland and fresh water, as well as its environment rich in historical and archaeological sites. The old manor could be adapted at little expense to house up to sixty students, chiefly sixth-formers, whose fees were needed to make each Centre viable and pay for the staffing and maintenance . . .

Behind this offer was surely the guiding hand of an old friend, Cyril Hurcomb (lately elected President of the Field Studies Council), and also, the enthusiasm of the archaeologist and historian Professor W. F. Grimes. My gloom suddenly lifted –

it was the right, the only solution. Although I knew from its latest published accounts that the Council had no money to purchase Orielton, I also knew I would gladly lease it to this splendid organisation which was bringing classes from city schools into the country to be taught nature's way, and the need to preserve what is left of the environment. The old manor would buzz with enthusiastic talk of the wild life these young people would study, and which they in turn would want to – nay must – save for their children . . . even under a smoky sulphurous sky!

Negotiations were to drag on over many months while the Council committee seemed to hesitate between leasing and buying. Some were for abandoning the project on second thoughts; it was perhaps too close to the Dale Fort Centre, and to the rapidly expanding oil refining industry, and couldn't the price be lowered? My agent Charles had already agreed with their agent on a modest figure; but it was now claimed that estimates for the cost of renovations and alterations had proved to be unexpectedly high. Patiently I lowered the figure – if only I could afford to make a gift of Orielton to this admirable national body which shared my aims: the study and protection of the pristine environment. Maybe the Council was hoping I would, and maybe I would have to, in the end?

But Professor Grimes remained buoyant and helpful on his several visits. He was urging the Council to buy rather than lease; a lot of money would have to be spent on the house and buildings to convert them to an effective Centre. He disclosed that he had already applied to the Historic Buildings Council (which had rejected my earlier appeal as a private owner) for a substantial grant to assist in repairing the roof, possibly rebuilding it completely.

'They'll hardly refuse a public body like the Field Studies Council,' he said, with a shake of his grey head as together we stared at the magnificent growth of golden Virginian creeper, cream-white clematis and purple musk rose which embraced the whole of the tall front of the manor so pleasingly, in my eyes. Rich in bird and insect life, it had sheltered and fed a handsome male blackcap over recent winters, when the bird should have been away in Africa. Often I had watched it feeding on flies, spiders and berries there, close to my window.

Grimes loved the place well, but he was worried about the

state of the roof, and of the walls beneath that hoary growth. Although I had kept the roof waterproof, it showed numerous weak spots on the exterior where repairs had taken place over two centuries of boisterous weather; and underneath it was still infested with bats, bees and owls.

'Of course, we shall have to have a thorough survey of the fabric,' he said dubiously. 'We'll send a man down as soon as possible.'

When an inspector from the pest control firm arrived he announced, 'I'll start at the top, please.'

He donned overalls and a dust helmet. I showed him the little trap doors, and warned him as he squeezed through into the darkness of the parapet roof: 'Please be careful not to disturb hibernating bats. Don't be alarmed by a sudden screech from the white owls in the north-east corner. But look out for a few active bees.'

Although it had been a cold night, the sun was now shining warmly from a clear sky. Presently, anguished cries arose above the tapping of hammer and probe. Half an hour later the inspector reappeared, extremely ruffled and dusty.

'It's simply terrible up there – bat-dung, bees and flies! Millions of flies! And I've been stung by bees several times!'

He had failed to examine more than a small proportion of the roof. Apart from the hazards of the small wild life sanctuary there, the trusses were too close together for his large body to squeeze through. But those timbers he had been able to reach were surprisingly sound, although very, very old. Just a few were worm-eaten.

'No dry rot that I can find, but it's buzzing with life, even on this cold day. Looks as if it hadn't been fumigated for a good many years.'

After he had changed, washed and sat down to the coffee brought by Victoria, he recovered his poise and was almost jovial. I could see by the bright gleam in his eyes that a grim report would be forwarded to the Council, and a profitable contract might ensue for his firm.

'Now I know where flies go in the winter time – into your roof!' he chuckled. 'Of course in these cases where you can't really get into a roof and check every corner and timber, there are only two courses of action. If you can't afford to strip the roof down and remove and renew all the rotten timber and treat the good beams with preservative, you will have to rely on repeated fumigation, once or twice a year. Do you mean to say you have never fumigated this old house in ten years?'

'Not yet. Probably it's never been fumigated. Our good Victoria insists on using flyspray in her kitchen, but fumigation of the whole house, no! I'm too interested in studying every form of natural life. I find that quite a healthy balance is established in nature if you don't interfere. After all, the old house has been here for centuries, and has become a fascinating sanctuary for all kinds of interesting creatures.'

'But all these flies!'

'A nuisance, I agree, but quite harmless. Some of them are beneficial; some, I admit, are not.'

At that moment, with a strong sun streaming its warm yellow light into the house, and aided by the disturbance the inspector had caused during his visit to the roof, considerable numbers of flies were crawling or buzzing inside the windows. I picked up a few of the sleepier individuals.

'Look, this one is a clusterfly *Pollenia rudis*, quite a handsome creature, a rich ebony, with golden hair. Quite harmless to man, and probably useful to keepers of smooth lawns who object to worm-casts. The clusterfly begins life as a tiny egg dropped in the grass or soil. The larvae are parasitic on earthworms. Those which leave their host as perfect flies in autumn seek warm cover for the winter. In any case their life span is very short; only if a clusterfly can find a moderately cool spot with a steady low temperature in which to pass the winter torpid, without being roused to waste its energy, will it survive to go forth in the spring and lay its eggs. See how the flies in this room are all trying to get out of the window into the sunshine; their instinct tells them – falsely – that spring has come!'

I flung open the windows in the room. The livelier flies at once escaped into direct sunshine – they would all die later in the frosty evening air when the windows were closed. Most people, in attempting to rid their homes of flies, shut the windows tight and fumigate or spray the room with insecticide which, incidentally, is dangerous to humans. Our winter routine was to open the windows on a sunny day to release the live flies, and sweep out the moribund and dead ones. Birds would attend this ceremony and hungrily devour the corpses and pursue the live ones. In summer the bats, martins, swallows, swifts and flycatchers could be relied on to control the winged insect population.

'Can't say I admire your clusterflies,' said the inspector, with a shrug of disgust. 'And look at all these tiny mosquitoes and midges – most unhealthy in a house. They bite and can carry disease!'

'These are neither mosquitoes nor midges. They do not bite humans, they are perfectly harmless and in fact beneficial. The life history of this midge-like fly *Thaumatomyia notata* is most interesting. The eggs are laid at the base of growing vegetation, and the larvae usefully gobble up aphids which suck the roots of plants. Most of the later generation winter below ground in the pupal stage, but in mild autumns numbers emerge as adult flies, and look for shelter and warmth for the night when the sun goes down. They accumulate in clouds, blown by the wind to the sheltered side of a house, and are apt to pass in through open windows. But they are all doomed to die, like these you see dead or dying here – without reproducing themselves – of cold, hunger and old age, long before the spring.'

Possibly this expert in the art of exterminating small life thought I was a complete crank? He departed without any further dissertation on the diptera of the old manor. I had said nothing about harmful and unpleasant so-called houseflies, the *Musca* and *Fannia* species, which entered the house in small numbers in summer. They were unwelcome because they laid their eggs in warm decaying animal matter, including horse, pig and human faeces, on which the maggots feed. After three months the larvae move to a cooler spot, pupate, and if born late in the year, hibernate in the pupal state. Those born earlier, however, provide generations of adult flies throughout the summer. The emerging adult forces open the lid of the pupal case by inflating a curious sac, never used again, between the eyes. Like other perfect aerial insects, it must then rest for a while to let blood flow through the veins of its unfolding wings, and stiffen and stretch them for its brief life on the wing.

Very occasionally the bloodsucking stable fly *Stomoxys calcitrans* found its way into the rooms, and was mistaken for a housefly, until it had sunk its proboscis into an exposed leg or arm, inflicting a painful bite. It was one of the many species, such as the green and blue bottle flies, which annoyed cattle and horses in summer. These also bred in decaying matter, and their larvae helped to clear up animal droppings so plentifully distributed about the fields. Good husbandry required that, as the Jersey herd grew to the capacity of the land to support it, we harrowed the land more often and scattered the nitrogenous cow pats which, left undisturbed, would kill the grass beneath during the weeks in which scavenging flies and beetles and their larvae were feeding, burrowing and pupating there.

Albeit reluctantly, I had sold the old water wheel, which I had hoped to restore to full use one day (but for what?) to Elijah and his tinker crew for a nominal sum as scrap iron, on condition that they removed it entirely. I had converted its splendid deep pit into a holding tank for the solid and liquid manure from the cow parlour and silage feeding shed. Such a tank might have been an ideal breeding ground for the biting and bottle flies; instead, by keeping it covered, the fermentation of the dung and straw produced methane gas which not only killed insect eggs and larvae but would one day be piped to provide the light and heat for the farm buildings. I had not yet got around to doing this, but already the liquid manure from the old waterwheel pit was providing the richest nourishment I could return to the land after an arable crop had been taken.

Among the insects which sought winter sanctuary in the house were the queen wasps, which crept into cool but frost-free corners under eaves, and in cellars and buildings where the temperature would not rise and rouse them unseasonably. The drones had died in the autumn, after a brief, ecstatic existence of idle feeding in the sun and of fertilising the queens. Whenever we could we killed the queens of these socialble *Vespa* wasps, each one the potential foundress of a new colony. Wasps troubled Victoria in her kitchen, seeking the sweetness of the honey and jam stores; and in the orchard they damaged ripe fruit.

Most people have a deep-seated fear of wasps, which in fact only use their sting to defend nests or themselves or, as I pointed out to Victoria one day as we watched a wasp seize a noisome house-fly, to immobilise their prey. In like manner the *Vespa* wasps will seize and devour, or feed to their larvae in the galleries of their marvellously intricate paper nests, the biting flies which annoy man and are serious parasites of farm animals.

Certain butterflies sought a winter retreat in the upper rooms, chiefly the *Vanessa* species, whose hairy caterpillars feed on the common *Urtica* nettles: peacock, red admiral and tortoiseshell. Sometimes a large migration of these and of cabbage white butterflies invaded this coast on a warm inland summer breeze during an anticyclone. Then thousands would drift westwards over the estate, very few pausing to feed but, as if driven by some irresistible inner force, sailing steadily, confidently onwards, towards Ireland and the open Atlantic. It was a curious and wonderful sight to watch these frail beauties head for a mass suicide, for the majority of these innocents perished by drowning; nature's way of reducing a surplus which might become a plague. As reported later, a very few of the hardiest reached Iceland and Greenland: an astonishing sea crossing of several hundred miles, ending in exhaustion, cold and starvation.

The buddleia in the Japanese Garden, flowering all summer, became a kaleidescopic metropolis with scores of butterflies fluttering to its scent and nectar. Humming-bird and convolvulus hawk-moths were among the migrant visitors which paused to sip there.

Newly-emerged small tortoiseshell butterflies of the second generation of the summer hibernated successfully in the plaster scroll-work of the upper, warmer rooms of the old manor; but few of the single-generation peacock and red admiral butterflies survived the winter. Their beautiful wings grew ragged, they suffered the cold and grew too feeble to escape the web-snares of the spiders when, on sudden warm days, they might be roused to flutter to a new corner of the ceiling. Even if these southern species survived to fly into the spring sunshine in March and April it is doubtful if they were in a fit condition to lay eggs. Their numbers, however, were recruited each summer by the migrants from the warmer lands of southern Europe.

Knowing that most of them would not survive, we felt compassion for these beautiful visitors when they entered the house in the cool of autumn. My sons would place any they could catch in perforated cardboard boxes and store them in the cool steady temperature of the barrel cellar, to be released in the spring. Here they were safe from spiders and other crawling predators.

Our Spanish helpers, like most tidy-minded souls, loathed the large spiders and would kill them. They took little notice of my occasional homily on their usefulness in killing flies and harmful insects in the house. Fortunately Victoria and Dulcinea, even with the long-handled feather brush, could rarely reach deep into the plaster scroll work and corners of the lofty ceilings, where the inconspicuous daddy-long-legs spider *Pholcus phalangiodes* hibernated or dozed away the cold days; a remarkable creature for which I entertained some admiration and a little nostalgic affection.

I was fond of this seemingly-timid domesticated spider because that expert arachnologist, Dr W. S. Bristowe, on a visit many years ago to Skokholm, had described its life history to me and so roused my curiosity that I had brought a female, complete with her silken cocoon containing her eggs, to live with us in the cottage I had rebuilt on the island. I had leisure to study her there, where her descendants yet thrive; for this species likes best a mild, humid Atlantic climate and does not survive in a dry heated house.

Pholcus spun a maze of fine silk lines attached to the joist beams of the ceiling, and suspended herself upside down – perfectly motionless most of the time. If I teased one of these lines with a feather she would vibrate her body, causing the central system of silk threads to quiver until she herself was no longer visible except as a blurred object. This is her method of disguising herself and shaking out of her snare any insect too large or undesir-

314

able to be captured and killed, such as a wasp or a bumblebee. She lived on flies and other small insects which, when they blundered into her web, she would approach cautiously, testing the nature of the victim with her enormously long front legs. These feelers are five times as long as her 10mm long body. If satisfied that the insect is edible she uses her long legs to fling silk from her spinnerets around it. She has no poison in her fangs with which to paralyse living prey like most spiders, but relies on her innate skill in swathing her victim until it becomes a helpless mummy. The bundle is then detached from the place of capture in the web and carried back to her lair where, if not hungry, she hangs it up alive. When ready to feed she bites a hole in the shroud, punctures the victim's skin with her fangs, and pumps digestive fluid into the body – as all spiders do – which assists in dissolving the soft parts. The prey is sucked dry and the hard chitinous carapace discarded.

The mating of spiders is notoriously strange. The male pholcus, even more elongated than the female, prepares for the ceremony some time before he touches the lady of his desire. He exudes a drop of sperm on to a thread of silk (some male spiders lay down a woven platform or mat of silk) which he draws tightly across his genital opening (placed not at the tip, as in most insects, but nearer the middle of the abdomen). The sperm on its thread (or in its bag of silk) is then transferred to the palps: the jointed, leg-like appendages attached to the side of the head which serve as a manipulative tool close to the mouth, and in the female may end in a claw. But in the male the last segment has no claw; instead it contains a unique organ with a cavity in which the sperm is stored preparatory to insertion in the body of the female. With his palps thus charged he approaches the female carefully, testing her reaction with the tips of his attenuated front legs, which he taps on her web. This is a necessary precaution in case she mistakes him for prey; if she does, she may capture him, wrap him in silk, and devour him. If his mistress is not in a mood for love, however, Pholcus is normally able to escape by withdrawing his legs before she can throw a lasso over him. Usually his gentle tapping on her web stimulates her to agree to the ceremonies of courtship.

The young hatch from a bundle of eggs which the mother lays at midsummer and nurses in a loose purse of silken threads which she patiently holds in her jaws – except when disturbed by a visitor to her web-snare. When this happens she hangs up her precious string-bag temporarily in order to deal with the next meal, or to repulse an amorous suitor.

The young daddy-long-legs spiders hatch in July, and for a while enjoy mother's further protection as they spread out along one of her silk lines, remaining motionless, like clothes put out to dry, until they have finished their first moult. Those which fail or are slow to complete this delicate operation may well provide a first meal for a more robust sibling which, having moulted, will spin its first web on the ceiling not far from the birthplace, and begin its independent solitary life.

The beautiful white silk ball containing the eggs of the cave spider *Meta menardi* was a conspicuous sight hanging from the higher part of the caverns which we explored with torches during the autumn marking of seals. These spiders live on minute flies which breed in the seaweed and jetsam washed up on the shore, and on the gammarids, silverfish and other crawlers of rock surfaces. I transferred two of these silken nursery spheres from a dank seal cave to our damp cellars, for this species takes readily to man-made cavities below ground level, where conditions are shady and humid enough. Their descendants are there still.

The common house spider *Tegenaria* prefers well-lit sites in which to build a sheet web, with a tunnel retreat leading to a niche, often in a window sash or the corner of two walls. For three years one matron of *T. atrica* lived in the space where a nib drawer was missing in my roll-top desk. She grew from her gossamer youth to become a handsome lady with pale stripes on her dark chestnut carapace and, including her eight legs, measured a total length of 40mm. Her large black eyes – all eight of them – seemed to recognise me, and after her first retreat on my arrival, she would partly emerge and straddle her long front legs (two pairs) upon her silken threshold. Sometimes in an idle moment I would remember to drop into her web a housefly, killed against the window glass, to compensate her for my presence, which reduced the number of insects flying near the sticky bluish strands.

My tame lady Tegenaria was safe in my desk, for I had forbidden anyone to close it or touch the papers and books it was normally strewn with. I was amused to study her desultorily; amused too to observe the reactions of visitors who, noticing the conspicuous untidy web first, spotted her somewhat devilish-looking face and dark hairy legs protruding from the central tunnel. Victoria screamed the first time she saw the 'Tarantila' as she called it, and warned me its bite was poisonous . . .

'My dear Victoria,' I cautioned her. 'You are confusing the country dance, the Tarantela – which doubtless you danced as a girl – with the tarantula spider of southern Europe, which is capable of inflicting a poisonous bite on anyone foolish enough to handle it. But even so, the poison is rarely fatal to humans.'

Victoria became accustomed to seeing 'Tarantila' at home in the roll-top desk, accepting my protection of the large spider as just another facet of her employer's lunatic ways. She told me she did not object to very small spiders – it was bad luck to kill these. In fact they had a medicinal value against certain disorders; she had even eaten them when a child, for her mother would crush and mix them with bread into a pill to be swallowed as a remedy, according to a time-honoured recipe.

It is a popular belief the world over that the tiny pink, pinhead-size spiders bring good fortune if you find one alive on your person. Hence their collective name, money-spiders. The minute *Linyphiidae* are the chief spinners of the silken parachutes on which they disperse by air after leaving the nursery, and so provide the gossamer which covers the land on late summer and autumn mornings, made glitteringly visible by the overnight dew. According to Dr Bristowe their populations reach over a million individuals to one acre in temperate lands. The numerous species of these smallest of spiders are found in diverse and often dark habitats, such as mines, sewage sprinklers and the nests of birds and ants. In the last they are tolerated and live unmolested by the ants, not spinning web-snares, but subsisting on small flies and other insect visitors, some of which may be harmful to the ant community.

Ants were sporadic visitors to the house. For a few years a large and unwelcome colony of the tiny Argentine species *Iridomyrmex humilis* lived close to the manor but inaccessible in the thick walls of the former laundry building, where had long been installed the electricity generating plant. This machine automatically started up when light or heat was switched on at the manor, and so the engine room was always warm at night and in winter, an essential condition for the survival of this tropical ant. Once established it is extremely difficult to eradicate. Probably it was introduced in furniture or crates imported during the occupation of Orielton by the RAF in the 1940s, for it is comparatively rare in our cool Atlantic climate.

As in other ant communities this colony sent forth thousands of the large winged females and tiny winged males on a hot day late in the summer. Their nuptials were conducted high in the calm air, much to the satisfaction of our swifts, swallows, martins and large birds – notably the gulls – which flocked to this abundant aerial feast. But other birds not so expert on the wing, and many small mammals (shrews and hedgehogs) snapped up the fat queens when these alighted on the ground, each fertilised by several males (the last suitor perhaps clinging to the rump of a queen, moribund or dead after the ejaculation of his sperm – a lethal consummation for the male ant).

The queen ant has an insatiable desire to mate during her nuptial flight and accepts as many of the tiny males as will fill her seminal receptacle. Here the sperm is stored which will last the rest of her life of several years – perhaps up to ten – during which she will lay a few million eggs. On reaching the ground the fertilised queen seeks a home, either within an existing colony, or founding one of her own. But first she must get rid of her wings, which she does by pulling each one forward with a middle leg and severing the base with knife-like blows of the sharp keel of a hind leg. She is now able to absorb the large wing-muscles, whose power carried her aloft as a bride, into her blood stream, and recycle this rich source of protein to develop her first eggs. If solitary at first she is able to do this without taking food externally, rearing the first of her children to an age – a few weeks – when they can go forth and forage for themselves and bring back food to break the fast of their devoted mother. Thereafter she lives entirely in darkness, never leaving the nest, laying up to several hundred eggs a day during the warmer months.

The Argentine ant has a repellent smell. When alarmed it squirts, not formic acid (a deadly poison) like most ants, but a sticky anal fluid. It was this faecal matter which offended Victoria's keen nose when she killed this ant on its far-flung night sorties. It also had the annoying habit of forming a ring of small daughter colonies far from the central one, where the worker class (of unfertilised females) laid eggs which, odd as it may seem, can produce workers, queens and even males. Occasionally we found a daughter colony of a few hundred individuals and their brood established in a warm spot in the house: for example – so tiny are these worker ants – in the space 1mm thick between the sash and frame of a sunny window. These outpost colonies would usually perish, or be withdrawn, at the onset of winter cold.

Another annoyance perpetrated by these aggressive Argentinian robots was the pasturing of considerable herds of cattle (green fly aphids) far and wide on the choice plants and shrubs around the manor, and on their roots, many of which sickened as a result. We were relieved when, after three years of their unwelcome attentions and our failure to extirpate the colony, Orielton was supplied with electricity from the National Grid (at that time holding no local menace to our way of life). I sold the obsolete engine and its shelves of batteries to the tinkers and wedged open the door of the empty engine room. The frosty air of winter penetrated to their inaccessible nursery beneath the thick stone walls. The dictatorship – for this ant dominates and drives out all other ants – was chilled to death.

In the unploughed parkland in front of the manor were the more democratic communities of the hardy black ant *Lasius niger,* and of its yellow cousin *L. flavus.* They are true pastoralists, building up their low farm mounds or fortresses with grains of soil excavated from their nurseries and stables beneath. On these convexities grew minuscule orchards of flowering plants, certain species which like a well-drained soil, tolerate burial, and flourish on the rich, constantly heaped debris: a pretty garden of centaury, pearlwort, milkwort and stonecrop, and the fine fescue grass. It was fascinating to study the herding of their aphid cattle which, like those managed by the Argentinian species, they pastured both above and below ground. Aphids suck plant juice and will exude a droplet of fluid, known as honeydew, from a pair of erect tubes at the rear, when these are lightly ticked by the ant. The touch must be gentle; if an ant or other visitor handles an aphis roughly it may squirt an unpleasant glue-like substance. As if in rage or revenge, the ant may then attack the misbehaving aphis, and cut it to pieces. Also, where aphids appear too numerous and are perhaps killing the host plant by excessive consumption of its sap, the herder ants may destroy a proportion of their cattle – an apparently reasoned operation. But is it?

Ants behave as instinctively as every other tiny-brained insect does which is also known to learn from experience. Normally the aphids are managed with seeming intelligence. If danger threatens they are removed to a safer place, as when high winds shake the host plant too violently; and in cold weather many of the aphids will be pastured below ground in stables excavated along the living roots. Aphid eggs are also taken below for safe-keeping over the winter. This apparently intelligent control argues that some leader has given the orders. But who?

Yet ants seem to act stupidly at times, as when two or more from the same colony can be observed to tug in opposite directions in attempting to move the same object; and there is much seemingly aimless running about as well as purposeful marching along regular routes. Again, since ants kill and devour a great many small insects, why do they not more often eat the juicy abundant aphids? Because, (according to one observer) the rear end and legs of an aphis closely resemble the head and antennae of an ant, especially when the aphis raises its hind legs in the air on being solicited by a thirsty ant. Gorged ants have been observed to offer nourishment to the backside of an aphis, mistaking it for the face of a fellow ant! Was it in this way that the symbiosis (mutual benefit) began and developed between ant and aphis – by mistake?

Like the domestic cow, the more the aphis is milked the more it will yield. In summer an individual aphis may be milked five or six times every twenty-four hours; and many hundreds of kilograms of honeydew must have been taken in a single year to nourish the numerous colonies of several species of herder ants in the parkland and woods of Orielton. The red ant *Formica*, scarce at Orielton because it prefers conifer woodland, climbs a pine, and after it has milked the aphids pastured aloft, it returns to the ant-heap on average 5.5mg heavier. A relatively small colony of *Formica* will contain a hundred thousand individuals; and it is estimated that twenty thousand of these will go aloft to milk the herds five times a day in summer. I leave it to the mathematicians to compute the output!

There are ants which cultivate and live on fungus, and ants which raid and make slaves of other species of ants. But the mystery of the highly successful organisation of ant communities remains. In his book *The World of Ants*, Remy Chauvin has this to say:

'On a planet swarming with life, but where man was not to appear for another eight hundred thousand centuries, the ants were already there, and had been for a very long time too, no doubt, very probably doing the same tasks as they do today. They practised agriculture, raised cattle, indulged in the art of war. Why did the flame of intelligence arise in us and not in them? They had a big start over us and had a greater chance of its happening. Or did they, perhaps – a theme taken up a thousand times by science fiction – acquire intelligence as we did, but without our knowing it, a true civilisation but one so different from ours that we cannot even see it?

'These are daydreams [but perhaps they are the force which impelled him to become a myrmecologist] . . . One is fascinated by ants, the only animals that seem to behave like men, who do not retreat before him or any other animal, whilst at the same time seeming completely to ignore him: is there not something here to excite a mind interested in the boundless cosmos which surrounds us?'

That flame of intelligence, which man values so much! Yet by multiplying like ants over the face of the earth, and building cities and destroying the countryside, was not man evolving a vast bureaucracy of communes? In exchange for the alleged security and comfort of dwelling in ant-like masses, these communes have inhibited freedom of thought and action, and necessitated dreary regimentation of behaviour as monotonous and soul-destroying as that of the ant.

Like Chauvin, an ardent admirer of the Provençal naturalist, Jean Henri Fabre, whose classic *Souvenirs Entomologiques* I had eagerly read from beginning to end several times, both for the brilliant studies and discoveries and for the lyrical, accurate descriptions, I could spend long hours watching the social insects, pondering this question, still unresolved, of where dwelt the brain or soul, the source of the apparently intelligent management of the community, of these tiny insect automatons.

If isolated for even a few hours the individual worker ant or honey bee sickens and dies. The nest or hive is the true organism and, like a computer composed of very many single components, the individual is a cell of little or no great importance – and replaceable. Provided there are enough replaceable units to operate the whole, the mechanism carries on indefinitely. The comparison is apt: the man-made computer and its components could not work as they do in such swift and masterly fashion unless fed the relevant information which is conveyed to the calculating centre by a continuous current of electrical energy. So too the whole and components of the ant or bee community are likewise energised by an electric current – the spark of life itself – through which flows the mysterious source of relevant information guiding each individual to perform the specialised tasks which, hour by hour, resolve the problems of its survival.

But perhaps the comparison breaks down somewhat in an emergency, when the living insect seems to have the advantage over the synthetic computer which must be repaired from outside, or fed instructions on how to act, if a major part of its machinery is destroyed. In such a crisis – the invasion and breaking of the citadel and loss of life from predator or weather – the ant and the bee soon undertake the restoration with a tenacity and apparent intelligence that is admirable, freely sacrificing the individual for the benefit of the whole. But only if a large enough group of survivors can concert together; for, if isolated by such a catastrophe, the individual will die, as if from loneliness and despair.

It is significant that if the queen (or queens), laying her thousands of eggs at the warm heart of the community, is removed or dies there is at first great agitation among her subjects which spreads rapidly through the whole colony. It is as if the computer had been struck a paralysing blow in its vital parts, as if the brain or soul had been smashed. A small colony of bees or ants may be so disorganised by the loss of the queen that it never recovers. The workers lose all interest in work, cease to defend the nest, and instead allow predators and robbers to invade and devour their food supplies.

In the larger colonies, however, if the fecund matriarch is lost, the workers, after a suitable period of agitation (as if mourning the death) gradually come together in more orderly fashion, almost as if a committee had been convened to discuss ways and means, and this close physical communion is evidently an essential preliminary to what follows. Under this stress bees huddle and vibrate together as if they really were plotting the restoration of the monarchy, the heart-beat of their corporate life.

322

In ants the procedure for replacing a lost matriarch varies with the species and has been less studied; but in the honey-bee it is well-known. The workers select one or more ordinary brood cells which they enlarge. When the egg hatches the larva is fed with a special mixture of honey and pollen rich in protein – the 'royal jelly'. In the enlarged cell, and fed with this special diet, the grub which emerges from what was laid as a common labourer's egg develops into a queen. Normally the first of these virgins to leave a royal cell will attack and sting to death later-hatching sisters; she will mate with a drone during a flight outside the hive, and be welcomed back eagerly by the workers who organised her metamorphosis from common egg to mated queen. Much the same recovery procedure is followed in the disrupted ant colony. How remarkable then, that if the lost queen was the brain or soul, the source of the will to survive (call it what you will) of the hive or the ant heap, and her death caused such disruption that the community almost died too, how odd that this soul can be re-generated and the community restored to normalcy as soon as a princess is in train to be born.

It has long been known that the honey-bee community is per-vaded by a mysterious substance emanating from the body of its egg-laying queen, which is distributed somehow between every worker bee, and which seems to be essential to their health and happiness (that is, the will and energy to work together). But so far the nature of this 'queen substance' has escaped complete analysis. Could it be that this substance, redolent of the lost queen and lingering in her dead body as well as in the live body of each worker who tended her – an effluvium of scent molecules perhaps – and which also clings to the combs and walls of the hive, could this pervading queen substance somehow contain the information for survival? Could it be that when they huddle together they are not only warming themselves for action (and bees will make wax for new combs as they mass together) but also sharing, even enriching, the quality and quantity of the molecules of the queen substance, the soul and intelligence of the hive? And reinvigorated by this, the survival and happiness of the colony is once more only a problem of hard work? The workers take up their duties again with their former ardour, some foraging to provide honey and nectar with which to provision the new royal cell being built by the architects among them, and all inspired by this 'soul' or queen substance, no matter how attenuated the original source has become, perhaps only a memory to live by (for insects do have memories), until the new young queen comes. The young mother's 'substance' will, of course, partake of the vanished queen's, since she will have been fed as a grub and groomed as a queen by workers carrying the effluvium of her predecessor. Every hive has its unique smell by which it is identified as home by those born in it, or as alien by other bees. Observation has proved that each ant colony too, has its peculiar scent, and evidently its queen special substance.

For years entomologists have endeavoured to discover the nature of the driving force of the communities of social insects by which individuals perform very different duties, like the different parts of a body, which keep the whole organisation in perfect running order – but without success. Remy Chauvin, after many months of experiment, extracted from a queen bee, without destroying it, the precious queen substance. It proved to be 'a white fatty substance having a faint smell which, put on a piece of paper, strongly attracts bees with no queen and also induces them to build beautiful wax combs. But that is not the whole story. Why, for example, do the bees at certain moments set to work to build large male cells instead of the small worker cells? Does it arise from some subtle modification of the queen's hormone output, or from something else? And the males themselves, traditionally considered as idle drones, of no use to the hives, is it unthinkable that they too might emit hormones? We know nothing about this.'

The mystery remains. 'God knows' . . . we are apt to shrug our shoulders when confronted by the unsolved wonders of nature and life, and utter this cliché; but does it perhaps contain the answer?

* * *

When told of the impending change of ownership Jesus and Victoria, Cortez and Dulcinea, did not at first believe it. Don Ronald could not possibly be giving up this lovely old house and its profitable farm and herd of Jersey cows – just because of the exciting new industry in the great waterway a few miles to the north? I promised them that I had made it a condition that they were to be taken on by the Field Studies Council at the same salary I had been paying them – that is, if they wished to work for what would be, in effect, an institution, an interesting sort of school for research into wildlife, the very things Jesus had become so knowledgeable about . . .

'Sixty young peoples in this house!' The practical Victoria, plumper than ever after a winter of ease, was shocked and unsure. 'How can Victoria cook for sixty hungry young peoples?'

'Of course you and Dulcinea will have a lot of help in the house. I believe the students have to make their own beds and help with the washing up.'

From his circuitous hints I could see that Jesus was principally worried about money. For some time now he had been asking for yet another rise in their wages. I had periodically given them an increase of less than he demanded. He had scowled and threatened to leave my employ, murmuring something about the very lucrative jobs available through Spanish friends working in London. Once, exasperated by what I, perhaps wrongly, considered was pure avarice on his part I had said, very well, you go to London and see how you would like living in the smell and grime backstairs in a city. I heard no more about London after that. But I was bound, as a peasant myself at heart, to respect his enterprising if devious mentality which naturally grasped all it could, from his tough Andalusian upbringing; and he would have despised me if I had not counter-argued and bargained just as vigorously.

In Jesus' unease I thought I detected a hidden intention, and this was presently confirmed by Victoria in one of those gossiping moments over morning coffee. Jesus had hinted that the new regime at Orielton would result in fewer gratuities than he now received from my guests – they were too generous, I was certain, – but everyone had liked and been amused by my helpers. Jesus asked openly, too about his garden. Would the new warden be as kind (lax would have been my word for it) as Don Ronald was about his spending so much time each day in his small but beautifully tilled walled garden which I had allowed him to cultivate entirely for his own profit? It produced double crops each summer: early potatoes followed by broccoli – generously manured free from the dung-pit at the farm – and Jesus had even managed to raise (and sell) some fine Spanish onions and melons.

'Why of course, Jesus. They'll be only too glad to buy your produce to help fill those sixty or more hungry stomachs!'

A few days later the forthright Victoria announced their decision, and the real reason for their hesitation emerged.

'We no like working any more in this country. No like working for stranger boys and girls. We only stay if Don Ronald stay. You beautiful señor, you and your beautiful wife and your beautiful young sons, you ver' kind to Victoria and Jesus. I no speak for Dulcinea and Cortez, but only for Jesus and Victoria. If Don Ronald go, Jesus and Victoria go – back home to Andalusia.'

'You are sure? What will you do when you get back home?'

'We no tell Don Ronald before, but when Jesus and Victoria go home four years ago on holiday we buy small farm near Jesus' village. All time first we save wages to buy small farm. Now we go home and buy cows for milk-selling business. You come 'long soon, Don Ronald, take holiday in Spain, bring señora and sons, see our nice farm?'

I was surprised but delighted that they had already amassed enough savings to realise their original declared ambition. The restless Jesus, now anxious to fix a date for returning home, explained his intention to sell milk in his native village, profitably, under the Spanish regulations for vending the commodity: there were three grades – dear, medium and cheap.

'Rich señoras buy milk straight from cow, with cream unseparated, they make butter from milk. Ordinary señoras buy ordinary milk with no cream – Jesus make butter to sell. Poor people buy half milk, half water cheap, Jesus boil water to kill germs before mixing milk and water – Spanish law very strict.'

*   *   *

At last all was settled. The original agreed price – too modest in my agent's opinion – had once more been lowered because of the report from the pest control inspector that at least £1,000 would have to be spent on the roof. Most likely, if the Historic Buildings Council made a grant available, as Grimes hoped, the old roof would be removed entirely (the considerable quantity of thick lead would be worth a substantial sum) and replaced by a new modern one, probably of tarred felt.

My heart was heavy with certain regrets on leaving this oasis of natural beauty, the little farm and my personal happiness in wildlife research. The moment had arrived to go, but I was uneasy too, thinking of the impending fate of the graceful long-eared bats, and the splendid white owls, even the bees, which had made the old manor so friendly to a naturalist. (Alas, the old slate and lead roof has been replaced by that ungracious tarred felt; and the creeper, clematis and musk rose stripped away – but I see the Virginia creeper begins to climb again, praise be.)

Nevertheless all those budding young naturalists arriving, week by week, that was splendid! They would roam the woods and fields, discovering new facts, making new records of (and I hoped, protecting) Orielton's wildlife. The history and antiquities would be under constant surveillance, guided by the master hand of the distinguished archaeologist Grimes, soon to become chairman of the Field Studies Council and retire from his numerous duties in London to live closer to his native county. I ought to be happy. Time would not stand still; Orielton would go forward more assuredly than I could ever have carried it into the future. Already the Council had energetically tackled the oil companies on the ceaseless fouling of sea and sky. As a result an oil pollution research unit was to be set up, in the steady temperature of the old barrel cellar where Rin-tin the greater horseshoe bat had once slept a winter, in the company of the cave spiders and boxes of dormant peacock, red admiral and tortoiseshell butterflies. The new electricity generating station would, of course, be invited to install a monitoring device to register the amount of sulphur falling on the woods and fields at Orielton . . .

Orielton had been saved. All was as well as it possibly could be in an unsatisfactory world. A warden had been appointed to the new establishment – to be known as the Orielton Field Centre – and he was about to take up his duties. As all the large furniture, except a few personal items, had been taken over by the Council at valuation, including those massive, ancient, yet still splendid sofas, settles and brassbound beds, which I had acquired with the old manor, the warden had only to walk in and I should walk out. My family had departed, and so had Jesus and Victoria, taking with them the adored but now more supine Mr X. There only remained the sheepdog Jack, and he lay waiting for me on the front doorstep.

The keys! The house had never been locked in ten years of my occupation, yet here was the final letter from the Council, demanding 'the handing over of the keys' – evidently a ceremonial occasion – on the date fixed for possession, 18th April. But where were the keys?

There was not a single key left in any of the locks of the doors of the manor. A search of the scrap in the workshop produced several small rusted keys and two large, intricately fashioned, rather splendid ones – probably of the great ornamental iron gates at the main road entrances to the estate, gates which had rusted into disuse long before I took possession. But none of the keys I unearthed and sandpapered to their original brightness seemed suitable to fit the old-fashioned bronze lock in the teak double doors of the hall, opening upon the Grecian portico.

In any case I did not try, for if a key had been found to fit that beautifully made mortice lock, it could not possibly have been turned. In the last few years the lock had been occupied by an interesting solitary insect, one of the lesser mason-bees whose history has been studied and vividly described by Jean Henri Fabre. I had often seen this busy little lady at work, passing in and out through the key-hole. I was reluctant now to unscrew the lock and clean away its living contents.

Strange it is to think that unlike the honey-bee or the ant each young mason-bee, as it emerges in spring from its single cell in that lock, will never see or know its mother. Instead it will fly in the sunlight for a brief moment, mate and die. Instructed by the programmed computer it has inherited, the female will proceed to seek out a crevice, or return to the lock, where she will clean out rubbish, including the remains of old cells, and build new ones, usually of mud worked into a plastic state with saliva. As each cell is completed she furnishes it with a store of honey and pollen; the egg is laid, and a lid sealed down. The solitary mother builds a second cell on top of the first – now hardened like concrete – complete with floor and sides, victuals it with food and lays one egg as before. She completes and furnishes as many cells – say up to eight in that lock at Orielton – as there is room for and depending on how many eggs she has yet to lay. If there are more than the lock can accommodate she will find another crevice to complete her task.

But here is a fresh mystery. It is important that the adult bees from those eggs laid in the last built cells should hatch or at least emerge first, despite the fact that the eggs in the bottom cells,

328

were laid first. This is for two reasons: if the lowermost young bees, hatching from their winter pupal case, attempt to reach the open they will have to gnaw a way through the several layers of cells above them – which might be a serious matter for their sisters and brothers not yet ready to depart; secondly, it is essential for the male bee to reach the open air before his sisters.

So what happens? The solitary bee mother, writes Fabre (after intensive experiments with tubes in which he persuaded mason-bees to build cells), 'decides' the sex of each egg. In each of the lowermost cells she deposits a female egg, making the cell slightly larger to accommodate the large cocoon her daughter will spin and hibernate in; but the cells nearest to the top, she makes smaller to fit the small male cocoon, and deposits a male egg on its heap of victuals.

No one knows yet how the solitary bee 'decides' on the sex of her eggs in this apparently intelligent fashion. When the warm spring air steals into the tubes and crevices, or the lock of the door, the young bee wakes and gnaws open first the lid of its silken prison; above is the concreted lid of its own cell, and above that may well be the hardened mud of the floor of the next cell, containing a brother or sister. Perhaps the activity of the first sleeper to awake – most likely the lowermost, the bee from the first-laid egg – gnawing and knocking, sets up a chain reaction through the fabric of the elongated nursery of many cubicles, waking up every inhabitant? Perhaps the cells nearest to the outside are first to be warmed into activity by the spring air? At any rate the bees in the topmost cells emerge first and from these only male bees appear. But now we see why. They are ardent to mate immediately they feel the sun on their new glistening carapace; they search for other mason-bee nests, eager to seize upon an emerging female. In this way they usually avoid mating with their sisters, who will be some hours or days later escaping from the innermost cells; but, in default of finding an unrelated female, brothers have no compunction about squabbling over and fertilising a sister as she struggles into the open, and perhaps before she has quite dried and stretched her wings.

Yet another act of natural wisdom; for if the colony in the lock is the only one within a bee-flight distance, or the only one surviving in the district, such incest assures its survival for at least another year.

329

The lot of the female mason-bee seems hard. She is born to instant marriage, and thereafter works herself to death. We see that as a virgin, struggling to reach the sun and stretch and harden her wings, she is beset by several suitors. The courtship is rough, and completed in a few seconds, the males fighting to fill her seminal receptacle with sperm. The honeymoon is non-existent; she shakes off the last ravisher and rises into the sunlight. First she circles above her birthplace, with her eyes fixing its location in her mind, processing her computer if you like, by which she will remember its exact location. For very soon, after a short spell of wandering from flower to flower and enjoying her first meals of nectar, instinct informs her she must begin building the nursery for the eggs ripening within her. She is not a great rambler; she prefers to build somewhere near home. If possible she will return to clean out the old cells in the corridor in which she and her sisters, and her brothers in the flats upstairs, were born. But if she has been forestalled by a married sister or other nest-building insect, she will be driven away angrily by the matron in possession. She will find the nearest suitable crack or hole – she is simply obeying nature's law of expanding outwards in the good, and contracting to the centre in the lean, seasons.

There is much work to be completed by midsummer; to be precise, she needs to build and provision between ten and twenty cells to accommodate the clutch of eggs which the mason-bee normally lays in her brief life. Fabre describes how this bee built her cells in his glass tubes, in empty snail-shells and other natural cavities. She enters head-first when carrying the mud to plaster the floor and walls of each cell, and backs out; then enters, again head-first, to bring in the provisions, first the droplets of honey which she disgorges to form a pallet on the floor. Retreating when this is complete, she turns around and backs down in order first to scrape the pollen (accumulated during her visits to flowers) on to the larder of honey, from the hairy basket on her hind legs. In this position too, she is able to lay an egg on top of the victuals; then once more she turns round and immediately seals off the cell with mud, often held ready in her jaws during the deposition of the pollen and the precious egg. She needs to be swift now to close the lid, because there are parasites which may enter if she delays.

Once her ovaries are exhausted her usefulness to posterity is at an end. Now is the moment to enjoy a few days of idleness in the sun? But no, she is so habituated to hard work that, as long as the sun shines and she can sip nectar to keep alive, she continues to buzz around suitable nesting holes, sometimes adding another crust of mud to the concreted cover with which she has already sealed her tunnel of cells. She may continue building new cells, sealing each carefully without being able to lay an egg within. Occasionally this industry creates a dangerous situation for her progeny. Sometimes the last eggs from her marriage fail to hatch; they are infertile because her seminal receptacle has run out of sperm, used up on the first laid eggs; she can give them neither sex nor life – there is none left to give. Unlike the social honey-bee and the ants, whose workers can lay unfertilised eggs which hatch into live grubs, the unfertilised egg of the solitary mason-bee can only wither away. Thus the surplus sealed nursery cell, provisioned with or without an infertile egg, becomes a tomb. Unless the virgins in the first and lowermost cells are strong and determined enough in the spring to gnaw through the barren vaults above them, they too must perish and their cubicles become coffins.

Such is the perilous life of the little bee which inhabited the lock of the main door at Orielton. The worn-out matron dies soon after midsummer. She never sees the sons and daughters whose sex she so carefully yet unconsciously planned, and for whom she made provision. At that moment, as I stood in the doorway, staring at the lock and pondering the marvellous intricacy of the life it contained, the unmated queens and drones would be stirring in their separate chambers, discarding the silken robe in which each had slept away the winter in peace and safety. It was April 18th, and time for the first young males to fly forth in the sun (from darkness begun as an egg ten months ago), fully equipped to sip nectar briefly, hopefully – if hope is instinctive – to find a mate, and soon to die of requited love.

My reverie of wonder at the complex ecology by which the solitary bee had survived a million years was interrupted by the call of the cuckoo from the alders by the Lily Pond, above which the newly-returned swallows were skimming. A few days before I had removed the labels covering the doorways to the nests of the house-martins, which normally arrive a week later than the swallows.

The song of the woodlark amid the chorus of the birds was

drowned by the roar of a vehicle changing gear as it came up the front drive. I placed my hand on Jack's rising neck-hackles to restrain the growl in the dog's throat.

The new warden and his wife stepped from their splendid van – likewise new.

'Mr and Mrs Page? Welcome to Orielton! You'll find the keys, such as they are, on the table in the library – in any case, you'll hardly need them . . .'

I explained too, about the lesser mason-bee.